WORKBOOK FOR
AUTOMOTIVE
MECHANICS
NINTH EDITION

William H. Crouse
Donald L. Anglin

GREGG DIVISION
McGraw-Hill Book Company

New York   Atlanta   Dallas   St. Louis   San Francisco
Auckland   Bogotá   Guatemala   Hamburg   Lisbon
London   Madrid   Mexico   Montreal   New Delhi   Panama   Paris
San Juan   São Paulo   Singapore   Sydney   Tokyo   Toronto

Workbook for
Automotive Mechanics, Ninth Edition

6 7 8 9 0 SEMSEM 8 9 1 0

ISBN 0-07-014861-9

CONTENTS

Preface   v

How to Use This Workbook   vi

The *Workbook for Automotive Mechanics,* Ninth Edition, is a combination shop guide, study guide, notebook, and student progress report. In addition, it covers shop exercises and jobs that will familiarize students with the construction and operation of each part of today's automobile. This workbook provides students with a series of tested interrelated jobsheets that take them step by step through many actual automotive repair jobs.

At the top of each jobsheet is a student performance objective for use by both students and instructors. By reading the objective for each jobsheet, students know the task to be performed. Instructors can then measure how well the student performed that task. Each student can keep an individual progress chart by posting the date and grade of each completed jobsheet in the space provided to the right of each title on the contents page.

References used in the *Workbook for Automotive Mechanics* are to the textbook *Automotive Mechanics* (AM), automotive manufacturers' service manuals, and auto shop equipment manufacturers' operating instructions.

All safety precautions are not repeated for every job because of space limitations. However, students must keep in mind the safety precautions outlined in the textbook, references, and other jobsheets as they progress through the workbook. Also, students should make full use of fender and seat covers when working on cars even though the covers are not mentioned specifically in every job. The covers protect the cars from dirt and grease and from damage to the paint.

Instructors should discuss with the students the safety precautions applying to the job about to be done. They should place special emphasis on local shop conditions. Students should be shown the locations of fire extinguishers and first-aid kits and taught how to use them. Periodically, the safety plan for handling auto-shop emergencies should be reviewed with the students by the instructor. Both instructors and students should note that the service procedures outlined in this text will not always apply to all vehicles. Instructors and students must make sure that service procedures will not endanger the student, the vehicle, or the tools and equipment being used. Where special tools are called for, they should be used. When in doubt about procedures or tools, students should check with the instructor.

The *Workbook for Automotive Mechanics* introduces students to the full range of automotive services and repairs that is recommended for entry-level automotive mechanics training by the automotive industry. These recommendations are the consensus of service experts in the automotive industry and of authorities in vocational education.

The workbook, along with the *Automotive Mechanics* textbook, is correlated with federal, state, apprenticeship, and industry guidelines for automotive mechanics training. These materials may be used for reference, study, and test preparation by anyone preparing for automotive mechanics certification programs. In addition, the *Testbook for Automotive Mechanics* provides a series of tests that may be used as part of the instructional program by instructors and used by students to check their own progress or for review.

Available to the instructor is the *Instructor's Planning Guide for Automotive Mechanics,* which discusses in detail automotive mechanics training. Also, the *Instructor's Planning Guide* explains each of the different parts of the automotive mechanics training program and how these parts can be individually tailored to each learning situation.

Included in the guide are teaching suggestions for using the correlated media and materials effectively in automotive mechanics training. The guide also contains an answer key for the testbook, the workbook, and the text.

The authors would like to acknowledge and thank the many people, both in education and in industry, who by their assistance and counsel have contributed so much to the present workbook. It is the authors' hope that this workbook will help to achieve the aims of all who work in the field of automotive service instruction: to train high-caliber automotive mechanics and technicians who are capable of taking their proper place in the automotive service industry.

William H. Crouse
Donald L. Anglin

———— 1   As you read through the jobsheets, notice that there is a line to the left of each numbered step in each procedure. Place a check mark above the line as you complete each step.

———— 2   Before attempting a job, carefully read the reference material that your instructor assigns. Read it more than once if necessary, to gain a good understanding of the principles involved.

———— 3   Read the jobsheet through to the questions. This will tell you the purpose of the job and how it is to be done.

———— 4   Make sure the equipment, tools, and supplies needed to complete the job are on hand. Check with your instructor if you are not sure that you have everything required.

———— 5   Carefully note the safety cautions. If references are made to safety cautions in previous jobs, be sure to reread those safety cautions. Do not assume that you remember them.

———— 6   Follow the procedure, step by step, as de-tailed in the jobsheet. If anything is not clear, ask your instructor about it.

———— 7   After completing each job, answer the questions assigned by your instructor. To answer a multiple-choice question, select the word or phrase that is the correct, best, or most probable answer. Then write the letter that precedes the word or phrase in the space provided. For example

1.   Before the clutch is removed from a car with front-engine and rear-wheel drive, you must first remove the
   a   engine
   b   differential
   c   transmission
   d   rear wheels   1. ————

Since "(c) transmission" is the correct answer, you would put a c on the line at the right.

———— 8   Notice that there is room on the contents page to write in the dates you complete the various jobs and the grades you were assigned by your instructor. This information will serve as your work-progress guide. It will tell you how you are getting along in your shopwork.

JOB 1
Introduction to the Automobile

Objective: To learn the names and locations of the major components of the automobile.

References: *Automotive Mechanics* (AM)♦1-1 to 1-13, *Study Guide* (SG) Chap. 1, automotive manufacturers' service manuals.

Equipment: Various automobiles.
Tools: None.

SHOP FACTS

Chapter 1 in AM describes briefly the various types of businesses associated with the automotive service business. Now let us take an introductory look at the various major components in the automobile. Later in AM these components are described in detail.

There are four basic components of the automobile:

1. The *engine* (Fig. 1-1), or source of power that moves the car.
2. The *framework,* or support for the engine and wheels. This includes the frame (if used) and the steering and braking system. The assembly is often called the *chassis* (Fig. 1-1).
3. The *power train,* which carries the engine power to the drive wheels. The car may have either rear-wheel drive (Fig. 1-1) or front-wheel drive (Fig. 1-2).
4. The *body,* which encloses and protects the passengers (Figs. 1-1 and 1-2).

To these could be added the heater, air conditioner, radio, CB transceiver, lights, and other devices. These accessories add to the safety, comfort, and convenience of the driver and passengers.

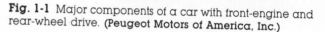

Fig. 1-1 Major components of a car with front-engine and rear-wheel drive. (**Peugeot Motors of America, Inc.**)

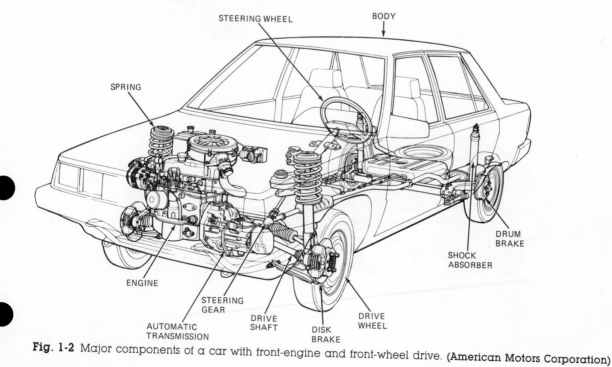

Fig. 1-2 Major components of a car with front-engine and front-wheel drive. (**American Motors Corporation**)

THE ENGINE

The engine is the source of power that makes the car move. In the automobile, a *motor* is usually an electrical device that runs on electricity. Most automobile engines run on petroleum—either gasoline or diesel fuel.

Two major types of engines are used in automobiles today. The first is the widely used *piston* engine (Fig. 1-3)—either spark ignition or diesel. In the piston engine, pistons move up and down, or reciprocate. The second is the *rotary* engine, in which one or more rotors spin (Fig. 1-4).

The two kinds of rotary engines are the Wankel and the gas turbine. There are no gas-turbine-powered production cars today. However, the Wankel (Fig. 1-4) is operating in hundreds of thousands of cars. The principal manufacturer is Mazda in Japan.

All of these engines must have four basic systems:

♦ Fuel system
♦ Electronic ignition system (not in diesel engines)
♦ Lubricating system
♦ Cooling system

In the spark-ignition engine, the fuel system (Fig. 1-5) mixes gasoline with air to make a mixture that will burn. When this mixture burns in the engine, it produces high pressure. The high pressure forces the pistons to move. The movement turns shafts that turn the wheels so that the car moves.

The ignition system (Fig. 1-6) supplies sparks to the engine cylinders at the right time. These sparks set fire to, or *ignite*, the mixture of air and fuel. The mixture burns to produce the power.

The lubricating system (Fig. 1-7) keeps all moving parts coated with oil so that they will move easily.

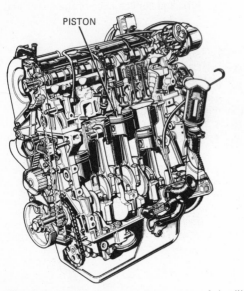

Fig. 1-3 A passenger-car type of spark-ignition piston engine. (Citroen)

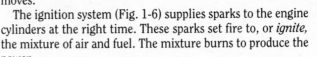
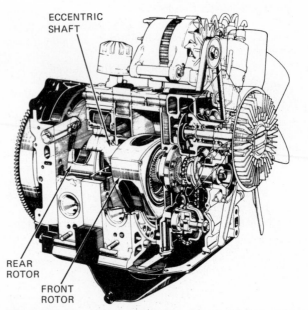

Fig. 1-4 A Wankel rotary engine. (**Mazda Motors of America, Inc.**)

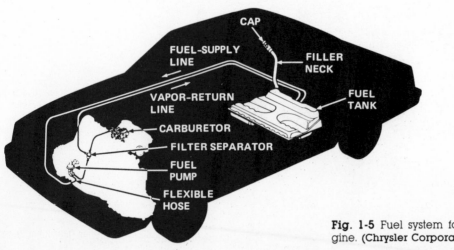

Fig. 1-5 Fuel system for a carbureted spark-ignition engine. (**Chrysler Corporation**)

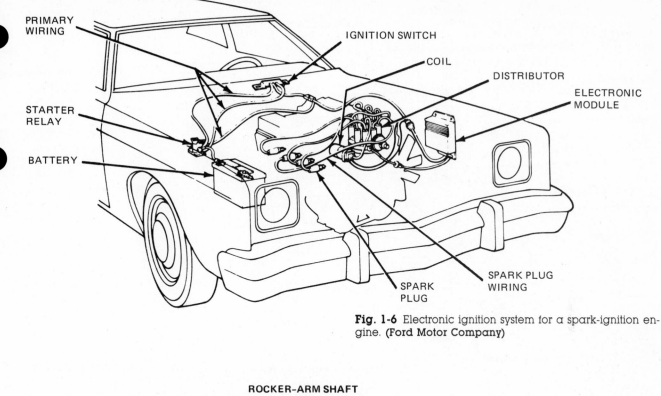

PRIMARY WIRING

IGNITION SWITCH

COIL

DISTRIBUTOR

ELECTRONIC MODULE

STARTER RELAY

BATTERY

SPARK PLUG

SPARK PLUG WIRING

Fig. 1-6 Electronic ignition system for a spark-ignition engine. **(Ford Motor Company)**

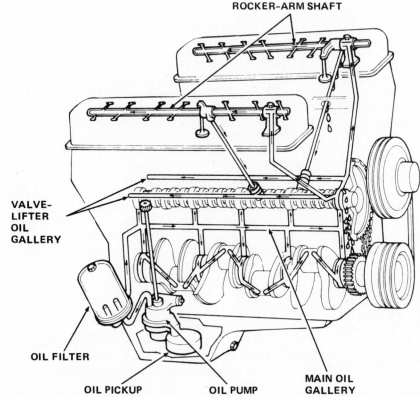

ROCKER-ARM SHAFT

VALVE-LIFTER OIL GALLERY

OIL FILTER

OIL PICKUP

OIL PUMP

MAIN OIL GALLERY

Fig. 1-7 Lubricating system for a V-8 engine. **(Chrysler Corporation)**

The cooling system (Fig. 1-8) circulates a mixture of water and antifreeze between the engine and a radiator. This mixture is called the *coolant*. The coolant carries heat away from the engine to prevent it from getting too hot or overheating.

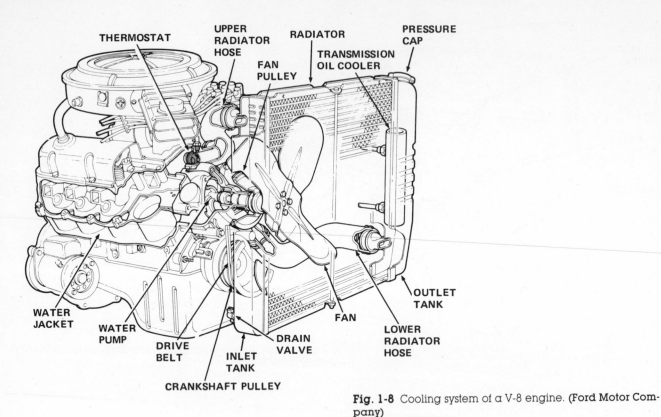

Fig. 1-8 Cooling system of a V-8 engine. **(Ford Motor Company)**

POWER TRAIN

The power train (Figs. 1-1 and 1-2) includes the parts that carry the engine power to the drive wheels. These are:

1. The transmission
2. The clutch (on some cars)
3. The drive shaft
4. The differential
5. The wheel axles or drive axles

TRANSMISSION

There are two types of transmission, manual or hand shifted (Fig. 1-1) and automatic (Fig. 1-2). Both do the same job. They allow the engine to run fast when the car first starts to move. This sends more power to the wheels, so the car can accelerate, or increase in speed. Once the car is moving, the transmission gears are changed, or shifted. This reduces the difference between engine speed and wheel speed. Less fuel is used, and the engine does not work so hard. To start, the engine shaft might rotate 12 times to turn the car wheels once. This is called a "12-to-1 gear ratio" (12:1). Then the transmission might shift so that 8 engine shaft rotations turn the car wheels once. This is an 8-to-1 gear ratio (8:1). In high, or direct, gear the shaft would rotate 4 times to turn the wheels once.

If the car has a manual transmission, the driver moves the shift lever to shift gears. Automatic transmissions do the job automatically, without any effort by the driver.

CLUTCH

In a car using a manual transmission, a clutch is needed (Fig. 1-1). The clutch allows the driver to temporarily disconnect the engine from the power train while the gears are shifted. This is necessary because it is very difficult to shift from one gear to another if power is flowing through the gears. Therefore, the clutch is operated by the driver before shifting so that no power flows from the engine through the gears. The gears can then be shifted easily. To operate the clutch, the driver pushes down on the clutch pedal. This disconnects the engine from the gears. Then, after the gears are shifted, the driver releases the clutch pedal to reengage the clutch. Now power can flow through the gears.

DRIVE LINE

The drive line, or drive shaft, carries power from the transmission toward the car wheels (Figs. 1-1 and 1-2). It is a shaft with two types of flexible joints. The joints permit the shaft to drive the wheels when the wheels are moving up and down.

DIFFERENTIAL AND DRIVE AXLES

Power from the drive shaft is sent to the differential. It splits the power and sends it through the two wheel axles to the wheels. The differential allows the drive wheels to turn different amounts when the car goes around a curve. In going around a curve, the outer wheel travels farther than the inner wheel. The differential allows this and still delivers power to both wheels.

More and more cars today have front-wheel drive (Fig. 1-2). In these cars, the front wheels, rather than the rear wheels, receive the power from the engine and drive the car.

FRAME AND CHASSIS

The frame supports the car body, engine, and power train. The frame is supported by springs placed between the frame and the wheel axles. The assembly is called the *chassis*. However, many cars now have *unibody* construction. In it, no separate full frame is used. The body itself may support the engine power train and suspension.

SPRING AND SHOCK ABSORBERS

The wheels are attached to the frame by springs (Figs. 1-1 and 1-2). The springs absorb, or "soak up," up-and-down motions of the wheels due to holes and bumps in the road. Therefore, these up-and-down motions do not reach the frame or passengers in the car.

Springs alone do not give a good ride. They need a control to prevent excessive bouncing. That is the job of the shock absorbers. Shock absorbers are connected between the car frame and the wheel axles. They restrain, or hold back, the springs. This prevents too much movement, or bounce, after a hole or bump has been passed.

STEERING SYSTEMS

The steering system (Fig. 1-2) allows the front wheels to be pivoted, or turned, to the right or left. This steers the car. The steering wheel is mounted on a steering shaft that extends down into the steering gear. When the steering wheel is turned, the steering gear pushes or pulls on rods connected to arms on the front axles. This movement pivots, or turns, the wheels for steering.

BRAKES

Brakes (Fig. 1-9) are necessary to slow or stop the car. All cars have foot-operated brakes that work by putting pressure on a fluid. These are called *hydraulic brakes*. The system contains a fluid-filled cylinder, called the *master cylinder*. When the brake pedal is pushed down by the driver, fluid is forced out of the cylinder. The fluid flows through pipes and hoses to the brake mechanisms at the wheels. There the fluid forces the brakes to work. This slows or stops the wheels so that the car slows or stops.

There are two different kinds of wheel-brake mechanisms. They are the drum type and the disk type. In the drum brake, curved plates, called *shoes*, are pressed against round drums on the wheels to produce braking. In the disk brake, flat shoes, or *pads*, are pressed against flat round disks on the wheels to produce braking.

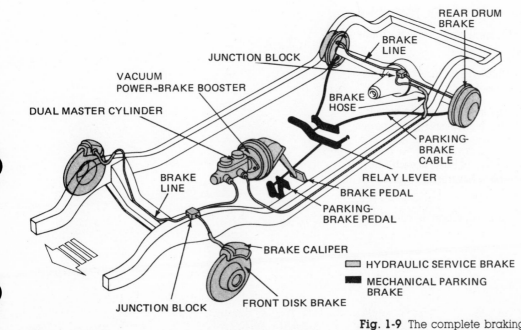

Fig. 1-9 The complete braking system on an automobile. (Texaco, Inc.)

SHOP SKILLS

_____ **1.** Raise the hood of the car, and locate the engine. Determine whether the engine is a piston engine or a rotary engine.

_____ **2.** Locate the parts of the fuel system. Under the hood, identify the carburetor and the fuel pump. Raise the car on a lift, and locate the fuel tank and fuel lines. Then lower the car and raise the hood again.

♦ CAUTION ♦ Raising a car on a lift can be dangerous if all safety precautions are not followed. Damage to the vehicle can also result from not knowing how to position a car on a lift. If you have not received instruction on how to operate the lift, call your instructor.

_____ **3.** Locate the ignition switch, ignition coil, distributor, spark plugs, and wiring.

_____ **4.** Locate the oil pan, oil pump, oil-filler cap, oil filter, crankcase dipstick, and oil-pressure-indicator light or gauge.

_____ **5.** Locate the radiator, radiator cap, upper and lower radiator hose, thermostat, fan, water pump, and engine water jackets.

_____ **6.** Locate the brake master cylinder and the brake lines connected to it. Determine if the vehicle has power brakes.

_____ **7.** Observing all safety cautions, raise the vehicle on a lift. Now locate and identify the parts of the automotive power train.

_____ **8.** Locate the transmission. Determine whether it is manual or automatic transmission.

_____ **9.** If the vehicle has manual transmission, locate the clutch.

_____ **10.** Identify the drive shaft, universal joints, and slip joint.

_____ **11.** Locate the differential. Identify the wheel axles.

_____ **12.** Locate the frame of the car, if used. Trace the frame completely around the vehicle.

_____ **13.** Locate the rear springs. Then locate the front springs. Locate the shock absorber for each spring.

_____ **14.** Locate the steering gear and the steering linkages. Determine whether the vehicle has manual steering or power steering.

_____ **15.** Locate and identify the type of brake at each wheel. Then determine whether the vehicle has front disk brakes or four-wheel disk brakes.

_____ **16.** After the under-the-car inspection is completed, lower the car.

JOB 1   MULTIPLE-CHOICE TEST

1. The four basic parts in the automobile are
   a. engine, chassis, power train, and body
   b. fuel, lubricating, cooling, and emission systems
   c. radiator, engine, clutch, and drive axle
   d. none of the above   1. _____

2. The four basic systems that a spark-ignition engine must have to run are
   a. heating, air conditioning, ventilating, and emissions systems
   b. fuel, ignition, lubricating, and cooling systems
   c. both a and b
   d. neither a nor b   2. _____

3. The purpose of the fuel system is to
   a. mix air and water with fuel
   b. prevent engine overheating
   c. transmit power to the drive wheels
   d. provide the engine with an air-fuel mixture that will burn   3. _____

4. A manual transmission is shifted
   a. automatically
   b. by hand
   c. both a and b
   d. neither a nor b   4. _____

5. All cars have
   a. foot-operated brakes
   b. hydraulic brakes
   c. both a and b
   d. neither a nor b   5. _____

JOB 2
Safety in the Shop

Objective: To learn about the automotive shop and how to work safely in the shop.

References: AM ♦2-1 to 2-14, SG Chap. 2, automotive manufacturers' service manuals.

Equipment: None.
Tools: None.

SHOP FACTS

_____ 1. Shopwork is varied and interesting. In the shop, you will learn many vehicle and engine jobs. But before you work in the shop, you should know about safety. Safety in the shop means protecting yourself and others from possible danger and injury. In this job sheet, we discuss some important safety rules that you should follow in the shop to protect yourself from harm. Remember this: When everybody obeys the safety rules, the shop is a much safer place to work in than your home! Many more people are hurt in the home than in the shop.

_____ 2. Safety is your job. In the shop, you are "safe" when you protect your eyes, your fingers, your hands—all of yourself—from danger and, just as important, when you look out for the safety of those around you. Some very important safety rules are listed and discussed in the next few pages. Your instructor will discuss these and many more safety rules with you. Follow the rules for your own protection and for the protection of your coworkers.

_____ 3. There is one rule that you should always keep in mind in the shop. It is extremely important when you are working with tools or around vehicles. It is called the *ABC of Safety* (Fig. 2-1): Always Be Careful!

Fig. 2-1 ABCs of safe auto shopwork.

_____ 4. When you first go into the shop, take a good look around. Notice the shop layout. The term *shop layout* means the locations of workbenches, car lifts, power tools, and so on. Shop layouts vary. So the first thing you should do in a shop is find out where everything is located. This includes the different power tools and the workbenches, car lifts, and work areas. Many shops have painted lines on the floor to mark off work areas. These lines guide customers and workers away

from danger zones where machines are being operated. The lines also remind workers to keep their tools and equipment within work areas.

_____ 5. Many shops have warning signs posted around machinery. These signs are there to remind you about safety and about how to use machines safely. Follow the posted instructions at all times. The most common cause of accidents in the shop is failure to follow instructions.

_____ 6. Locate the first-aid kits so that you can get one when it is needed. Note the location of the telephone and the nurse's office. This will allow you to get help quickly in case of an accident or a fire. If there is an accident and someone gets hurt, notify your instructor at once. Your instructor knows what to do. Be very careful in attempting first aid. You must know what you are doing. If first aid is done wrong, it can do more harm than good. For example, a serious back injury could be made worse if the injured person is moved. On the other hand, quick mouth-to-mouth resuscitation may save the life of a person who has suffered an electric shock. Talk to your instructor if you have any questions about safety and first aid.

_____ 7. Notice the location of the fire extinguishers. Make sure you know how to use them. Figure 2-2 is a chart showing the different types of fires and the types of fire extinguishers used to fight them. Take a moment right now to study Fig. 2-2. The quicker you begin to fight a fire, the easier it is to control. But you have to use the right kind of fire extinguisher, and use it correctly. Ask your instructor if you have any questions about fire extinguishers, where they are located, and how to use them.

_____ 8. Gasoline is used so much in the shop that people forget it is very dangerous if not handled properly. A spark or lighted match in a closed place filled with gasoline vapor can cause an explosion. Even the spark from a light switch can set off an explosion. So you must always be careful with gasoline.

_____ 9. Suppose there is gasoline vapor around, because someone spilled gasoline or a fuel line is leaking. Then you should have the shop doors open and have the ventilating system running. Wipe up the spilled gasoline at once, and put the rags outside to dry. Never smoke or light cigarettes around gasoline. When you work on a leaky fuel line, carburetor, or fuel pump, catch leaking gasoline in a container or

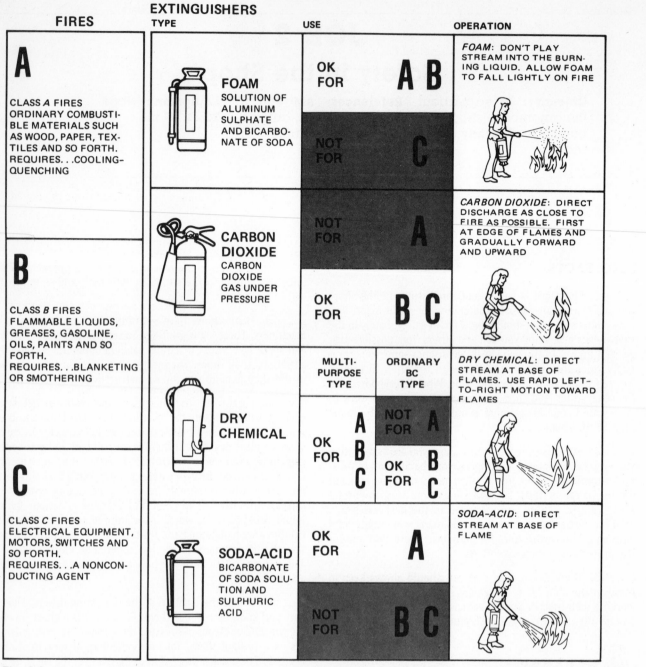

Fig. 2-2 Chart showing types of fire extinguishers and the classifications of fires. (Ford Motor Company)

with rags. Put the soaked rags outside to dry. Fix the leak as quickly as possible. Don't make sparks around the car, for example, by connecting a 12-volt test light to the battery.

_____ 10. Store gasoline in an approved safety container. It has a spring-loaded cap that prevents leakage if the container is dropped or knocked over. Never, _never_ store gasoline in a glass jug. The jug could be broken and could cause a terrible explosion or fire.

_____ 11. Oily rags can also start fires. They can catch fire without a spark or flame. Oily rags and waste should be put into special closed metal containers. In these special containers, they can do no harm if they ignite from spontaneous combustion or another cause.

_____ 12. Never siphon gasoline from a tank using your mouth and a piece of hose. Swallowing even a small amount of gasoline can cause respiratory infection and pneumonia. In addition, the lead added to gasoline is poisonous. If you should get gasoline in your mouth, spit it out. Rinse your mouth several times, and avoid taking deep breaths. If you swallow some gasoline, do not try to vomit. Get immediate help. Your life may depend on it!

_____ 13. Some people say, "Accidents will happen!" But safety experts do not agree. They say, "Accidents are caused: They are caused by careless actions, by inattention to the job at hand, by using damaged or incorrect tools. And sometimes accidents are caused by plain stupidity!" Here are some simple safety rules that will help prevent accidents in the shop.

____ 14. Work quietly, and give the job your full attention. This means no horseplay! Never indulge in horseplay or other foolish antics in the shop. You could cause yourself or someone else to get seriously hurt. Give your attention to the job you're doing.

____ 15. Keep your tools and equipment under control. Jack handles should be kept up, out of the way. Don't leave tools, creepers, and other items on the floor where someone could trip on them and get hurt. After using a creeper, prop it against a wall.

____ 16. Don't put sharp objects, such as screwdrivers, in your pocket. You could cut yourself or get stabbed. Or you could ruin the upholstery in a car.

____ 17. Make sure your clothes are right for the job. Dangling sleeves or ties can get caught in machinery and cause serious injuries. Keep long hair out of machinery by wearing a cap.

____ 18. No bare feet in the shop! There are too many ways to get hurt without shoes in the shop. Do not wear sandals or open-toe shoes. Wear full leather shoes with nonskid rubber heels and soles. Steel-toe safety shoes are best for shopwork.

____ 19. Keep your hands and tools free of excess grease and oil. Otherwise, you will not be able to get a good grip on your tools.

____ 20. If you spill oil, grease, or any liquid on the floor, clean it up so that no one will slip and fall.

____ 21. Compressed air can be dangerous. Never use compressed air to blow dirt from your clothes. Never point the compressed-air blowgun at another person. Flying particles could put out an eye. The Occupational Safety and Health Act (OSHA) requires that compressed-air blowguns discharge air at a pressure of not more than 30 pounds per square inch (psi) [207 kilopascals (kPa)] (Fig. 2-3).

____ 22. Always wear a face shield, safety glasses, or safety goggles when you are doing any job that could endanger your eyes (Fig. 2-4). Always wear suitable eye protection when using a grinding wheel or when cutting or welding. Watch out for sparks from a grinding wheel or welding equipment. The sparks can set your clothes on fire.

____ 23. To protect your eyes, wear safety goggles when using any chemical cleaner, such as solvent or carburetor

Fig. 2-4 Always wear safety glasses, goggles, or a face shield when using a bench grinder. **(Ford Motor Company)**

cleaner. If you get a chemical in your eyes, wash them with water at once (Fig. 2-5). Then see the school nurse or a doctor as soon as possible.

____ 24. When using a jack to lift a car, make sure the jack is properly positioned. Make sure it won't slip and let the car fall. *Never* jack up a car while someone is working under it! People have been killed when the jack slipped and the car fell on them! Always place safety stands or supports in proper position under the car before you go under it yourself.

____ 25. Never run an engine in a closed garage unless a working shop ventilation system is hooked up to the tail pipe of the car. Engine exhaust gases contain carbon monoxide (CO). Carbon monoxide is a colorless, tasteless, odorless, poisonous gas that can kill you! In a closed one-car garage, enough carbon monoxide to kill you can collect in only 3 minutes.

____ 26. Remember your personal responsibility to work safely while you are in the shop. Look out for yourself and for the safety of those working around you. In other words, Always Be Careful.

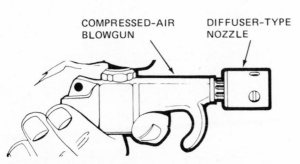

COMPRESSED-AIR
BLOWGUN

DIFFUSER-TYPE
NOZZLE

Fig. 2-3 A diffuser nozzle on a compressed-air blowgun. The maximum allowable discharge pressure is 30 psi (207 kPa). **(Ford Motor Company)**

Fig. 2-5 If solvent or some other chemical splashes in your eye, immediately wash your eye with water.

JOB 2 MULTIPLE-CHOICE TEST

1. Horseplay in the shop is
   a. permitted
   b. seldom permitted
   c. never permitted
   d. frequently permitted   1. ____

2. Carrying screwdrivers in your back pockets can
   a. injure you
   b. keep tools handy
   c. keep tools clean
   d. protect the tools   2. ____

3. Long, loose sleeves worn around moving machinery could
   a. keep you clean
   b. improve your appearance
   c. get caught in the machinery
   d. protect the machine   3. ____

4. Tools may slip out of your hands if your hands are covered with
   a. gloves
   b. sand
   c. grease or oil
   d. protective cream   4. ____

5. A compressed-air blowgun must never be
   a. used in the automotive shop
   b. pointed at someone else
   c. left pressurized overnight
   d. kept on a reel   5. ____

6. The right time to jack up a car is
   a. when someone is working under it
   b. never
   c. when several people are working under it
   d. when no one is working under it   6. ____

7. Before you get under a car to work on it, you must make sure that
   a. the jack handle is up
   b. you use a creeper
   c. the tires are inflated
   d. the car is supported on stands   7. ____

8. Creepers left sticking out from under a car can
   a. get dirty
   b. keep the car from rolling
   c. cause someone to trip
   d. add speed to your work   8. ____

9. You should wear safety goggles
   a. when doing any job that could endanger your eyes
   b. when told to wear them by the instructor
   c. only if you do not wear glasses
   d. while welding   9. ____

10. Oil-soaked rags should be
    a. washed in the sink
    b. stored in a safety container
    c. thrown in a corner
    d. used to mop the floor   10. ____

JOB 3
Shopwork and Shop Manuals

Objective: To learn the steps in shopwork and how to use the manufacturers' service manuals.

References: AM ♦3-1 to 3-6, SG Chap. 3, automotive manufacturers' service manuals.

Equipment: None.
Tools: None.

SHOP FACTS

Servicing jobs vary from simple to difficult, but no automotive-service job requires more than six steps. These are measuring, disassembling, machining, installing new parts, reassembling, and adjusting. Some jobs may be completed in fewer steps. Let's review the six steps in automotive service.

1. **Measuring** Before you can work on a car, you must find out what is wrong with it. You begin by measuring. There are various types of measurements. Linear measurements are the most common kind of measurement. They are the measurements that you take in a straight line. For example, you might measure the diameter of a hole or cylinder. Using the metric system, you take measurements in millimeters, centimeters, or meters. Many cars are measured in the metric system. There are other ways to measure. Sometimes measuring is done by listening. For example, when you listen to noises in a running engine or feel the steadiness of the exhaust gas (Fig. 3-1), you are making a measurement. When you check the oil in an engine, you measure its level in the crankcase. You use test instruments to measure battery conditions. When you check engine vacuum or compression, you measure engine performance. The results of the measurements tell you what service or repair job is needed.

2. **Disassembling** Sometimes the measurements show that there is trouble. Then you have to disassemble, or take

apart, the component to fix the trouble. Suppose your measurements show that the engine valves are leaking. This means you must take off the cylinder head to get to the valves and reface or replace them.

Note Disassembly is also called *teardown*. For example, you disassemble, or tear down, an engine. However, you do it carefully, part by part.

3. **Machining** Sometimes you have to remove metal from a part. Using a machine to remove metal is called *machining*. Suppose you find valve trouble. This could require machining, or grinding, the valves and valve seats. Or you might find that the engine cylinders require machining. Then a *boring bar* is required to machine, or bore, the cylinders.

4. **Installing new parts** You might find that some parts are so worn that they must be thrown away. Then new parts must be installed in their place. This is called *replacing* a part. For example, engine bearings sometimes wear out, and new bearings must be installed to replace the old ones. Even new parts may require machining to make them fit.

5. **Reassembling** After you fix a trouble, you may have to put some parts back together. This is called *assembly* or *reassembly*. This means that you put the parts back together to make a complete assembly.

6. **Adjusting** When a car is driven, parts normally wear. This requires occasional adjustments. Also, adjustments may be required after a service or repair job. For example, after grinding the valves, you reassemble the engine. Then you measure the valve clearance. If it is not right, you have to adjust the valves.

SPECIFICATIONS

You will hear the word "specifications," or "specs," quite often in the shop. The specs give you the right measurements for the vehicle you are working on. The automotive manufacturer sets the specs. You find the specs in the manufacturer's service manual, or in its specifications book. These specs include valve clearance, ignition timing, piston clearance, piston-ring clearances, and many other measurements.

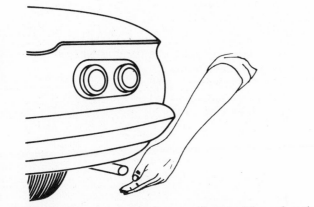

Fig. 3-1 When you feel the smoothness of the exhaust-gas flow, you are taking a measurement. **(ATW)**

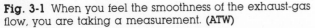

MANUFACTURERS' SERVICE MANUALS

With each new model of vehicle, the manufacturer issues a service manual covering that model. The manual covers all service procedures, provides the specs, names the tools needed, and explains how to do service jobs on the vehicle.

When you get a chance, take a careful look at a manufacturer's service manual. Note how it is arranged in groups or sections covering the engine, clutch, transmission, brakes, and other parts and systems. Each section in a service manual is further divided into descriptions of specific components. These explain how to find and fix troubles with those components, and they list the special tools required to service them. Get acquainted with automotive manufacturers' service manuals. You will be using them when you work in the shop.

OTHER USEFUL PUBLICATIONS

Many automotive magazines are published. Such magazines sometimes contain information on servicing vehicles and articles on specific service jobs. They often have tips on how to make hard jobs a little easier.

Testing-equipment manufacturers, parts makers, and tool and service-equipment manufacturers publish manuals on how to install their parts or use their equipment. These publications can be very helpful, especially the test-equipment operating instructions.

SHOP SKILLS

_____ 1. Locate where the manufacturers' service manuals are kept in the shop. Find out how to use them for reference and study.

_____ 2. Find the title page and study the table of contents. Note how the names of the major parts and systems of the car are separate headings. You must know what you are looking for to determine in which section of a service manual the information is found.

_____ 3. To better understand how the service manual is used, read the foreword and any notices, such as safety notices, that appear before the table of contents. Most automotive manufacturers' service manuals follow the same general format.

_____ 4. Do you know the steps in performing a valve adjustment on a four-cycle engine? Here is a chance to check up on yourself and to compare two different manufacturers' procedures. Open two different service manuals to the same section. Notice the slightly different instructions given and the differences in the sequence in which the steps are performed.

_____ 5. Thumb through a complete section in a service manual. Notice the illustrations. Some are line drawings, while others are photographs, just as in your AM textbook. Some manuals have pictures or drawings of the special tools required to do each job. As you study automotive mechanics, you will find that seeing a picture of the tool used often makes it easier to understand how to do the job.

_____ 6. Practice using these manuals. Look up "fuel system," "transmission," "brakes," and the names of other major parts in the manual. Notice how each section is divided into specific service jobs.

_____ 7. Select several basic jobs that you will have to do. In the manufacturer's service manual, review the manufacturer's procedure for each. Then locate the specifications that you must have to complete the job. Sometimes the specs are not given in the text of the service manual. Instead, they are printed as tables or charts at the front or back of the manual, or as a separate specifications book.

JOB 3   MULTIPLE-CHOICE TEST

1. The six basic steps in any automotive repair job are measuring, disassembling, machining, and
   a. removing parts, replacing parts, and adjusting parts
   b. removing and installing parts and making adjustments
   c. checking, testing, and inspecting
   d. installing new parts, reassembling, and adjusting

   1. _____

2. Using a boring bar to rebore a cylinder is an example of
   a. measuring
   b. adjustments
   c. machining
   d. none of the above

   2. _____

3. The specifications for service work on an automobile are set by
   a. the federal government
   b. state and local laws
   c. the Society of Automotive Engineers
   d. the automobile manufacturer

   3. _____

4. A manual that tells the time it normally takes to do any service job is called
   a. a service manual
   b. a flat-rate manual
   c. an owner's manual
   d. a parts manual

   4. _____

5. When you listen to noises in a transmission, you are
   a. taking a measurement
   b. making adjustments
   c. locating specifications
   d. none of the above

   5. _____

Name _____   Date _____

JOB 4-1
Using Thickness Gauges

Objective: To learn how to use thickness gauges.

References: AM ♦4-9, SG Chap. 4, automotive manufacturers' service manuals.

Equipment: Five pieces or parts with gaps to be measured.
Tools: Various sets and types of thickness gauges.

♦ _____ ♦

SHOP FACTS

Thickness gauges are strips or blades of hardened steel or other material. They are ground or rolled to the proper thickness. This is the reason they are called thickness gauges. Thickness gauges are generally supplied in sets (Fig. 4-1). Each blade in the set is marked with its thickness in thousandths of an inch, hundredths of a millimeter, or both. For example, in Fig. 4-1 the gauge marked 0.003 inch is also marked with its metric equivalent of 0.08 mm.

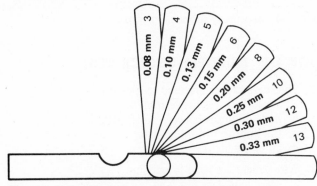

Fig. 4-1 Set of blade-type thickness gauges.

Some thickness gauges have two steps, or thicknesses. These are *stepped* thickness gauges. The tip of the blade of a stepped thickness gauge is thinner than the rest of the blade (Fig. 4-2).

Stepped thickness gauges are handy on certain jobs. For example, the specifications might call for a clearance of 0.005 inch [0.13 mm]. With the 0.004 to 0.006 inch [0.10 to 0.15 mm] gauge, the clearance is adjusted so that the 0.004-inch [0.10-mm] portion fits but the 0.006-inch [0.15-mm] portion does not fit. For this reason, stepped thickness gauges are often called "go–no-go" gauges.

Wire thickness gauges are similar to flat thickness gauges, but they are made of carefully calibrated steel wire of the proper thickness. They are useful in checking spark-plug gaps and similar dimensions. Metric wire thickness gauges are also available. When specifications are given in the metric system, and you do not have metric gauges, you can convert the measurements with the conversion table in Chap. 4 of AM.

Thickness gauges are made in many shapes and sizes.

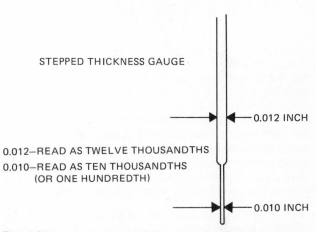

STEPPED THICKNESS GAUGE

←— 0.012 INCH

0.012—READ AS TWELVE THOUSANDTHS
0.010—READ AS TEN THOUSANDTHS
(OR ONE HUNDREDTH)

←— 0.010 INCH

Fig. 4-2 Blade of a stepped thickness gauge. The tip is thinner than the rest of the blade.

Some thickness gauges, or blades, are straight, as in Fig. 4-1. Others are bent at an angle. A thickness-gauge set usually consists of several blades, which often range in thickness from 0.0015 to 0.040 inch [0.04 to 1 mm]. Sometimes you will need to measure a space for which your set does not have a blade. You can make up the proper size of gauge by combining several clean, undamaged blades. The total thickness of all the blades used to fill the space is the measurement between the surfaces.

Before using a thickness gauge, wipe the blade with a clean oiled cloth. This will remove any dirt from the blade, and prevent inaccurate readings (especially if two or more blades are combined). After you use the thickness gauges, and before returning them to your toolbox, again wipe the blades and holder with a clean oiled cloth. This prevents the acids and moisture on your hands from rusting the blades.

SHOP SKILLS

____ 1. Most thickness gauges are made of steel. However, sometimes a mechanic needs a nonmagnetic thickness gauge. Brass thickness gauges are available for work around permanent magnets. They are used, for example, to measure the air gap in an electronic distributor. The permanent magnet in the distributor attracts the steel gauge and prevents accurate measurement.

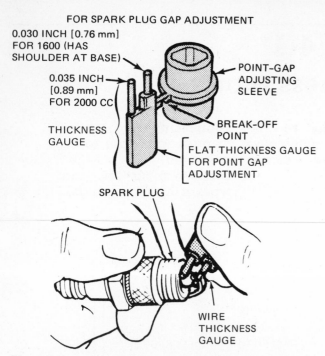

FOR SPARK PLUG GAP ADJUSTMENT

0.030 INCH [0.76 mm]
FOR 1600 (HAS
SHOULDER AT BASE)

0.035 INCH
[0.89 mm]
FOR 2000 CC

THICKNESS
GAUGE

POINT-GAP
ADJUSTING
SLEEVE

BREAK-OFF
POINT

FLAT THICKNESS GAUGE
FOR POINT GAP
ADJUSTMENT

SPARK PLUG

WIRE
THICKNESS
GAUGE

Fig. 4-3 Round and flat plastic thickness gauges that are included in some tuneup kits. **(Ford Motor Company)**

____ 2. Many engine tuneup kits contain a plastic disposable, or throwaway-type, thickness gauge. Figure 4-3 shows such a gauge and how it is used. Note that, on this particular gauge, one end is a round wire gauge for use in gapping the spark plugs. The other end is a flat thickness gauge for use in gapping the contact points in the ignition distributor.

____ 3. Examine various thickness gauge sets. Notice the difference between them.

____ 4. Next, compare the flat-blade type with a set of round wire thickness gauges. Note how the stepped thickness gauge is marked to indicate the thickness of each part of the blade.

____ 5. Now, obtain five pieces or parts which have clearances or gaps to be measured. Using a standard gauge set, take each measurement. Write it down in the left column of the chart in Fig. 4-4. Then, using the conversion table in Chap. 4 of AM, figure the metric measurement for each gap. Write the metric equivalent in the proper place in the right column of the chart in Fig. 4-4.

Piece 1	_____ in	_____ mm
Piece 2	_____ in	_____ mm
Piece 3	_____ in	_____ mm
Piece 4	_____ in	_____ mm
Piece 5	_____ in	_____ mm

Fig. 4-4 Measurements with thickness gauges.

____ 6. Using a set of stepped thickness gauges, measure each gap or clearance again. Write the measurement in the left column of the chart in Fig. 4-5. (When using a stepped thickness gauge, if the tip of the blade goes into the gap, and the bigger part of the blade does not, the measurement is halfway between the two thicknesses of the blade.) Then con-

vert each measurement to its metric equivalent. Enter that measurement in the right column.

Piece 1	_____ in	_____ mm
Piece 2	_____ in	_____ mm
Piece 3	_____ in	_____ mm
Piece 4	_____ in	_____ mm
Piece 5	_____ in	_____ mm

Fig. 4-5 Measurements with stepped thickness gauges.

____ 7. Now, use the wire gauges to measure the gaps of five used spark plugs. Write the measurements in the left column of the chart in Fig. 4-6. Next measure the gaps of the same five used spark plugs with the flat gauges. Write these measurements in the right column.

	WIRE THICKNESS GAUGE	FLAT THICKNESS GAUGE
Piece 1	_____ in	_____ in
Piece 2	_____ in	_____ in
Piece 3	_____ in	_____ in
Piece 4	_____ in	_____ in
Piece 5	_____ in	_____ in

Fig. 4-6 Measuring spark-plug gaps.

JOB 4-1   MULTIPLE-CHOICE TEST

1. Thickness gauges are used to measure
   a. small distances between parts
   b. large distances between small parts
   c. the thickness of round wire
   d. all of the above   1. ____

2. Wire gauges are used to measure
   a. spark-plug gaps
   b. contact-point openings
   c. both a and b
   d. neither a nor b   2. ____

3. A thickness blade that has two thicknesses on it is
   a. a stepped thickness gauge
   b. a go–no-go gauge
   c. both a and b
   d. neither a nor b   3. ____

4. After using steel thickness blades, you should
   a. clean the blade with emery cloth
   b. wipe the blade and holder with a clean oiled cloth
   c. wash the blade and holder with soap and water
   d. all of the above   4. ____

5. When measuring the air gap in some electronic distributors, you will need
   a. steel thickness gauges
   b. stepped thickness gauges
   c. wire thickness gauges
   d. brass thickness gauges   5. ____

JOB 4-2
Using Micrometers

Objective: To learn how to use micrometers.

References: AM ♦4-11 to 4-20, SG Chap. 4, automotive manufacturers' service manuals.

Equipment: Round and flat pieces to be measured; an engine cylinder.
Tools: Outside and inside micrometers.

♦ **SAFETY** ♦ *Never attempt to measure a part that is moving such as a shaft that is turning. The micrometer might jam on the shaft, be whirled around, and break. If this happens, you might be injured by flying particles.*

SHOP FACTS

READING A MICROMETER

A micrometer is a special form of caliper. A micrometer measures very accurately. In addition, measurements can be read directly from a micrometer. However, instead of reading in fractions of an inch like many rules, a micrometer reads in tenths, hundredths, thousandths, and sometimes ten-thousandths of an inch. It uses the decimal system.

In the shop, a micrometer is usually called a "mike." Measuring something with a mike is called "miking."

Examine an outside micrometer. Identify the anvil, frame, spindle, hub, and thimble.

Note the locknut and the ratchet stop. Here's how the locknut is used. Suppose, for example, that you are measuring a shaft, but that the position of the micrometer does not allow you to see the reading. In this case, you can turn the locknut with your fingers. This locks the spindle at the final setting so that you can remove the micrometer from the shaft and take the reading.

The ratchet stop is a friction clutch that is built into the micrometer. If you turn the ratchet stop instead of the thimble, when the proper force is applied by the anvil to the piece being measured, the ratchet stop will slip. This prevents the spindle from turning any further. The use of the ratchet stop makes taking readings faster and more accurate, especially for someone not accustomed to using a micrometer.

Hold the micrometer in your hand and turn the thimble so that the spindle moves away from the anvil. Note the markings on the hub and the thimble. The measurement is read from the hub and the thimble.

Note in Fig. 4-7 that the hub, or barrel, is marked off in uniform spacings of 0.025 inch. The circumference of the thimble is marked off by 25 graduations. Each graduation represents 0.001 inch.

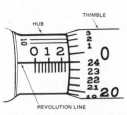

Fig. 4-7 Hub and thimble markings on a micrometer.

To measure with a micrometer, turn the ratchet screw until the piece being measured is a light-drag fit between the anvil and the end of the spindle. Then read the measurement on the barrel and the thimble.

Each barrel marking indicates 0.025 inch. Four markings make 0.100 inch. If three of the numbers are visible, then the thimble has uncovered 12 markings. The measurement is at least 0.300 inch.

Notice the words "at least" above. Checking the barrel is only the first step in reading the measurement. The second step is to note exactly where the markings on the thimble are, relative to the line on the barrel.

Assume, for example, that the thimble has been turned so that the fourth line after the zero aligns with the barrel line. This means that the thimble has been turned 0.004 inch past the 0.300-inch mark. Each thimble marking represents 0.001 inch. Therefore, the actual measurement is 0.304 inch (0.300 plus 0.004).

THE METRIC MICROMETER

A metric micrometer (shown in AM Fig. 4-15) reads in millimeters and hundredths of a millimeter. The barrel is marked off in millimeters above the line and in half millimeters below the line. The thimble is marked off into divisions of 0.01 mm.

To read the micrometer in AM Fig. 4-15, add the reading on the barrel (11 mm) to the reading on the thimble (0.45 mm). The total measurement is 11.45 mm.

THE INSIDE MICROMETER

Inside micrometers (AM Fig. 4-11) are used to measure hole diameters, such as the diameter, or bore, of an engine cylinder (AM Fig. 4-17). Extension rods, such as those above the inside micrometer in AM Fig. 4-11, can be attached so that the mike will measure large diameters.

SHOP SKILLS

USING A MICROMETER

_____ 1. Use an outside micrometer to measure the thickness or diameter of a piece of stock or a blade from a set of thickness gauges. Turn the thimble back enough so that the anvil and spindle surfaces pass over the stock without interference. Then turn the thimble slowly forward (clockwise), while repeatedly passing the micrometer over the stock. Continue until the micrometer drags slightly as it passes over the piece being measured.

_____ 2. After adjusting the micrometer to the correct fit, read the measurement. Note first the micrometer size. Then count the exposed markings on the hub. Finally, note the marking on the thimble that is aligned with the heavy line on the hub. Adding these together gives the dimension of the piece that was miked. Write the measurement in the first space on the chart in Fig. 4-8. Then measure four other objects, and record the readings. Have your instructor check your work.

_____ 3. Examine an inside micrometer. Note the markings on the hub and thimble. They correspond to the markings on the hub and thimble of the outside micrometer (Fig. 4-7). The extension rods allow you to measure cylinder diameters from 1½ inches to several inches.

_____ 4. When inserting an extension rod in an inside micrometer, be sure that the extension seats properly. The shoulder on the rod must seat fully for the micrometer to read correctly.

_____ 5. AM Fig. 4-17 shows an inside micrometer being used to measure the bore of an engine cylinder. To measure a cylinder bore, first turn the thimble clockwise until the length of the assembled micrometer is smaller than the diameter of the bore.

_____ 6. With one hand, hold the head end of the micrometer squarely against the cylinder wall. Then, with your other hand, turn the thimble to increase the length of the micrometer. As you do this, feel for the maximum diameter by moving the rod end slightly from left to right and up and down. Read the mike when no left-to-right movement of the rod end is possible, and a slight drag is felt as you move the rod end up and down.

Piece 1	_____ inch	_____ mm
Piece 2	_____ inch	_____ mm
Piece 3	_____ inch	_____ mm
Piece 4	_____ inch	_____ mm
Piece 5	_____ inch	_____ mm

Fig. 4-8 Measurements with an outside micrometer.

_____ 7. Write the cylinder diameter in the first space in Fig. 4-9. Then measure four other cylinders, and enter the measurements.

Piece 1	_____ inch
Piece 2	_____ inch
Piece 3	_____ inch
Piece 4	_____ inch
Piece 5	_____ inch

Fig. 4-9 Measurements with an inside micrometer.

_____ 8. To check the accuracy of the inside micrometer, mike the inside micrometer (Fig. 4-10) with an outside micrometer. This transfers the reading from the inside mike to the outside mike. Both readings should be the same. If they are not, check the zero setting on each micrometer.

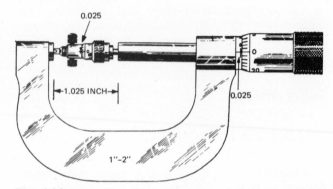

Fig. 4-10 Measuring the setting of an inside micrometer with an outside micrometer.

JOB 4-2   MULTIPLE-CHOICE TEST

1. On an outside micrometer, the part that turns to indicate the reading is the
   a. barrel
   b. anvil
   c. ratchet screw
   d. thimble   1. _____

2. Each complete revolution of the thimble changes the micrometer reading by
   a. 0.100 inch
   b. 0.250 inch
   c. 0.025 inch
   d. 0.001 inch   2. _____

3. A cylinder diameter is given in a service manual as 3⅛ inches. On a micrometer, the reading would be
   a. 3.375 inches
   b. 3.125 inches
   c. 3.1875 inches
   d. 3.750 inches   3. _____

4. To measure the amount of taper in a cylinder, you would use
   a. an outside micrometer
   b. an inside micrometer
   c. a steel scale
   d. a tape measure   4. _____

Name _____ Date _____

JOB 5
Automotive Fasteners

Objective: To learn about the fasteners used on automobiles.

References: AM ♦5-1 to 5-20, SG Chap. 5, automotive manufacturers' service manuals.

Equipment: Assorted screws, bolts, nuts, lock washers, cotter pins, and keys, as supplied by the instructor; shafts and housings with undercuts for snap rings.

Tools: A steel rule; calipers or a micrometer; a thread gauge; snap-ring pliers.

SHOP FACTS

Fasteners are the parts that hold the engine and the vehicle together. Fastener is the name given to any device that holds other parts together. A screw, a nut and bolt, and a stud and nut are examples of fasteners widely used in automobiles. Other types of fasteners are cotter pins, snap rings, splines, and rivets.

There are also permanent ways of fastening parts together, such as welding and brazing. The vehicle frame is welded together. Welding and brazing are specialized jobs sometimes required during automotive service.

METRIC BOLTS, SCREWS, AND THREADS

Metric bolts, screws, and nuts are measured in millimeters, as shown in Figure 5-1. The threads are also different from the threads used on some engines built in the United States. A mechanic working on both domestic and imported cars needs two sets of fasteners and two sets of wrenches.

The different ways that wrench sizes for bolts are measured are shown in Fig. 5-1. In both the USCS (inch system) and the metric system (millimeter system), the wrench size is determined by measuring across the flats of the bolt head. In past years, the British Standard System was used on engines and cars built in England. In this system, the wrench size is determined by measuring, in inches, across the outside diameter of the threads.

Cars, trucks, and motorcycles imported into the United States are dimensioned in the metric system. Also, some engines built in the United States are already completely metric. This means that all measurements and fasteners are in metric units.

Many metric fasteners are very close in dimension to "inch" fasteners in the USCS. You must not mix metric and customary fasteners. Mismatched or incorrect fasteners can result in automobile damage, automobile malfunction, or personal injury. Fasteners removed from the vehicle should be saved for reuse whenever possible. When fasteners are not reusable, select a replacement fastener that is equal to or better than the original.

In general, automobile manufacturers use certain metric

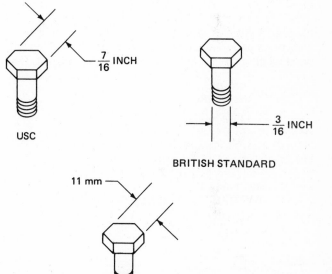

Fig. 5-1 Different ways in which the wrench size for a bolt is determined.

fastener sizes as defined by the International Standards Organization (ISO). This is done to reduce the number of fastener sizes while retaining the best strength characteristics in each thread size. For example, the customary ¼-20 and ¼-28 screws are replaced by the metric M4.3×1 screw. It has nearly the same diameter and 25.4 threads per inch. The thread pitch is between the USCS coarse and fine thread pitches.

Bolt strength, in the metric system, is embossed on the head of the bolt just as in the USCS. In both systems, the higher the number, the higher the strength of the bolt.

When working on automobiles, be sure that metric and inch nuts and bolts are not interchanged. This could result in cross-threading and in a dangerous loosening of the fastener.

If a new metric fastener is to be bought and installed, it must be the equivalent of the original fastener in dimensions, strength, and the pitch of the threads. If an equivalent metric fastener is not available from your local fastener supplier, the proper fastener can be obtained from the dealer for the vehicle you are repairing.

All pipe-plug threads are the same in both the USCS and the metric system.

SHOP SKILLS

___ 1. Examine different screws and bolts. Note the types of heads on them. Select several bolts of different types and sizes. With a steel rule, calipers or a micrometer, and a thread gauge, take various measurements, as shown in Fig. 5-2. Write the measurements in the spaces provided in the table in Fig. 5-3. The threads per inch can be counted or checked with a thread gauge.

___ 2. Examine various nuts. Then, using a thread gauge, select a nut to fit a particular bolt.

___ 3. Examine the various types of lock washers. Some lock washers depend for their locking on the biting of the split or twisted sections into the bolt or nut and metal part. Others depend for their locking action on tangs that are bent up along the flat on the bolt head or nut.

___ 4. A different locking action is obtained with a cotter pin. Examine several sizes of cotter pins. The cotter pin is inserted through slots in the nut and a hole in the shaft. Then the cotter-pin ends are cut off to the desired length and bent back around the nut to lock it in place.

___ 5. Examine the keys and keyways, such as the ones used in alternator rotors and pulleys and on wheels and axles. Note how the key locks the shaft and the rotating part together. Splines, such as those used with shafts and sliding gears, are a special form of key and keyway. The "keys," or splines, on the shaft and the rotating part fit between each other.

___ 6. Study other fastening and retaining devices used on automobiles. These include snap rings, which snap into undercuts on shafts or other parts to hold them in the proper relationship; C washers, which perform a similar function; and rivets. Use snap-ring pliers to install and remove external and internal snap rings.

JOB 5 MULTIPLE-CHOICE TEST

1. A fastener is
   a. any device that holds other parts together
   b. any type of welding or soldering
   c. any type of solvent
   d. none of the above   1. ___

2. The strength of a bolt usually is marked on its
   a. shank, or diameter
   b. threads, with a dab of paint
   c. head
   d. none of the above   2. ___

3. If metric and "inch" bolts are interchanged, the result could be
   a. a perfect fit
   b. cross-threading and loosening
   c. a fit that requires the use of a locking cement
   d. none of the above   3. ___

4. All pipe threads are
   a. the same in both the USCS and the metric system
   b. interchangeable between the USCS and the metric system
   c. both a and b
   d. neither a nor b   4. ___

5. Splines are a form of
   a. screw and thread
   b. lock and lock washer
   c. rivet and pin
   d. none of the above   5. ___

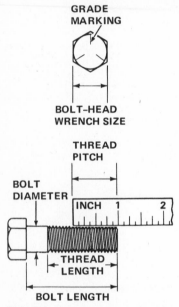

Fig. 5-2 Various measurements of a bolt. (ATW)

BOLT NUMBER	A LENGTH	B DIAMETER	C THREADS PER INCH	D LENGTH OF THREAD	E WRENCH SIZE

Fig. 5-3 Bolt-measurement practice.

JOB 6
Shop Hand Tools

Objective: To learn about the types and uses of hand tools used in the automotive shop.

References: AM ♦6-1 to 6-21, SG Chap. 6, automotive manufacturers' service manuals.

Equipment: Various engines and vehicles.
Tools: Various types and sizes of shop hand tools.

♦ ——————————————————————————————— ♦

SHOP FACTS

HAND TOOLS AND MACHINE TOOLS

Two main types of tools are used in the shop. One type is called *hand tools* because your hand supplies the energy to operate them. The hammer is a good example of a hand tool. The other type is called *machine tools* or *power tools*. Electricity, compressed air, or hydraulic pressure supplies the power for these tools.

An example of a machine tool that uses electric power is an electric drill. It has an electric motor that spins a drill bit. Tools using compressed air for power are called *pneumatic tools*. "Pneumatic" means "of or related to air." An impact wrench is an example of a pneumatic tool.

SCREWDRIVERS

A screwdriver is used to drive, or turn, screws with slotted or recessed heads. The most common type is the driver for slotted screwheads (Fig. 6-1).

A Phillips-head screw (Fig. 6-1) has two slots that cross at the center. There is less chance that a screwdriver will slip out of the slots and damage the finish. Three sizes of Phillips-head screwdrivers, 4, 6, and 8 inch [100, 150, and 200 mm] are the minimum needed for most automotive work.

HAMMERS

The ball-peen hammer (Fig. 6-2) is the one most commonly used by mechanics. It should be gripped on the end, and the face should strike the object squarely. Hammers for striking on easily marred surfaces also are shown in Fig. 6-2. These include the rawhide-faced, plastic-tip, and brass hammers.

PLIERS

There are two basic types of pliers, gripping pliers and cutting pliers. Do not use pliers to grip hardened-steel surfaces. This

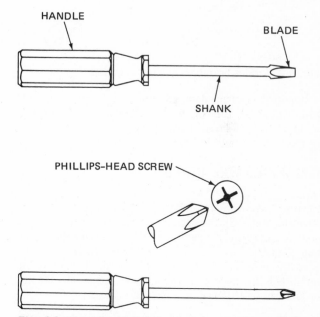

Fig. 6-1 (Top) Typical slotted-head screwdriver. (Bottom) Phillips-head screwdriver.

dulls the teeth of the jaws of the pliers. Do not use standard pliers on nuts or bolts. This damages the nut or the bolt head so that wrenches will not fit on it.

WRENCHES

A variety of wrenches are used in the automotive shop. To work on both domestic and imported vehicles, you will need two sets of wrenches. Some vehicles made in the United States use bolts that have heads which are measured in fractions of an inch (Fig. 5-1). These need inch-type wrenches. A 10-piece set (⅜ to 1 inch) will handle most jobs.

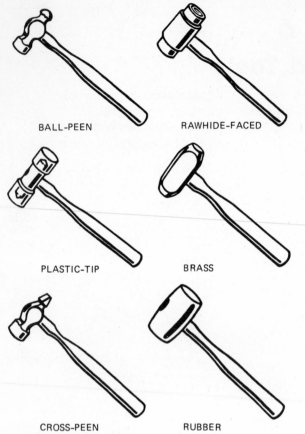

BALL-PEEN   RAWHIDE-FACED

PLASTIC-TIP   BRASS

CROSS-PEEN   RUBBER

Fig. 6-2 Various hammers used in the shop.

Imported and some domestic vehicles use metric nuts and bolts. On these, the bolt heads and nuts are measured in millimeters. A 10-piece metric wrench set (6 to 19 mm) will fit most metric nuts and bolts.

OPEN-END WRENCHES

Open-end wrenches are designed to tighten or loosen nuts and bolts (Fig. 6-3). The opening is usually on an angle to the body of the wrench to permit turning in a tight space. The nut or bolt is turned as far as the space allows. Then the wrench can be flipped over to permit further turning of the nut or bolt. By flipping the wrench after each swing, the nut or bolt can be loosened or tightened satisfactorily.

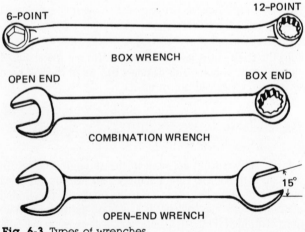

6-POINT   12-POINT
BOX WRENCH

OPEN END   BOX END
COMBINATION WRENCH

15°
OPEN-END WRENCH

Fig. 6-3 Types of wrenches.

BOX WRENCHES

Box wrenches (Fig. 6-3) do the same job as open-end wrenches. However, the opening for the nut or bolt head surrounds, or "boxes," the nut or bolt head. Box wrenches can be used in very tight spaces because the wrench head is very thin. Also, a box wrench seldom slips off the nut.

The 12-point box wrench (Fig. 6-3) is now used almost everywhere. It has 12 notches in the head. This means that a nut or bolt can be turned even where there is a swing of only 15 degrees. Some box wrenches have the head at an angle of 15 degrees to the handle. This provides added clearance for your hand.

COMBINATION OPEN-END AND BOX WRENCHES

A combination wrench has a box wrench on one end and an open-end wrench on the other (Fig. 6-3). A box wrench is more convenient for the final tightening or breaking loose of a nut or bolt. It is less convenient for rapidly turning the nut or bolt. The box must be lifted completely off and then placed back on for each swing. An open-end wrench is more likely to slip off and is less convenient for the final tightening or breaking loose of a nut or bolt. But an open-end wrench is more convenient for running a nut or bolt off or on. A combination wrench lets a mechanic use first one type and then the other by reversing ends.

SOCKET WRENCHES

Socket wrenches are similar to box wrenches, except that the sockets are detachable. Figure 6-4 illustrates a set of socket wrenches with several types of handles. The sockets fit onto the handles. The mechanic uses the handle that best suits the job. For example, for speed in turning a loose nut or bolt, use the speed handle. But for breaking loose a nut or bolt, use the ratchet or the breaker bar (nut spinner).

If you are going to work on automobiles, you will need a set of metric sockets. Sockets sized according to the USCS will not fit some nuts and bolts on imported automobiles. Study Fig. 6-5 to familiarize yourself with the difference between metric and USCS sizes of sockets.

ALLEN WRENCHES

An Allen wrench is a special form of turning tool. It has a hexagonal (six-sided) shape and fits into a hexagonal hole in the head of an Allen screw. Allen wrenches fit many set-screws.

ADJUSTABLE WRENCHES

An adjustable wrench has an adjustable jaw that can be moved back and forth to narrow or widen the distance between the jaws. Moving the jaw allows an adjustable wrench

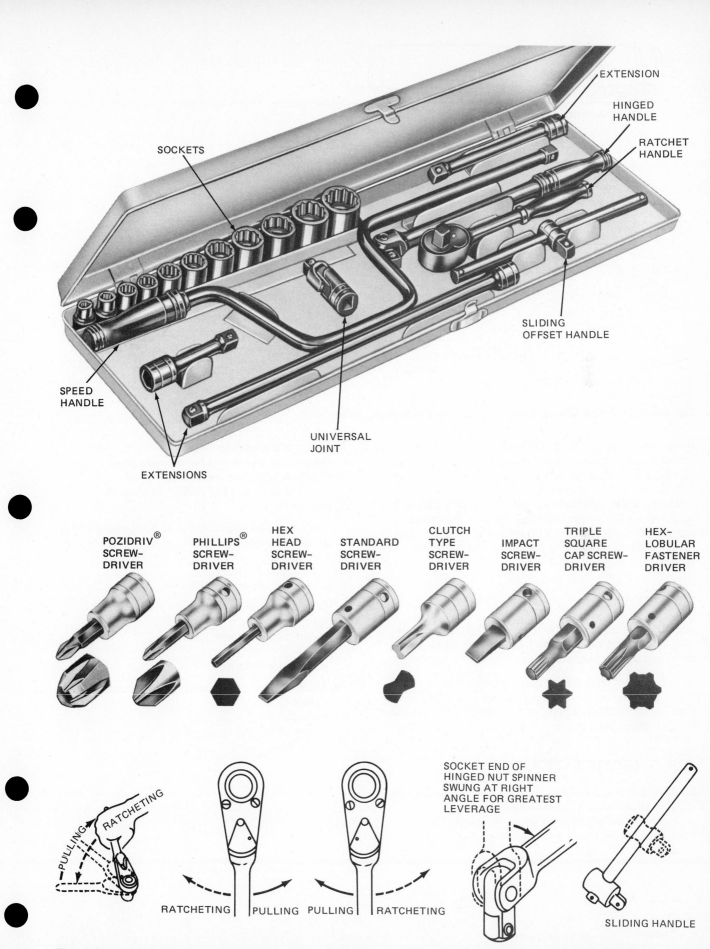

SOCKETS

EXTENSION

HINGED HANDLE

RATCHET HANDLE

SLIDING OFFSET HANDLE

SPEED HANDLE

EXTENSIONS

UNIVERSAL JOINT

POZIDRIV® SCREW-DRIVER

PHILLIPS® SCREW-DRIVER

HEX HEAD SCREW-DRIVER

STANDARD SCREW-DRIVER

CLUTCH TYPE SCREW-DRIVER

IMPACT SCREW-DRIVER

TRIPLE SQUARE CAP SCREW-DRIVER

HEX-LOBULAR FASTENER DRIVER

PULLING RATCHETING

RATCHETING PULLING PULLING RATCHETING

SOCKET END OF HINGED NUT SPINNER SWUNG AT RIGHT ANGLE FOR GREATEST LEVERAGE

SLIDING HANDLE

Fig. 6-4 Set of sockets with handles, extensions, screwdrivers, and a universal joint. (Snap-on Tools Corporation)

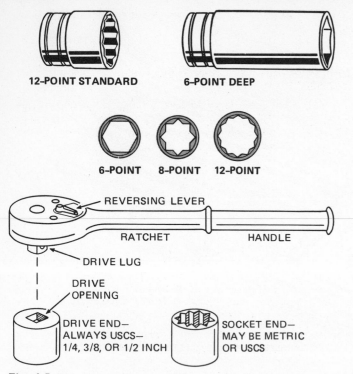

12–POINT STANDARD **6–POINT DEEP**

6–POINT **8–POINT** **12–POINT**

REVERSING LEVER

RATCHET HANDLE

DRIVE LUG

DRIVE
OPENING

DRIVE END—
ALWAYS USCS—
1/4, 3/8, OR 1/2 INCH

SOCKET END—
MAY BE METRIC
OR USCS

Fig. 6-5 Difference between metric and USCS sizes of sockets. **(ATW)**

to fit many sizes of nut or bolt heads. This tool is not intended to take the place of the standard wrench. However, an adjustable wrench is handy for special jobs or odd sizes of nuts or bolts.

When using an adjustable wrench, make sure it is properly tightened on the nut or bolt head. Position the wrench so that the adjustable jaw is on the inside of the turning motion. In this position, the pulling force keeps the adjustable jaw tight against the nut or bolt head.

SHOP SKILLS

____ 1. In the shop, you may be assigned a set of hand tools. Your instructor should give you an inventory sheet, listing each item in your assigned toolbox.

____ 2. Lay out on the bench the tools assigned to you. Then mark off on the inventory sheet each tool as you inspect it. Note any abnormal conditions, such as bent screwdrivers and loose heads on hammers.

JOB 6 MULTIPLE-CHOICE TEST

1. A hand tool is a tool that
   a. you can hand to another person
   b. your hand supplies the energy to operate
   c. must be insulated from your hand
   d. none of the above   1. ____

2. Two types of screwdrivers are for
   a. slotted-head screws and hollow-point screws
   b. Phillips-head screws and locking screws
   c. slotted-head screws and Phillips-head screws
   d. none of the above   2. ____

3. A wrench that has one open end and one closed end is
   a. an open-end wrench
   b. a box wrench
   c. an adjustable wrench
   d. none of the above   3. ____

4. To use a wrench safely, always
   a. pull it toward you
   b. push it away from you
   c. place a pipe over the end
   d. hit it with a hammer   4. ____

5. The hammer used most commonly by mechanics is a
   a. rawhide-faced
   b. plastic-tip
   c. cross-peen
   d. ball-peen   5. ____

JOB 7
Air Tools and Impact Wrenches

Objective: To learn how to use air tools and impact wrenches.

References: AM ♦7-7 to 7-13, SG Chap. 7, automotive manufacturers' service manuals.

Equipment: Practice engine.
Tools: Shop air tools.

♦ **SAFETY** ♦ *Compressed-air tools are safe and reliable when properly and sensibly used. However, compressed air can be dangerous, even deadly, when it is misused. Never look into the air outlet or nozzle of any compressed-air tool or device such as a blowgun. Never point discharging air at any part of your body or at anyone else. When you do, you change a useful labor-saving tool into a dangerous weapon that can cause permanent injury and even death.*

SHOP FACTS

Tools and equipment operated by compressed air are *pneumatic* devices. "Pneumatic" means "of or related to air." We use the common terms "air tools" and "air equipment" when talking about air-powered shop tools.

First, let us see how to get air pressure in the shop. Air pressure is produced by an air compressor (Fig. 7-1). The air-compressor unit includes an electric motor that drives an air pump. This pump starts running automatically when the pressure falls below a preset value. The pump sends air into the compressor air tank for storage. That way, there is always a reserve of compressed air ready to serve the air tools and equipment in the shop. A schematic of a complete shop air-supply system is shown in Fig. 7-1.

Impact wrenches are used to run nuts and bolts in and out rapidly. The direction of rotation can be changed with a reversing control on the impact wrench.

Most shop impact wrenches have a standard ½-in [12.7-mm] socket drive. However, only special impact sockets should be used with the impact wrench. Standard sockets crack and round out when used on an impact wrench. Impact sockets are frequently black in color.

Some impact wrenches are powered by an electric motor (Fig. 7-2). The electric impact wrench is usually larger and bulkier than a comparable air impact wrench. In addition, you must be careful not to cut or damage the electric cord while working with an electric impact wrench.

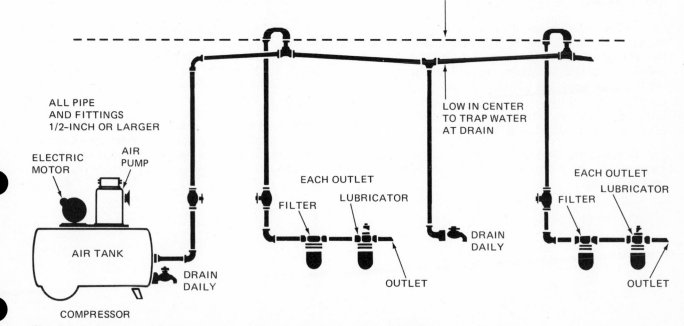

Fig. 7-1 A shop compressed-air system. **(Chicago Pneumatic Tool Company)**

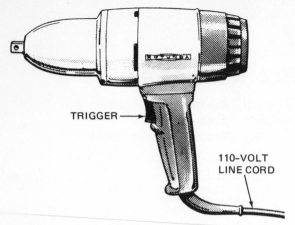

Fig. 7-2 An electric impact wrench. (Ford Motor Company)

Here are some recommendations for using an impact wrench:

1. Always use impact sockets on an impact wrench.
2. Use only the correct size socket for the bolt or nut.
3. Use the simplest possible assembly of sockets, extensions, and universal joint.
4. Use a deep socket, where possible, rather than a standard-length socket and an extension.
5. Hold the wrench so that the socket fits squarely on the bolt or nut. Apply a slight forward pressure to hold the socket in place.
6. Once a nut or bolt tightens, never impact it beyond an additional one-half turn of the socket. Continued impacting might strip the threads or break the bolt.
7. Never use an impact wrench beyond its rated capacity. If a bolt or nut remains tight after impacting for 5 seconds, use a larger wrench.
8. Soak large rusty nuts and bolts with penetrating oil before impacting them.

SHOP SKILLS

____ 1. Every day, before using an air tool or impact wrench, apply three or four squirts of flushing oil into the tool air inlet. (See Fig. 7-12 in Chap. 7 of AM.) Then connect and operate the tool. This flushes any gum, dirt, or moisture out of the air motor and lubricates the moving parts. Any deposits in the wrench are flushed out through the air exhaust. Do not flush the wrench around an open flame. Always point the tool air exhaust away from your body.

____ 2. Locate the compressed-air outlets in the shop and in your work area. Practice connecting and disconnecting an air hose at the outlet.

____ 3. Check out an impact-wrench set. Identify the trigger, reversing control, and air or power regulator. Squirt a few drops of air-tool oil into the air inlet. Connect the hose to the impact wrench, and press the trigger. Then reverse the direction of rotation with the reversing control. Change the position of the power regulator to note how it changes the operation of the impact wrench.

____ 4. Examine the impact sockets. Compare an impact socket with a standard socket. Most impact sockets are six-point sockets. The impact socket is often heavier and slightly thicker than a comparable standard socket.

____ 5. Practice using the impact wrench on an engine or some other assembly with several sizes of nuts and bolts. Run the bolts in and out. The impact wrench is a time-saver. But for accurate tightening of nuts and bolts, a torque wrench is still required.

JOB 7 MULTIPLE-CHOICE TEST

1. In the shop, the source of compressed air is
   a. the shop air compressor
   b. bottles of compressed air
   c. an air hose
   d. none of the above   1. ____

2. The electric impact wrench, when compared to an air impact wrench of comparable size, is usually
   a. lighter and more compact
   b. the same weight and size
   c. never predictable in weight and size
   d. larger and bulkier   2. ____

3. Looking into the nozzle of a compressed-air tool
   a. can be safe if the tool has worked properly before
   b. is never safe to do
   c. is safe at low air pressure
   d. none of the above   3. ____

4. Once a nut or bolt tightens, never impact it beyond an additional
   a. one-half turn of the socket
   b. one-quarter turn of the socket
   c. one whole turn of the socket
   d. none of the above   4. ____

5. When using an impact wrench,
   a. occasionally use impact sockets on an impact wrench
   b. always use impact sockets on an impact wrench
   c. never use impact sockets on an impact wrench
   d. none of the above   5. ____

Name _____ Date _____

JOB 8
Engine Fundamentals: Measurements

Objective: To learn about the fundamental measurements of the engine.

References: AM ♦8-1 to 8-15, SG Chap. 8, automotive manufacturers' service manuals.

Equipment: None.
Tools: None.

SHOP FACTS

Most of the thermometers we use measure temperature based on the Fahrenheit (F) scale. On this scale, water freezes at 32°F and boils at 212°F. With the increasing use of the metric system, temperatures now often are given in degrees Celsius (C). The Celsius scale formerly was called the centigrade scale. Figure 8-1 compares the two temperature scales.

A frequent problem for the automobile mechanic is that the thermometer reads in degrees F and the specification is given in degrees C. To convert from degrees F to degrees C, use the following formula:

$$C° = 0.56 (F° - 32)$$

Here is an example of how to use the formula. We know that water boils at 212°F (at sea level). To find the boiling point of water in degrees C, we proceed as follows:

$$C° = 0.56 (F° - 32)$$
$$C° = 0.56 (212 - 32)$$
$$C° = 0.56 (180)$$
$$C° = 100$$

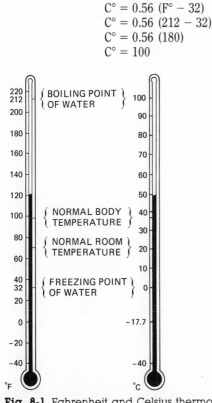

Fig. 8-1 Fahrenheit and Celsius thermometers.

In a few simple arithmetic steps, we find that the boiling point of water in the metric system is 100°C.

SHOP MATH

____ 1. Using the formula and following the example given above, find the temperature in degrees C for the following:
   a. Water freezes at sea level at 32°F.

   32°F = _____°C

   b. A mixture of 50 percent water and 50 percent antifreeze in the radiator will protect the engine against freeze to −34°F.

   −34°F = _____°C

   c. The *hot* temperature indicator light on a new car is set to come on at 260°F.

   260°F = _____°C

____ 2. Most of us have always measured pressure in pounds per square inch. However, many specifications for pressure are now given in the metric term of kilopascals. To change a reading in psi to kPa, use the following formula:

$$kPa = psi × 6.9$$

For example, the oil pressure in an engine is given as 40 psi. To find the pressure in kPa, proceed as follows:

$$kPa = psi × 6.9$$
$$kPa = 40 × 6.9$$
$$kPa = 276$$

____ 3. Using the formula and following the example in step 2 above, find the pressure in kPa for the following: The fuel-pump pressure on a car is given as 3 to 5 psi.

   3 to 5 psi = _____ to _____ kPa

JOB 8   MULTIPLE-CHOICE TEST

1. Another word for combustion is
   a. water
   b. gasoline
   c. vapor
   d. fire

   1. ____

2. An engine runs because combustion produces
   a. atoms
   b. vapor
   c. heat
   d. hydrocarbons   2. ___

3. When a piece of iron is heated, it
   a. expands
   b. contracts
   c. gets weaker
   d. gets stronger   3. ___

4. When gas is compressed, its temperature
   a. decreases
   b. increases
   c. stays the same
   d. may increase or decrease   4. ___

5. As an automobile engine operates, it produces a partial vacuum in the
   a. engine cylinders
   b. crankcase
   c. fuel tank
   d. muffler   5. ___

Name _____ Date _____

JOB 9
Piston-Engine Operation

Objective: To learn the principles of the four-stroke-cycle engine.

References: AM ♦9-1 to 9-16, SG Chap. 9, automotive manufacturers' service manuals.

Equipment: Engines partly disassembled so that movement of parts can be seen when the crankshaft is rotated.
Tools: None.

SHOP SKILLS

_____ 1. Slowly turn the engine. Note that, while the piston moves up and down *twice,* each valve opens and closes *once.*

_____ 2. Note which is the intake valve and which is the exhaust valve in the cylinder head so that four cycles can be identified.

_____ 3. Turn the engine to the intake stroke on the cylinder you are watching.

_____ 4. Notice that as the piston moves down on the intake stroke, the intake valve is open. (See Fig. 9-11 in Chap. 9 of AM.) In an operating engine, this allows the piston to pull into the cylinder a mixture of fuel and air.

_____ 5. On the next stroke (the compression stroke) both valves are closed. In an operating engine, the piston would therefore compress the air-fuel mixture.

_____ 6. Note that, as the piston reaches and passes (top dead center (TDC), the power stroke has begun, and both valves are closed. Just before the start of the power stroke, an electric spark at the spark plug ignites the compressed air-fuel mixture.

_____ 7. As the piston approaches bottom dead center (BDC) on the power stroke, the exhaust valve opens.

_____ 8. As the piston moves up on the exhaust stroke, the exhaust valve is open. This allows the piston to force from the cylinder the burned gases or products of combustion.

_____ 9. Note that the exhaust valve closes and the intake valve opens as the piston reaches TDC at the end of the exhaust stroke.

_____ 10. The engine has rotated through one complete four-stroke cycle. The crankshaft has turned two complete revolutions, with each valve opening and closing once. Continue turning the crankshaft. Study the piston and valve action until you completely understand the principle of the four-stroke-cycle engine.

JOB 9 MULTIPLE-CHOICE TEST

1. In the four-cycle engine, the exhaust stroke immediately follows the
   a. power stroke
   b. intake stroke
   c. compression stroke
   d. outlet stroke   1. ____

2. In the four-cycle engine, the compression stroke immediately follows the
   a. outlet stroke
   b. power stroke
   c. intake stroke
   d. exhaust stroke   2. ____

3. In the four-cycle engine, the intake stroke immediately follows the
   a. exhaust stroke
   b. power stoke
   c. outlet stroke
   d. compression stroke   3. ____

4. In the four-cycle engine, the power stroke immediately follows the
   a. exhaust stroke
   b. outlet stroke
   c. compression stroke
   d. intake stroke   4. ____

5. The piston movement from TDC to BDC is called
   a. two cycles
   b. four cycles
   c. a stroke
   d. a strike   5. ____

JOB 10
Engine Types

Objective: To learn about the types of engines used in various automobiles.

References: AM ♦10-1 to 10-19, SG Chap. 10, automotive manufacturers' service manuals.

Equipment: Five different cars or engines to be examined.
Tools: None.

♦ ——————————————————————————— ♦

SHOP SKILLS

____ 1. Your instructor will point out a minimum of five different cars or engines for you to examine. Each of these cars or engines will be assigned a number from 1 to 5.

____ 2. Identify Car 1. Enter the make and model year of the car in the space provided in the chart in Fig. 10-1.

____ 3. Raise the hood and determine how many cylinders the engine has. Write this information in the space provided in the chart.

____ 4. From the information found in the engine compartment and from reference to the automobile manufacturers' service manuals, determine the displacement of the engine in cubic inches and liters (or cubic centimeters). Enter this information in the chart.

____ 5. Examine the engine, and determine the cylinder arrangement—such as "in line," or "V type." Enter this information in the chart.

____ 6. Determine the camshaft location of the engine and enter this information in the chart. If you need help, refer to your AM textbook or to the automobile manufacturers' service manuals.

____ 7. After you complete all the information needed for each car in the chart, move on to the next engine to be studied. When the chart is completely filled in, have the instructor check your work.

JOB 10 MULTIPLE-CHOICE TEST

1. Most new engines are of the
   a. four-in-line type
   b. V-6 type
   c. eight-in-line type
   d. rotary type   1. ____

2. Most new engines have
   a. in-line valves
   b. in-block valves
   c. L heads
   d. I heads   2. ____

3. Engines are classified as
   a. liquid-cooled and air-cooled
   b. liquid-cooled and statically cooled
   c. liquid-cooled and solid-cooled
   d. air-cooled and ground-cooled   3. ____

4. When an engine has one set of valves in the head and none in the block, it is known as
   a. a T-head engine
   b. an F-head engine
   c. an I-head engine
   d. an L-head engine   4. ____

5. Automotive engines are of the
   a. four-cycle type
   b. three-cycle type
   c. two-cycle type
   d. one-cycle type   5. ____

	EXAMPLE	CAR 1	CAR 2	CAR 3	CAR 4	CAR 5
Make	Ford					
Model Year	1983					
Number of Cylinders	4					
Displacement	97.6 CID/1.6 L					
Cylinder arrangement	in-line					
Camshaft location	in head					

Fig. 10-1 Types of engines.

JOB 11
Engine Construction

Objective: To learn about the construction of various types of pistons, rings, connecting rods, and bearings and to learn the details of construction of cylinder blocks and cylinder heads.

References: AM ♦11-1 to 11-42, SG Chap. 11, automotive manufacturers' service manuals.

Equipment: Various pistons, piston rings, connecting rods, cylinder blocks, and cylinder heads.
Tools: Micrometers.

♦ _____ ♦

SHOP SKILLS

____ 1. From an examination of the block, determine how many main bearings are used in the engine. Examine each main-bearing bulkhead carefully to locate the thrust-bearing position in the engine.

____ 2. Note whether the main-bearing caps are secured in place with studs or bolts.

____ 3. Determine how many camshaft bearings are used in the engine.

____ 4. Identify each hole in the block. Be sure you can name the bolt-head holes, pushrod holes, valve-lifter holes, etc. If you are unable to identify any hole, refer to the automobile manufacturers' service manuals, or ask your instructor for assistance.

____ 5. Note the water jackets and the coolant circulation ports, which permit coolant to pass between the block and the head.

____ 6. Notice the numerous machined surfaces of the block. Identify the surfaces as to the engine components that mount on them (head, oil pan, clutch housing, etc.).

____ 7. Identify the general shape of the combustion chamber, such as "hemi," "wedge," or "open."

____ 8. Note the shape of the water jackets and how the water jackets surround the combustion chamber. Notice how the water jackets are designed to permit free circulation of coolant over the top of the combustion chamber and around the spark-plug openings.

____ 9. Examine the formation of the water jackets and the provisions for coolant circulation around the intake-valve and exhaust-valve seats.

____ 10. Note how the valve guides are mounted in the head. Determine whether the valve guides are integral or replaceable.

____ 11. Examine the intake- and exhaust-valve ports and the intake- and exhaust-valve seats. Determine whether replaceable valve-seat inserts are used for any of the intake- or exhaust-valve seats.

____ 12. Examine several pistons to note their construction. Note struts and reinforcing sections in pistons.

____ 13. Note the shapes of piston heads and pistons. Carefully examine how the tops of some pistons are cut away to prevent the valves from striking them.

____ 14. Use a micrometer to measure piston-skirt diameters in line with and at 90 degrees to the piston pin. Note that there is a difference on cam-ground pistons (Fig. 11-1). Also, note the smaller diameter of the piston at the head. This compensates for the greater expansion that is due to the higher temperatures of the piston head.

____ 15. Notice how most pistons have the skirts cut away to provide rod clearance and reduce weight.

____ 16. Examine various pistons, piston pins, and connecting rods to find different methods of attaching connecting rods to pistons.

____ 17. Examine various piston rings to note the types of compression and oil-control rings. Identify the top side of each piston ring.

____ 18. Determine whether the piston pin is "offset." If it is, toward which side of the piston is it offset?

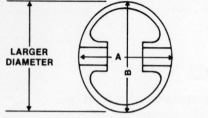

Fig. 11-1 When a cam-ground piston is cold, its diameter at A is smaller than at B. **(Chrysler Corporation)**

JOB 11   MULTIPLE-CHOICE TEST

1. Most spark-ignition engines have
   a. two rings per piston
   b. three rings per piston
   c. four rings per piston
   d. five rings per piston   1. ____

2. The piston pin may be free floating or
   a. locked to the piston *and* rod
   b. static
   c. integral with the piston
   d. locked to the piston *or* rod   2. ____

3. The escape of burned gas from the combustion chamber past the pistons and rings is called
   a. blowoff
   b. passed gas
   c. gas loss
   d. blowby   3. ____

4. Piston rings do three jobs: They seal between the piston and cylinder wall, they help control the oil, and they
   a. help heat the piston
   b. keep coolant off the piston
   c. help cool the piston
   d. keep oil off the piston   4. ____

5. The ring expander combined with the ring offers the advantage of
   a. high flexibility with high tension
   b. extra rigidity with high tension
   c. high flexibility with low tension
   d. low flexibility with light tension   5. ____

6. The water pump is usually attached to the cylinder block at the
   a. back
   b. top
   c. side
   d. front   6. ____

7. On overhead-valve V-8 engines, the manifolds are attached to the
   a. block
   b. frame
   c. heads
   d. head   7. ____

8. The V-8 I-head engine has
   a. one intake manifold
   b. two intake manifolds
   c. three intake manifolds
   d. a combination intake-exhaust manifold   8. ____

9. V-8 engines have
   a. one head
   b. two heads
   c. single heads
   d. V heads   9. ____

10. The part that, in effect, hangs from the bottom of the cylinder block and is supported by caps is the
    a. crankshaft
    b. pistons
    c. connecting rod
    d. pan   10. ____

JOB 12
Valves and Valve Trains

Objective: To become familiar with valves and valve trains.

References: AM ♦12-1 to 12-14, SG Chap. 12, automotive manufacturers' service manuals.

Equipment: Cylinder heads partly disassembled so that the valves and valve mechanisms can be studied; valve-train parts, including hydraulic valve lifters.
Tools: None.

♦ _____ ♦

SHOP SKILLS

____ 1. Study the various valve trains and valve-train parts until you understand how the rotation of the camshaft causes the valves to open.

____ 2. Examine the different types of rocker arms. Some are cast and some are stamped. Notice the different methods of adjustment. Some rocker arms have an adjusting screw in one end, and others have an adjusting nut on a ball stud.

____ 3. Notice that some heads use replaceable valve guides, and others have integral valve guides cast into the cylinder head.

____ 4. Be sure you understand the operation of the various overhead-camshaft valve trains, and how to adjust them.

JOB 12   MULTIPLE-CHOICE TEST

1. Two types of rocker arms used on I-head engines are
   a. solid and machined
   b. cast and machined
   c. cast and stamped
   d. stamped and metal   1. ____

2. In operation, the coolest part of the valve is the
   a. margin
   b. stem
   c. face
   d. head   2. ____

3. Some valves are cooled by having their hollow stem partly filled with
   a. water
   b. hydrogen
   c. cadmium
   d. sodium   3. ____

4. On many engines, a special, heat-resistant steel-alloy ring is used
   a. as the oil seal
   b. for the valve guide
   c. for the intake-valve seat
   d. for the exhaust-valve seat   4. ____

5. One part of the I-head valve train that is not included in the L-head valve train is the
   a. valve spring
   b. valve lifter
   c. rocker arm
   d. valve guide   5. ____

JOB 13
Engine Measurements and Performance

Objective: To learn about engine measurements and the measurements of engine performance.

References: AM ♦13-1 to 13-15, SG Chap. 13, automotive manufacturers' service manuals.

Equipment: Engine with cylinder head removed.
Tools: Inside micrometers, depth gauge, basic hand tools.

SHOP SKILLS

____ 1. The size of an engine cylinder is referred to in terms of its bore and stroke. The *bore* is the diameter of the cylinder (Fig. 13-1). Set up an inside micrometer, and measure the bore of an engine that has the cylinder head removed. Turn the crankshaft until the piston is at BDC in the cylinder you are measuring.

_____ inch
cylinder bore

____ 2. Now, if a metric-reading inside micrometer is available, measure the bore with it. If a metric micrometer is not

available, use the conversion table in your AM textbook, and convert the bore to millimeters.

_____ mm
cylinder bore

____ 3. Using a depth gauge, or other suitable measuring instrument, measure the stroke of the engine. The *stroke* is the distance the piston travels from BDC to TDC, as shown in Fig. 13-1. To check the accuracy of your reading, turn the crankshaft until the piston is at TDC, and take a reading. Then turn the crankshaft until the piston returns to BDC, and take a second reading. Always turn the crankshaft in its normal direction of rotation.

_____ inch
piston stroke

____ 4. Now, if a metric-reading depth gauge is available, measure the piston stroke in millimeters. If a metric measuring instrument is not available, use the conversion table in your AM textbook, and convert the piston stroke to millimeters.

_____ mm
piston stroke

____ 5. To figure the piston displacement for one cylinder, the following formula can be used: Displacement = $0.7854 \times D^2 \times L$ where D is the diameter, or bore, of the cylinder, and L is the length of the piston stroke.

For example, if the engine you measured has a 4-inch bore and a 3-inch stroke, here is how to figure the displacement of that one cylinder:

$$\text{Displacement} = 0.7854 \times D^2 \times L$$
$$\text{Displacement} = 0.7854 \times (4 \times 4) \times 3$$
$$\text{Displacement} = 0.7854 \times 16 \times 3$$
$$\text{Displacement} = 0.7854 \times 48$$
$$\text{Displacement} = 37.6992 \text{ cubic inches}$$

____ 6. The formula used in step 5 determines the displacement of only *one* cylinder. To find the piston displacement of the engine, multiply by the number of cylinders.

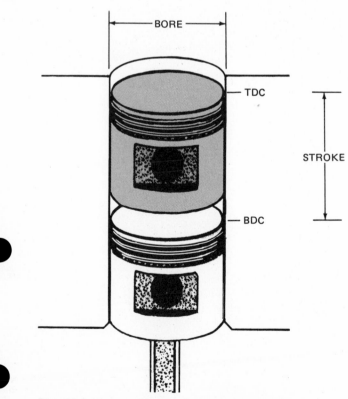

Fig. 13-1 Bore and stroke of an engine cylinder.

For example, if the cylinder used in the example above was in an eight-cylinder engine, the engine displacement is found by multiplying by eight, as follows:

Engine displacement = cylinder displacement × number of cylinders
Engine displacement = 37.6992 × 8
Engine displacement = 301.5936, which would be rounded off to the nearest cubic inch

Engine displacement = 302 cubic inches

_____ 7. In the space below, figure the engine displacement for the engine you have measured.

Engine displacement = _____ cubic inches

_____ 8. Now, check your work by looking up the displacement for the engine you measured in the manufacturer's service manual or in a shop manual.

JOB 13 MULTIPLE-CHOICE TEST

1. In the metric system, power output from an engine may be measured in
   a. kilowatts
   b. horsepower
   c. torque
   d. kilogram-meters   1. ____

2. Torque is measured in
   a. foot-pounds
   b. pound-feet
   c. rpm
   d. volts   2. ____

3. In the metric system, torque is measured in
   a. kilogram-meters
   b. meters-kilogram
   c. foot-pounds
   d. pound-feet   3. ____

4. Average automobile-engine compression ratio is about
   a. 5.0:1
   b. 0.9:1
   c. 16:1
   d. 9.0:1   4. ____

5. A dynamometer measures
   a. indicated horsepower
   b. brake horsepower
   c. friction horsepower
   d. taxable horsepower   5. ____

JOB 14
Automotive Engine Fuels

Objective: To learn about gasoline and its use as an automotive engine fuel.

References: AM ♦14-1 to 14-15, SG Chap. 14, automotive manufacturers' service manuals.

Equipment: Cars with spark-ignition engines.
Tools: Mechanic's stethoscope.

SHOP FACTS

Gasoline is the most commonly used fuel for automotive engines. Historically, automotive gasolines have been classified as premium and regular on the basis of octane number. As a concern about auto emissions grew, low-lead and unleaded grades of gasoline were introduced. However, the combustion process is little changed by burning different brands and grades of gasoline.

GASOLINE

Gasoline is a mixture of hydrocarbons. A hydrocarbon (HC) is a compound made up of hydrogen and carbon. These two elements unite readily with oxygen, a common element which makes up about 20 percent of our air. When hydrogen unites with oxygen, water (H_2O) is formed. When carbon unites with oxygen, carbon monoxide (CO) and carbon dioxide (CO_2) are formed. If all the gasoline burned completely in the engine, all that would come out of the tail pipe would be H_2O and CO_2. However, perfect combustion is not achieved in the engine. Therefore, some CO and HC are present in the exhaust gases. These two compounds, plus a third compound (nitrogen oxides, or NO_x), are the pollutants emitted from automobiles.

Note Gasoline is often referred to as "gas," which can cause some confusion. The sort of gas you burn in a gas stove or use to heat a house is actually a gas that is delivered through gas lines or pipes. So there is "gas" that is a gas, and "gas" that is slang for the liquid fuel gasoline.

Actually, gasoline is not a simple substance. It is a mixture of many different hydrocarbons. Each hydrocarbon has its own characteristics. Aside from the combustibility of gasoline, one of its important properties is its volatility.

Volatility refers to the ease with which a liquid vaporizes. The volatility of a simple compound like water is found by increasing its temperature until it boils, or vaporizes. A liquid that vaporizes at a low temperature has a high volatility; it is highly volatile. If its boiling point is high, its volatility is low. A heavy oil with a boiling point of 600°F [315.5°C] has a low volatility. Gasoline has a high volatility. It boils at 188°F (87°C) at sea level under atmospheric pressure.

Gasoline is blended from different hydrocarbon compounds. Each has a different volatility, or boiling point. The proportions of high-volatility and low-volatility hydrocarbons in gasoline must be correct for engine operating requirements. These requirements include:

1. Easy starting
2. Freedom from vapor lock
3. Quick warm-up
4. Smooth acceleration
5. Good economy
6. Freedom from crankcase dilution

COMBUSTION

During normal combustion in the engine cylinder, shown at the top in Fig. 14-1, the pressure increases evenly. Under some conditions, the last part of the compressed air-fuel mixture explodes, or detonates, as shown at the lower right in Fig. 14-1. This produces a sudden, sharp pressure increase that may cause a pinging noise. It sounds almost as if the cylinder wall has been tapped with a hammer. Actually, the sudden pressure increase does put a sudden heavy load on the piston, almost like a hammer blow. This can be very damaging to the engine. It can wear moving parts rapidly and even cause parts to break. Also, some of the energy in the gasoline is wasted. The sudden pressure increase does not permit best utilization of the fuel energy.

Some types of gasoline produce more pinging than others. Because detonation is such an undesirable characteristic, gasoline producers try to reduce this tendency. Certain chemicals (tetraethyl lead, for example) have been found to reduce detonation when added to gasoline. The actual rating of the antiknock tendencies of a gasoline is given in terms of octane number.

Most late-model cars are designed to operate on unleaded fuels of at least 91 octane research octane number (RON). These fuels minimize spark-plug fouling and emission-control-system deterioration.

Normally, the spark at the spark plug starts the fuel burning in the combustion chamber. A wall of flame spreads out in all directions from the spark (moving outward almost like a rubber balloon being blown up). The flame travels rapidly through the compressed mixture until all the charge is

NORMAL COMBUSTION

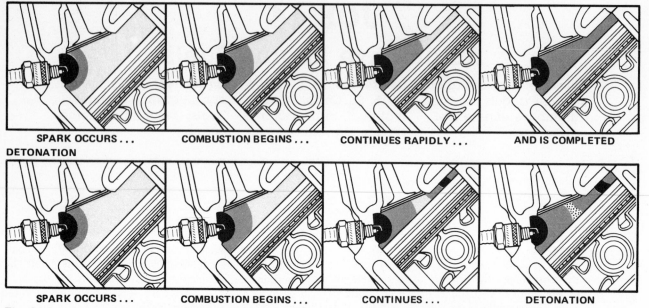

SPARK OCCURS . . .　COMBUSTION BEGINS . . .　CONTINUES RAPIDLY . . .　AND IS COMPLETED

DETONATION

SPARK OCCURS . . .　COMBUSTION BEGINS . . .　CONTINUES . . .　DETONATION

Fig. 14-1 Normal combustion is shown in the top row. Detonation is shown in the bottom row.

burned. The speed with which the flame travels is called the *rate of flame propagation*. The movement of the flame wall during normal combustion is shown in the row of pictures at the top of Fig. 14-1. During combustion, the pressure may exceed 1000 psi [6895 kPa].

Under certain conditions, the last part of the compressed air-fuel mixture, or the end gas, explodes before the flame front reaches it (Fig. 14-1, lower right). The unburned mixture is subject to increasing pressure as the flame moves through the combustion chamber. This increases the temperature of the end gas because of heat of compression and heat from the combustion process. If the temperature goes high enough, the end gas explodes before the flame front arrives. This effect is called *detonation*. The sudden shock load due to detonation increases wear on bearings. Severe detonation may actually break engine parts.

DETONATION AND PREIGNITION

Let us define these two terms. Detonation is a secondary explosion that occurs after the spark at the spark-plug gap. *Preignition* is ignition of the air-fuel mixture prior to the occurrence of the spark at the spark-plug gap.

So far, we have discussed the type of abnormal combustion that results from detonation, or sudden explosion, of the last part of the fuel charge. The pinging sound of detonation is usually regular in character. It is most noticeable when the engine is accelerated or when the car is climbing a hill. Detonation also may occur when the throttle valve is nearly or fully wide open. The engine is taking in a full air-fuel charge on every intake stroke. This means that maximum compression pressures are reached. Detonation pressures are most likely to be reached after the mixture is ignited.

There are other types of abnormal combustion, including surface ignition, preignition, and rumble. Surface ignition can start at hot spots in the combustion chamber from a hot exhaust valve or spark plug or from combustion-chamber

deposits. In some cases the deposits break loose and the particles float free and become hot enough to produce ignition. Surface ignition can occur before (preignition) or after the spark occurs at the spark plug. It can cause engine rumble and rough operation or mild to severe detonation. In some engines, the hot spots act as substitutes for the spark plugs. Then the engine continues to run even after the ignition switch is turned off. This can cause engine damage.

Preignition, surface ignition, and rumble are usually service problems. They may result from inadequate servicing of the engine as well as from the installation of the wrong spark plugs (which run too hot). Abnormal combustion may also result from the use of incorrect fuels and lubricating oils. With incorrect fuel or oil, engine deposits may occur and lead to surface ignition and rumble. Engine deposits also increase the compression ratio so detonation tends to occur more.

COMBUSTION CHAMBER

The shape of the combustion chamber has a great effect on detonation. The top of the combustion chamber of an overhead-valve engine is actually the cylinder head, intake and exhaust valves, and spark plug. The bottom is the piston head and top compression ring (Fig. 14-2). There are two general shapes of combustion chambers, wedge and hemispheric

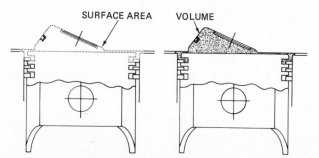

Fig. 14-2 Combustion chamber. The surface area is shown by the dotted line.

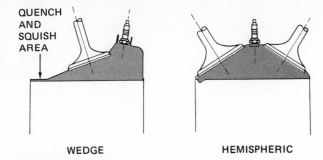

QUENCH
AND
SQUISH
AREA

WEDGE   HEMISPHERIC

Fig. 14-3 Wedge and hemispheric combustion chambers. (General Motors Corporation)

(Fig. 14-3). The shape determines turbulence, squish, and quench, three factors that affect detonation.

When you stir coffee, you swirl it, or impart turbulence to it, so that the cream and sugar mix with the coffee. In the same way, turbulence in the air-fuel mixture entering the combustion chamber assures more even mixing. This makes the combustion more even. Turbulence also reduces the time required for the flame front to sweep through the compressed mixture.

In some combustion chambers, the piston squishes, or squeezes, a part of the air-fuel mixture at the end of the compression stroke. The squish area in a combustion chamber is shown on the left in Fig. 14-3. As the piston nears TDC, the mixture is squished, or pushed, out of the squish area. As it squirts out, it promotes turbulence and further mixing of the air-fuel mixture.

Detonation results when the end-gas temperature is too high. The end gas explodes before the flame front reaches it. However, if some heat is taken from the end gas, its temperature will not reach the detonation point. In the cylinder shown on the left in Fig. 14-3, the squish area is also a quench area. The cylinder head is close to the piston, and these metallic surfaces are cooler than the end gas. This allows heat to be removed from the end gas. Therefore, the tendency for detonation to occur is quenched. However, this causes a problem with exhaust emissions because the air-fuel mixture does not burn completely.

With the hemispheric combustion chamber, the spark plug can be located near the center of the dome (Fig. 14-3, right). Then, when combustion starts, the flame front has a shorter distance to travel. There are no distant pockets of end gas to detonate. The chamber has no squish or quench areas. However, there is relatively little turbulence.

With the wedge combustion chamber, the spark plug is located to one side. The flame front must travel a greater distance to reach the end of the wedge (Fig. 14-3, left). The end of the wedge has a squish and quench area which cools the end gas to prevent detonation. At the same time it imparts turbulence to the mixture.

The shape of the combustion chamber also affects the amount of exhaust pollutants that appear in the exhaust gases. The cooler metal surfaces of the cylinder head and piston top slow combustion. Therefore, the layers of air-fuel mixture next to these metal surfaces do not burn completely. The wedge combustion chamber has a larger surface area. Because its surface area is larger, it produces more exhaust pollutants than does the hemispheric combustion chamber.

SHOP SKILLS

_____ 1. Being able to diagnose the sounds of abnormal combustion is an important tool for the mechanic. Try to locate a car with a spark-ignition engine that is pinging, which is the characteristic sound of detonation.

_____ 2. Try to locate a car with a spark-ignition engine that has a dull thudding sound. This may be preignition. Use a mechanic's stethoscope to locate the source of the noise.

JOB 14   MULTIPLE-CHOICE TEST

1. A gasoline that is too volatile will have a tendency to cause
   a. carburetor flooding
   b. vapor lock
   c. easy starting
   d. higher engine power   1. ____

2. The explosion of the last part of the air-fuel mixture before the spark reaches it is called
   a. detonation
   b. preignition
   c. normal combustion
   d. squish   2. ____

3. Engines must be operated on unleaded gasoline if they are equipped with
   a. electronic ignition
   b. a resonator
   c. fuel injection
   d. a catalytic converter   3. ____

4. The two general shapes of combustion chambers are
   a. wedge and Ricardo
   b. wedge and hemispheric
   c. Wankel and hemispheric
   d. square and over-square   4. ____

5. Low-octane gasoline
   a. will not detonate
   b. detonates under all conditions
   c. detonates easily
   d. none of the above   5. ____

JOB 15

Automotive Fuel Systems

Objective: To learn about automotive fuel systems.

References: AM ♦15-1 to 15-14, SG Chap. 15, automotive manufacturers' service manuals.

Equipment: Various vehicles.

Tools: None.

SHOP FACTS

Two types of engines are used in automobiles, gasoline and diesel. They have different operating cycles and burn different fuels. The gasoline engine uses an electric ignition system to ignite the air-fuel mixture in the engine cylinders. In the diesel engine, the fuel oil is ignited by *heat of compression*. Air alone is compressed in the engine cylinders during the compression strokes. The air gets very hot as it is compressed. Temperatures of the compressed air can exceed 1000°F [555°C]. The fuel oil is sprayed into the hot air just before the compression stroke is finished. Then the hot air ignites the fuel oil and the power stroke follows.

For many years, the gasoline engines used in automobiles have had carburetors in their fuel systems. The *carburetor* is a mixing device which mixes air and gasoline vapor in the proper proportions to produce a combustible mixture. This mixture flows from the carburetor through the intake manifold to the engine cylinders.

In recent years, many spark-ignition engines have been equipped with a gasoline *fuel-injection system*. The basic difference between the carbureted system and the fuel-injection system is how the fuel is metered. In the carburetor, the air passing through creates a vacuum which causes fuel to discharge from the main nozzle. In the fuel-injection system, fuel is pressurized by a pump and forced to discharge through an injection valve into the intake air. The amount of gasoline discharged from the injection valve is determined electronically (electronic fuel injection) or mechanically (mechanical fuel injection).

Both the carbureted fuel system and the fuel-injection system do the same job. That job is to supply a combustible mixture of air and fuel to the engine cylinders.

The fuel system must vary the proportions of air and gasoline to handle different operating requirements. For example, when a cold engine is started, the fuel system must deliver a very rich mixture (rich in gasoline). The proportions may be about 9 pounds [4.08 kilograms (kg)] of air to 1 pound [0.45 kg] of gasoline. After the engine is running and has warmed up, the fuel system "leans out" the mixture (makes it less rich) to about 15 pounds [6.80 kg] of air to 1 pound [0.45 kg] of gasoline. For acceleration or high-speed operation, the mixture is again enriched.

The carbureted fuel system (Fig. 15-1) consists of the fuel tank, the fuel pump, the carburetor, the fuel gauge, the in-take manifold, the connecting fuel lines, and the accelerator pedal and linkage. The accelerator pedal controls the amount of air-fuel mixture entering the engine cylinders and, therefore, the amount of power the engine produces. The fuel tank holds a supply of gasoline for the engine. The fuel-level indicating system includes a gauge on the car instrument panel which shows the level of fuel in the fuel tank. The fuel pump draws gasoline from the fuel tank and delivers it to the carburetor. The carburetor mixes the gasoline in varying proportions and delivers it through the intake manifold to the cylinders.

SHOP SKILLS

Figure 15-1 shows the fuel system for one model of car. Study the illustration until you have a general understanding of the fuel-system components and their locations. Then follow the procedure below to locate and identify the fuel-system components on several vehicles.

_____ 1. Raise the vehicle on a lift. Locate the fuel tank (Fig. 15-1). Check for a drain plug in the bottom of the tank. Locate the fuel-gauge tank unit. Note the wire that leads to the fuel-gauge dash unit.

_____ 2. Locate the fuel line at the fuel tank. Trace the line to the front of the car. Note how the line is secured in position with clips and is routed around moving parts and the heat from the exhaust system.

_____ 3. Find the flexible fuel line, usually called the "flex line." It is used to absorb any vibration or movement that occurs between the engine and the car frame.

_____ 4. Lower the car. Locate the fuel pump (Fig. 15-1). Check for the use of a vapor-return line to help prevent vapor lock.

_____ 5. Note that a metal line is used to carry fuel from the fuel pump to the carburetor. Locate the fuel filter (Fig. 15-1).

_____ 6. Remove the air cleaner from the carburetor and determine the type of filter element used. Check the inside of the air cleaner for a small filter used to clean the fresh ventilating air on some cars equipped with a positive crankcase ventilation (PCV) system.

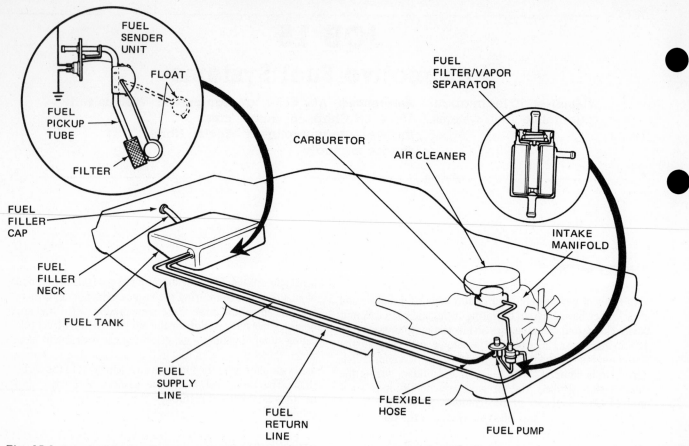

Fig. 15-1 A typical fuel system for a carbureted spark-ignition engine. **(Chrysler Corporation)**

JOB 15 MULTIPLE-CHOICE TEST

1. Mechanical fuel pumps are operated by an eccentric on the
   a. camshaft
   b. crankshaft
   c. carburetor
   d. rocker-arm shaft   1. ____

2. Under-the-hood temperatures are likely to be higher on a car
   a. without air conditioning
   b. with air conditioning
   c. with power steering
   d. with automatic transmission   2. ____

3. A charcoal canister is used in the
   a. evaporative control system
   b. thermostatic air cleaner
   c. crankcase emission control system
   d. exhaust-gas recirculation system   3. ____

4. An electronic fuel-injection system takes the place of
   a. the air cleaner
   b. the intake manifold
   c. the mechanical fuel pump
   d. the carburetor   4. ____

5. LPG stands for
   a. liquid propane gas
   b. liquefied petroleum gas
   c. light-pressure gas
   d. lost pure gas   5. ____

Name _____ Date _____

JOB 16
Automotive Carburetors

Objective: To learn the construction and operation of automotive carburetors.

References: AM ♦16-1 to 16-41, SG Chap. 16, automotive manufacturers' service manuals.

Equipment: Various carburetors and carburetor parts.
Tools: None.

♦ _____ ♦

SHOP FACTS

Two types of carburetors are used on automobiles. These are the *fixed-venturi* (FV) carburetor and the *variable-venturi* (VV) carburetor. In an FV carburetor, air flowing through the constricted passage produces a partial vacuum that causes fuel to discharge from the fuel nozzle. In a VV carburetor, the size of the passage varies as operating conditions change. This then controls the amount of fuel that is delivered to the air flowing through.

Most carburetors installed in cars made in the United States are FV carburetors. However, an increasing number of cars made in the United States have a VV carburetor, as do many imported cars.

The various passages in the FV carburetor through which fuel and air are metered are called *systems* (or *circuits*). Different systems supply fuel during idle, part throttle, full throttle, and acceleration. These systems work together or separately during certain operating conditions to supply the required air-fuel ratio. The systems in the FV carburetor are:

1. Float system
2. Idle system
3. Main-metering system
4. Power system
5. Accelerator-pump system
6. Choke system

Note These are essentially the internal systems that meter fuel in FV carburetors. Fixed-venturi carburetors also have several additional external devices to help control engine operation. These include:

1. Antidieseling, or idle, solenoid to prevent engine run-on after it is turned off.
2. Dashpot to prevent sudden closing of the throttle valve, which eliminates a sudden peak of HC in the exhaust gas.
3. Linkage to the automatic transmission which causes a downshift when the throttle is opened wide.
4. Several openings, or ports, in the carburetor which send vacuum signals to other components so that they can perform a function. For example, a vacuum passage runs from the carburetor to the ignition-distributor vacuum-advance unit. Also, a vent connects the float bowl to the charcoal canister in the evaporative emission control system to trap fuel vapors.

Most FV carburetors, including single-barrel carburetors, can be divided into three basic parts. These are the air horn, the main body or float bowl, and the throttle body.

SHOP SKILLS

____ 1. Figure 16-1 shows a simplified FV carburetor with the basic parts named. Identify these parts on the carburetor you are examining. Study the action of the throttle valve. Note that the throttle valve can be tilted in the air horn to allow more or less air to flow through. When it is tilted to allow more air to flow, larger amounts of air-fuel mixture are delivered to the engine. But if the throttle valve is tilted to throttle off most of the air, only small amounts of air-fuel mixture are delivered. The engine produces less power and tends to slow down.

____ 2. Locate the fuel nozzle. A partial vacuum occurs in the venturi where the end of the fuel nozzle is located. The other end of the fuel nozzle is in the float bowl covered by fuel (Fig. 16-1).

____ 3. Atmospheric pressure pushes the fuel through a vent in the float-bowl cover. With the vacuum at the upper end of the nozzle, fuel is pushed up through the nozzle. The fuel enters the passing airstream as a fine spray. It quickly turns to vapor as the droplets of fuel evaporate. The more air

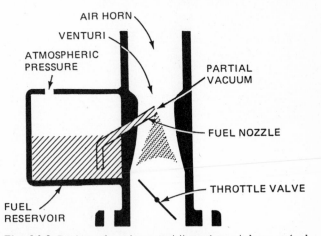

Fig. 16-1 Basic carburetor, consisting of an air horn, a fuel nozzle, a throttle valve, and a fuel reservoir.

flowing through the air horn, the greater the vacuum in the venturi. The greater the vacuum, the more fuel delivered.

_____ 4. Note in Fig. 16-1 and on the carburetor that you are studying that the venturi end of the fuel nozzle is slightly above the level of fuel in the float bowl. This prevents fuel from running out when the engine is off. It requires a slight vacuum (*venturi vacuum*) to cause fuel to discharge from the nozzle.

_____ 5. The float system (Fig. 16-2) includes the float bowl and a float and needle-valve arrangement. The float and the needle valve maintain a constant level of fuel in the float bowl. If the level is too high, too much fuel will feed from the fuel nozzle. If the fuel level is too low, too little fuel will feed. In either event, poor engine performance will result.

_____ 6. Figure 16-2 is a simplified drawing of the float system. If fuel enters the float bowl faster than fuel is withdrawn, the fuel level rises. This causes the float to move up and push the needle valve into the valve seat. This, in turn, shuts off the fuel inlet so that no fuel can enter.

_____ 7. When the fuel level drops, the float moves down and releases the needle so that the fuel inlet is opened. Now fuel can enter. In actual operation, the fuel is kept at an almost constant level. The float tends to hold the needle valve partly closed so that the incoming fuel just balances the fuel being withdrawn.

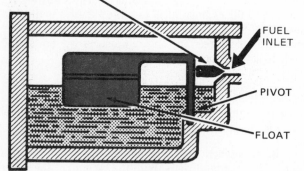

Fig. 16-2 A basic carburetor float system.

_____ 8. Locate the parts of the float system on the carburetor you are studying. Identify the float, needle and seat, and gasoline inlet. Many late-model carburetors have more than one hose or tube connected to the float bowl. Fuel enters the float bowl through the line that has the needle valve and seat assembled in it.

_____ 9. Making use of the references, examine different carburetors. Disassemble the carburetor, if possible, and locate and identify the various parts and systems of each.

JOB 16   MULTIPLE-CHOICE TEST

1. The device on the carburetor that removes dust from the air entering the air horn is called the
   a. air duster
   b. air screen
   c. air cleaner
   d. oil cleaner   1. _____

2. The system that maintains a constant level of fuel in the carburetor float bowl is called the
   a. flow system
   b. idle system
   c. float system
   d. reserve system   2. _____

3. The main nozzle does not deliver fuel during idling because of insufficient
   a. fuel velocity
   b. venturi vacuum
   c. fuel pressure
   d. air pressure   3. _____

4. With the engine idling, all fuel discharges past the
   a. idle-speed screw
   b. main nozzle
   c. low-speed port
   d. idle-mixture screw   4. _____

5. As the metering rod is lifted by movement of the throttle to wide open, more fuel is permitted to pass through the
   a. metering rod
   b. idle system
   c. low-speed system
   d. high-speed system   5. _____

JOB 17-1
Air-Cleaner Service

Objective: To learn to service various types of air cleaners.

References: AM ◆17-16 and 17-17, SG Chap. 17, automotive manufacturers' service manuals.

Equipment: Various engines and air cleaners.
Tools: Basic hand tools.

SHOP FACTS

Car manufacturers previously recommended that the filter element should be periodically removed, cleaned, and reinstalled. Today, only replacement of the filter element is recommended. Now, the carburetor is internally vented to the air cleaner. With this arrangement, a partial clogging of the filter element will not produce a richer mixture.

Because of this, and because of improved filter elements, most manufacturers recommend replacing the filter element after a certain time or mileage, whichever occurs first. Manufacturers no longer provide cleaning instructions. The typical recommendation today is to install a new filter element every 30,000 miles [48,000 kilometers (km)] or more often for dusty conditions.

SHOP SKILLS

SERVICING THE PAPER-ELEMENT AIR CLEANER

____ 1. Figure 17-1 shows an air cleaner and its related parts. The filter element is removed from some air cleaners by taking off the wing nut and air-cleaner cap. Then the element can be lifted out.

____ 2. On other air cleaners, the cap is part of the air-cleaner cover. The assembly includes the snorkel, the connections to the PCV system, and the heat stove for the heated-air-intake system. On these, the air-cleaner cover can usually be lifted up enough to remove the element. If not, the hoses must be disconnected.

____ 3. Chrysler recommends that if the air cleaner must be loosened for any purpose, it should be removed from under the hood. If the air cleaner rests on or hooks into linkage parts, the parts could be damaged. Cap all air fittings which could leak air if the engine is started while the air cleaner is removed.

____ 4. With the filter element out, the bottom of the air cleaner, gasket surfaces, and cover should be cleaned. Check the cover seal for tears or cracks, and replace it if damaged.

____ 5. Examine the filter element for oil. If it is wet with oil over more than half of its outside surface, or circumference, check the PCV system. It is carrying oil up to the air cleaner.

____ 6. Chevrolet recommends inspection of the element for dust leaks after the first 15,000 miles [24,000 km] of operation. Look for dust in the air-cleaner housing on the inside of the filter element. Dust could enter through the holes in

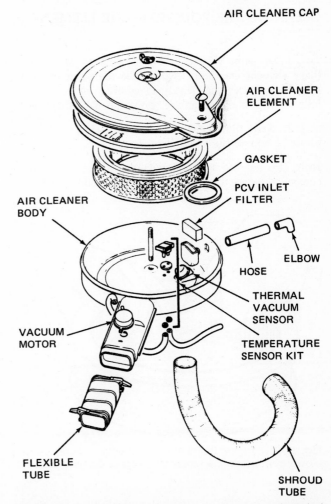

Fig. 17-1 Disassembled carburetor air cleaner and related parts for an in-line engine. **(American Motors Corporation)**

the filter element, and under or over the element, past the side seals. If no dust is found, rotate the element one-half turn, and reinstall it.

♦ CAUTION ♦ Do not operate the engine with the air cleaner off unless you are making tests. If the engine backfires with the air cleaner off, it could cause a fire in the engine compartment.

_____ 7. Here is the procedure that was recommended by Chrysler for cleaning the paper element on older cars. Examine the element, and if it is wet with oil over more than half of its circumference, discard it.

_____ 8. To clean the element, use compressed air to blow through the element from the inside (Fig. 17-2). Hold the nozzle at least 2 inches [51 mm] away from the inside screen of the element. Do not blow from the outside in. This will embed the particles in the paper.

_____ 9. After cleaning the element, examine it for punctures. If you can see any pinholes when the element is held up to the light, discard the element.

_____ 10. Make sure that the plastic sealing rings on both sides of the element are smooth and uniform. If these are in good condition, install the element. Be sure that it seals both top and bottom when the air-cleaner cover is reinstalled.

CLEANING THE POLYURETHANE ELEMENT

_____ 1. On some vehicles, a plastic wrapper, or polyurethane element, has been used outside the paper element. After the polyurethane element is removed, inspect it carefully for rips or other damage. Discard it if it is damaged.

_____ 2. Wash the element in kerosene. Then squeeze it gently to remove the excess kerosene.

Note Do not use solvents containing acetone or similar compounds, since they could ruin the polyurethane element.

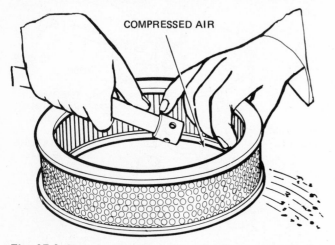
COMPRESSED AIR

Fig. 17-2 Cleaning the filter element with compressed air blown from inside the element. **(Chrysler Corporation)**

Never wring out, shake, or swing the element. This could tear it. Instead, fold over the element and gently squeeze it.

_____ 3. Clean the cover and other parts of the air cleaner. Then dip the cleaned element in SAE10W-30 engine oil, and squeeze out the excess.

_____ 4. Reinstall the element and its support in the air cleaner. Make sure that the element is not folded or creased and that it seals all the way around. Use a new gasket when installing the air cleaner on the carburetor.

SERVICING THE OIL-BATH AIR CLEANER

_____ 1. After removing the filter element, clean it by sloshing it up and down in clean solvent. Dry it with compressed air.

_____ 2. Dump the dirty oil from the air-cleaner body, wash it with solvent, and dry it.

_____ 3. Refill the body to the full mark with clean SAE10W-30 engine oil.

_____ 4. Reinstall the filter element and air-cleaner body on the engine.

JOB 17-1   MULTIPLE-CHOICE TEST

1. The most popular type of air cleaner is the
   a. oil bath
   b. oil-wetted
   c. dry-paper element
   d. wire screen   1. _____

2. The air cleaner filters fresh air going into the
   a. engine
   b. radiator
   c. heater
   d. air conditioner   2. _____

3. In normal usage, the filter element in the air cleaner should be replaced every
   a. year
   b. 30,000 miles [48,000 km]
   c. two years
   d. 15,000 miles (24,000 km)   3. _____

4. Cranking an engine without an air cleaner can cause
   a. a fire
   b. fuel-filter clogging
   c. battery failure
   d. air-filter clogging   4. _____

5. On older engines, the dry-paper element could be cleaned with
   a. gasoline
   b. soap
   c. solvent
   d. compressed air   5. _____

JOB 17-2
Testing Fuel Pumps

Objective: To learn how to inspect and test fuel pumps.

References: AM ♦17-21 to 17-25, SG Chap. 17, automotive manufacturers' service manuals.

Equipment: Various engines and fuel pumps.
Tools: Fuel-pump tester, graduated fuel container, and basic hand tools.

♦ **SAFETY** ♦ *Always observe all safety precautions when working around gasoline.*

SHOP SKILLS

The inspection and testing of fuel pumps are performed with the fuel pump installed on the engine.

_____ 1. Make certain that there is gasoline in the fuel tank. Inspect for signs of leakage at the lines and connections from the fuel tank to the carburetor. Tighten any loose connections. Inspect all hoses and lines for flattening or kinks which would restrict fuel flow. Fuel may not leak out of a leaking hose or connection on the vacuum side of the fuel pump. (The vacuum side of the fuel pump is from the fuel-pickup tube in the fuel tank to the fuel-pump inlet.) Instead, during engine operation, air may be pulled into the fuel system by fuel-pump vacuum. This outside air in the fuel line will reduce fuel-pump capacity.

_____ 2. If the engine will run, let it idle. Inspect for leaks at the fuel-pump diaphragm flange and in the pressure line from the fuel pump to the carburetor. Shut off the engine, and remove the air cleaner. Disconnect the fuel inlet line or the fuel filter from the carburetor. Make sure that the fuel filter is not partially plugged. An engine is more likely to have a plugged fuel filter or a restricted fuel line than a defective fuel pump.

♦ **CAUTION** ♦ Use care to prevent fire resulting from fuel spilling from the fuel line, filter, and carburetor.

_____ 3. Disconnect the distributor primary lead from the coil terminal to prevent the engine starting. Place the fuel container at the end of the fuel hose and crank the engine a few revolutions. If no gasoline or only a little gasoline flows from the pipe, the line is plugged or the pump is inoperative. If a sufficient quantity of gasoline flows from the fuel line at the carburetor, most automotive mechanics would assume that the fuel pump and lines are okay.

_____ 4. If a further check of the fuel line is indicated, disconnect the line from the fuel tank. Blow compressed air through the line to make sure that it is clear.

_____ 5. Connect a pressure gauge, a hose restrictor, and a flexible hose between the fuel line and carburetor, as shown in Fig. 17-3. Reconnect the distributor primary lead to the coil terminal. Before fuel-pump tests are made, the engine should be at normal operating temperature. Run the engine at normal idle speed. Open the hose restrictor momentarily to vent any air trapped in the fuel system. Then be sure that the hose restrictor is closed.

_____ 6. Idle the engine at the specified speed (rpm). As soon as the pressure-gauge needle is steady, read the fuel-pump pressure. Some cars are equipped with a vapor-return system. The vapor-return line from the fuel pump to the fuel tank must be squeezed closed to get an accurate reading.

_____ 7. Check the fuel-pump specifications in the shop manual. If the pump pressure is not within specifications, the pump is defective. If the fuel-pump pressure is within specifications, perform the fuel-pump capacity test.

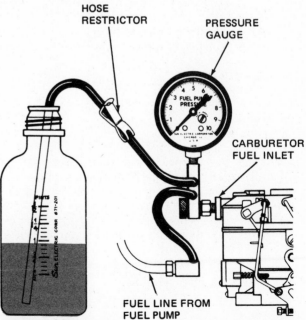

Fig. 17-3 Fuel-pump pressure and capacity tests. (Sun Electric Corporation)

____ 8. With the engine running at idle, open the hose restrictor. Allow the fuel to discharge into the graduated container for 30 seconds. On most full-size American-built cars, the fuel pump should deliver at least 1 pint [0.47 liter (L)] of fuel in 30 seconds or less.

____ 9. To make a fuel-pump vacuum test, attach the fuel-pump tester to the vacuum side of the fuel pump. Be sure that the fuel line is disconnected at the carburetor. Idle the engine for a few seconds while it runs on the gasoline in the float bowl. A typical fuel pump should have at least 10 inches [250 mm] mercury (Hg) vacuum at idle.

____ 10. Today most fuel pumps are crimped together instead of being held together by screws. When a fuel pump of this type fails one or more of the fuel-pump tests, it should be discarded.

JOB 17-2 MULTIPLE-CHOICE TEST

1. Small pinholes in the line from the fuel tank to the fuel pump will
   a. leak gasoline
   b. prevent fuel flow
   c. draw in air
   d. have no effect   1. ____

2. The most common cause of fuel starvation is
   a. too high fuel-pump pressure
   b. a plugged fuel filter
   c. carburetor flooding
   d. a defective fuel pump   2. ____

3. Three tests which can be made on a fuel pump are
   a. pressure, volume, and capacity
   b. volume, capacity, and vacuum
   c. capacity, volume, and speed
   d. pressure, vacuum, and capacity   3. ____

4. On full-size American-built cars, a good fuel pump should deliver
   a. less than 1 pint [0.47 L] in more than 30 seconds
   b. 1 gallon [3.79 L] in an hour
   c. less than 1 quart [0.95 L] in more than 1 minute
   d. more than 1 pint [0.47 L] in less than 30 seconds
                                                        4. ____

5. To get an accurate pressure reading, the mechanic must first squeeze closed the
   a. inlet line to the fuel pump
   b. outlet line from the fuel pump
   c. vapor-return line from the fuel pump
   d. none of the above   5. ____

JOB 17-3
Adjusting Carburetors

Objective: To learn how to adjust carburetors.

References: AM ♦17-26 to 17-41, SG Chap. 17, automotive manufacturers' service manuals.

Equipment: Various engines and carburetors.
Tools: Basic hand tools.

SHOP SKILLS

CHECKING THE CHOKE

____ 1. Remove the air cleaner. Hold the throttle half open, and open and close the choke valve several times (Fig. 17-4).

____ 2. If the linkage or choke sticks, clean the sticking parts with a spray can of choke or carburetor cleaner (Fig. 17-4). Follow the directions on the can. If the cleaner does

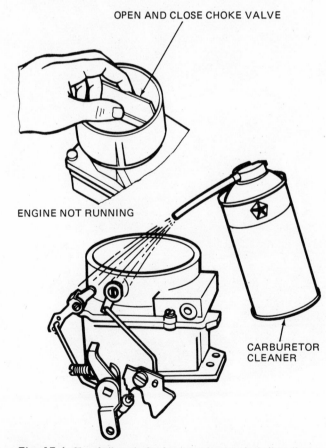

OPEN AND CLOSE CHOKE VALVE

ENGINE NOT RUNNING

CARBURETOR CLEANER

Fig. 17-4 Check the choke by opening and closing it several times. If it sticks, clean the sticking part with spray carburetor cleaner. **(Chrysler Corporation)**

not free the choke and linkage, remove the carburetor for additional cleaning.

____ 3. Make sure that all vacuum hoses are connected properly and are in good condition. Replace or tighten hoses as necessary.

____ 4. The vacuum-break-diaphragm shaft should be fully extended when the engine is off. If the shaft is not fully extended, replace the vacuum-break assembly.

____ 5. Check the position of the choke valve when the engine is cold. When the throttle is opened slightly, the choke valve should be closed completely. Install the air cleaner and make the following running test.

____ 6. Start the engine. Measure the time in seconds it takes the choke valve to reach the full-open position. If the valve fails to reach wide open within 3½ minutes, make these additional checks.

____ 7. Check the voltage at the choke heater connection with the engine running. If the voltage is between 12 and 15 volts, replace the electric choke unit.

____ 8. If the voltage is low or zero, check all wiring and connections. If the connections at the oil-pressure switch are faulty, the oil warning light will be off with the ignition key turned to ON with the engine not running. If a fuse is blown, the radio or turn signals will not work. Repair connections or wires as required.

____ 9. If step 8 does not correct the problem, replace the oil-pressure switch. Do not use a gasket between the choke cover and housing. This would prevent the necessary ground connection.

CHECKING THE IDLE SOLENOID

The idle solenoid allows the throttle valve to close completely when the engine is turned off, so that the engine cannot "diesel," or run after the ignition is turned off. If the solenoid is suspected of not working properly, check it as follows:

____ 1. Turn the ignition key to ON, but do not start the engine.

2. Open the throttle to allow the solenoid plunger to extend.

3. Hold the throttle wide open. Feel the end of the plunger, and disconnect the wire at the solenoid. The plunger should move as the spring pulls it back (on some cars).

4. If the plunger does not move, back out the hex screw one full turn, and repeat steps 2 and 3. If the plunger now moves, reconnect the wire to the solenoid and adjust idle speed.

5. If the plunger does not move, connect a test light between the solenoid feed wire and ground. If the light glows, replace the solenoid.

6. If the light does not come on, there is an open in the feed line. Check the wires and connections.

IDLE-MIXTURE CHECK AND ADJUSTMENT WITH PROPANE

1. Set parking brake and block drive wheels. On cars equipped with a vacuum parking-brake release, disconnect and plug the hose above the parking-brake foot pedal.

2. Disconnect and plug hoses as directed on the vehicle emission control information label in the engine compartment.

3. Connect a tachometer to the engine to measure engine rpm.

4. Disconnect vacuum advance, and set the ignition timing to the specification shown in the emission control information label. Reconnect the vacuum advance.

5. Engine must be at normal operating temperature. The choke must be open and the air conditioning off.

6. Set engine idle speed to rpm shown on the emission control information label.

7. Disconnect the PCV hose from the air cleaner.

8. Connect the hose from the propane-container valve to the PCV-hose nipple in the air cleaner (Fig. 17-5). When the propane valve is opened, propane gas will flow through the air cleaner, carburetor, and intake manifold and into the cylinders.

Note On some engines, the procedure is to make the connection at the evaporative-hose nipple on the air cleaner.

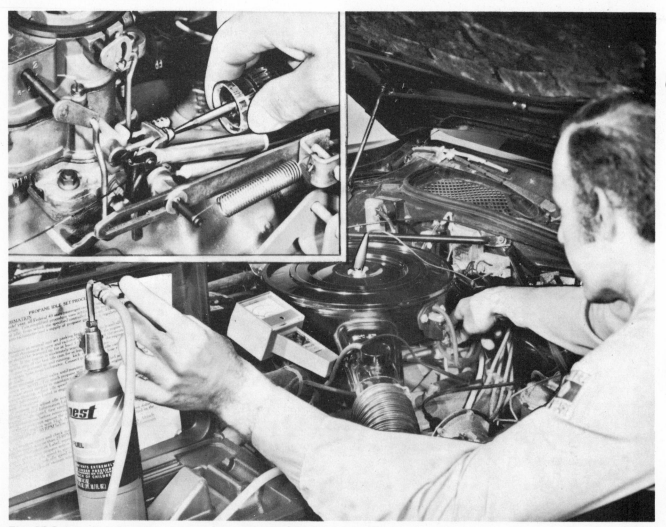

Fig. 17-5 Adjusting the idle mixture with propane. **(Chrysler Corporation)**

___ 9. With the propane container in a vertical position (Fig. 17-5) and the engine idling, slowly open the propane control valve while watching the tachometer. Engine speed will increase to a maximum (enriched idle speed) and then decrease as too much propane is fed into the engine.

___ 10. Note the maximum rpm. Then close the propane control valve. If the maximum rpm is within the enriched idle rpm range as shown on the emission control information label, the idle mixture is correct. Proceed to step 14 below.

___ 11. If the enriched idle speed is incorrect, remove the idle-mixture-screw limiter cap. Turn the mixture screw in until it is lightly seated. Then back out the mixture screw until the lean best idle point at the enriched idle speed is reached. This is the maximum engine idle speed with the least amount of fuel.

___ 12. Now, starting with a lean best idle setting at the enriched idle rpm, lean the idle mixture (turn screw in) until the specified curb idle speed is reached.

___ 13. Recheck the enriched speed with propane. If it is not within specifications, repeat the above procedure, starting with step 9.

___ 14. With the idle mixture properly set, turn off the engine and remove the propane container. Reconnect the PCV hose to the air cleaner.

___ 15. Reset the idle speed.

JOB 17-3 MULTIPLE-CHOICE TEST

1. Specifications for the idle-speed adjustment are found
   a. in the manufacturers' service manuals
   b. on the vehicle emission control information label in the engine compartment
   c. both a and b
   d. neither a nor b   1. ____

2. On a car with an electric choke, the choke valve should reach wide open
   a. in 3½ minutes or less
   b. as soon as the engine starts
   c. within 10 minutes
   d. as soon as the engine is cranked   2. ____

3. Mechanic A says that an improperly adjusted idle solenoid may cause an engine to idle too fast. Mechanic B says that an improperly adjusted idle solenoid may cause an engine to "diesel" after the ignition switch is turned off. Who is right?
   a. A only
   b. B only
   c. both A and B
   d. neither A nor B   3. ____

4. Adjustment of the idle mixture on cars equipped with a catalytic converter should be made
   a. using only a screwdriver and a tachometer
   b. using propane
   c. using only a screwdriver and a vacuum gauge
   d. none of the above   4. ____

5. To lean the idle mixture on a carburetor,
   a. turn the idle-mixture screw out
   b. turn the idle-speed screw in
   c. turn the idle-mixture screw in
   d. turn the idle-speed screw out   5. ____

JOB 18

Servicing Gasoline Fuel-Injection Systems

Objective: To learn how to check and service a typical gasoline fuel-injection system.

References: AM ♦18-13 to 18-18, SG 18, automotive manufacturers' service manuals.

Equipment: Various engines with gasoline fuel-injection systems.
Tools: Fuel-injection analyzer and basic hand tools.

SHOP SKILLS

VISUAL INSPECTION

____ 1. Visually check all wiring-harness connections for
a. Loose or detached connectors
b. Broken or detached wires
c. Terminals not completely seated in connector housings
d. Partially broken or frayed wires at terminal connections
e. Excessive corrosion

____ 2. Start the engine. Plug the idle bypass passage on top of the throttle body with a clean shop towel to make it easier to hear any vacuum leaks. Then visually check all vacuum lines to ensure that they are securely connected to the proper fittings and are not broken, pinched, or cracked.

____ 3. Visually check the fuel lines for kinks and for traces of fuel leakage. Correct any problem found.

♦ CAUTION ♦ Do not loosen any fittings in the fuel system until after you have relieved the pressure in the system! Fuel in the system may be pressurized to 41 psi (283 kPa) or more. When loosening a fitting, observe the proper precautions to prevent fuel from spraying out and causing a fire or injuring you. Cover the fitting to be loosened with a shop towel to absorb the fuel. Then place the gasoline-soaked towel in a safety container or outside in a safe place to dry.

ON-CAR SERVICE

Various components of the electronic fuel-injection system can be adjusted, or removed and replaced. Consult the manufacturer's service manual for the specific procedures.

Here are several important points about servicing components and making various adjustments to the Cadillac electronic fuel-injection system (Bosch D type).

____ 1. **Fuel-line Gaskets** Each time any of the five fuel-rail fittings (shown by the heavy arrows in Fig. 18-1) are

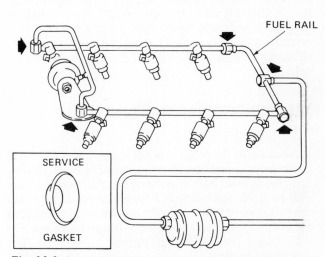

Fig. 18-1 A metal gasket must be installed in each fuel-rail connection any time the fitting is opened and reconnected. (Cadillac Motor Car Division of General Motors Corporation)

opened, a special conical-shaped metal gasket must be installed when reattaching the connection. The gasket is not installed during new car assembly. However, to minimize the chances of fuel leaks during service, a new gasket must be installed each time a fitting is separated and reconnected in the field. The gasket cannot be reused.

____ 2. **Electronic Control Unit (ECU)** Never open the ECU if it is to be used again or if it must be returned to the parts department in lieu of a core charge. The ECU is a pre-programmed, complex, expensive analog computer. There are no adjustments or repairs that can be made to it in the field.

____ 3. **Fuel-pump Fuses** Both of the fuel pumps are protected by a 10-ampere fuse located in the harness near the ECU. If the fuse blows, replace it only with an AGG-10-ampere or a 3 AC-10-ampere fuse of the same physical size. Never install a "slow-blow" or larger amperage fuse. This could result in damage to the ECU.

____ 4. **Electrical Precautions** When charging the battery on a car equipped with EFI, always make sure that the ignition switch remains off. If the ignition switch is turned to ON, a rapid false triggering of the injection valves may occur which will result in a flooded engine. In addition, electrical damage may occur to the ECU.

_____ 5. Fuel Filter When an engine fails to receive fuel, the problem may be a clogged fuel filter. Make certain that the filter has been serviced regularly.

_____ 6. In-tank Fuel Pump A filter or strainer is located on the inlet end of the fuel-pickup tube in the fuel tank. Sometimes the fuel pump appears to lack capacity and is replaced when only the filter needs replacement. The filter is a press fit on the end of the fuel-pump assembly and is available from the dealer's parts department. After installing a new filter, be sure to align it so that it cannot contact the float.

_____ 7. Hose Fuel hoses in the EFI system are made of special materials and cut to certain lengths. When replacing a fuel hose, use only a recommended type of replacement hose. Be sure that it is cut to the proper length. Hose material is designed to withstand the effects of gasoline and high temperatures. Correct hose length allows the new hose to be installed with the same routing so that it can be securely retained.

PRELIMINARY DIAGNOSIS

If the cause of the problem is not found during the visual inspection, a preliminary diagnosis should be made. Cadillac lists nine different types of problems that might occur in cars with electronic fuel injection. If the engine and all other systems are operating properly, these problems may be traced to the electronic fuel-injection system. The problems are:
1. Engine cranking but not starting
2. Hard starting
3. Poor fuel economy
4. Engine stalling after starting
5. Rough idle
6. Prolonged fast idle
7. No fast idle
8. Engine hesitating or stumbling on acceleration
9. Lack of high-speed performance

When the cause of any of these problems is not found during a visual inspection, a fuel-injection analyzer must be used to locate the cause.

CARBURETOR	ELECTRONIC FUEL INJECTION
1. Accelerator pump	1. Throttle position switch
2. Fast-idle cam	2. Electric fast-idle valve
3. Float	3. Fuel-pressure regulator
4. Power valve metering rods	4. Manifold absolute pressure sensor
5. Metering jets and idle fuel system	5. Injection valves, electronic control unit (ECU)

Fig. 18-2 Chart showing the relationship between carburetor components and electronic-fuel-injection system components.

During the preliminary diagnosis, keep in mind certain relationships between parts in the carburetor systems and components in the electronic fuel-injection system (Fig. 18-2). These relationships can help you to identify and pinpoint a defective component.

JOB 18   MULTIPLE-CHOICE TEST

1. The first step in checking a complaint about the electronic fuel-injection system is to
   a. make a visual inspection
   b. connect a fuel-injection analyzer
   c. make sure that the engine and ignition system are okay
   d. relieve the pressure in the fuel line   1. _____

2. A visual inspection includes checking the wiring-harness connections, fuel lines, and
   a. fuel-pump pressure
   b. fuel-tank capacity
   c. vacuum lines
   d. battery voltage   2. _____

3. After starting the engine, plug the idle bypass passage on top of the throttle body, and
   a. look for fuel leaks
   b. listen for vacuum leaks
   c. check for poor fuel economy
   d. note if the engine stalls   3. _____

4. If the fuel pump does not run, the cause may be a
   a. fouled spark plug
   b. sticking injection valve
   c. defective sensor
   d. blown fuse   4. _____

5. Excessive fuel consumption may be caused by
   a. a weak fuel pump
   b. a blown fuse
   c. an injection valve stuck closed
   d. defective sensors   5. _____

JOB 19

Servicing Diesel Fuel-Injection Systems

Objective: To learn how to service fuel-injection systems on diesel engines.

References: AM ♦19-18 to 19-31, SG Chap. 19, automotive manufacturers' service manuals.

Equipment: Various automotive diesel engines.
Tools: Basic hand tools.

♦ ——————————————————————————— ♦

SHOP FACTS

In a diesel fuel-injection system, the hydraulic lines must withstand very high pressures and must be noncorrosive. If a hydraulic line requires replacement, install a new line as recommended by the engine manufacturer. The hydraulic lines supplied as service parts are preformed and of the proper length. Care should be used in installing them to avoid twisting or bending them out of shape. If the line to be replaced is under other lines, you may have to remove the upper lines.

Whenever lines are disconnected, the lines, nozzles, and pump fittings must be capped. This will prevent dirt from entering the fuel system. Cleanliness is very important when working on the fuel system. A dirt particle so tiny as to be almost invisible can clog an injection nozzle.

In a diesel engine, the fuel must be clean and free of contaminants. Figure 19-1 shows the location of the fuel filter on one engine. A fuel filter works like the filter used in engine lubricating systems. It contains a cartridge of filtering material (special pleated paper or fiber mat) through which the fuel must pass. The filter traps any particles and keeps them from entering the fuel system. The filter should be replaced at specified intervals.

SHOP SKILLS

___ 1. Injection nozzles should not be removed unless there is evidence that they require servicing or replacement. Usual indications of trouble include:
    a. One or more cylinders knocking
    b. Loss of power
    c. Black exhaust smoke
    d. Engine overheating
    e. Excessive fuel consumption

___ 2. One way to check for a faulty injection nozzle is to run the engine at fast idle. Then loosen the connector at each nozzle in turn, one at a time. If loosening a connector causes the engine speed to drop off, the injection nozzle is probably working okay. If the engine speed remains the same, then the injection nozzle probably is not working properly. It could be clogged so that no fuel flows through. Or the holes could be partly clogged so that the spray is inadequate or does not have the required pattern.

___ 3. A variety of nozzles are used, but all have a check valve. The check valve opens when spray pressure is applied so that the fuel can flow through. When the pressure drops, the check valve closes to shut off the fuel flow rapidly and completely.

___ 4. To remove an injection nozzle, first remove the fuel-return-line clamps and return line. Then remove the nozzle hold-down clamp and spacer or other connector arrangement. Remove the nozzle. Cap the nozzle inlet line and the top of the nozzle. Figure 19-2 shows one installation arrangement which includes a compression seal and a carbon stop seal.

___ 5. Some manufacturers recommend a spray test of the detached nozzle. This requires a special hydraulic pump which has a pressure gauge. You attach the nozzle to the pump and then operate the pump. The fuel should spray from the nozzle when the pump reaches the specified pressure. When the pressure is released, the spray should stop abruptly without dripping.

♦ **CAUTION** ♦ Direct the spray from the nozzle into a suitable container. Do not allow the spray to hit your skin. The pressure is high enough to force fuel oil through the skin. This can cause serious trouble. You can be seriously injured because the oil could cause infections.

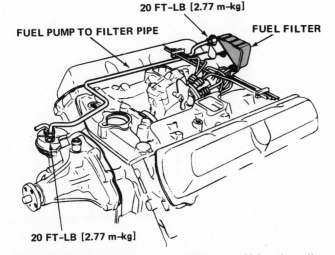

20 FT-LB [2.77 m–kg]

FUEL PUMP TO FILTER PIPE
FUEL FILTER

20 FT-LB [2.77 m–kg]

Fig. 19-1 Location of the fuel filter on a V-8 automotive diesel engine. **(Chevrolet Motor Division of General Motors Corporation)**

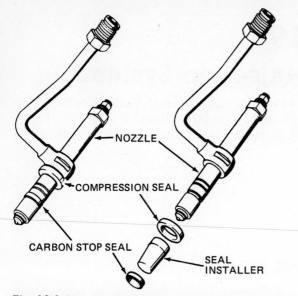

Fig. 19-2 Diesel fuel-injection nozzles with seals. **(Chevrolet Motor Division of General Motors Corporation)**

NOZZLE

COMPRESSION SEAL

CARBON STOP SEAL

SEAL INSTALLER

_____ 6. If the nozzle does not work properly, it can be disassembled and cleaned. Some manufacturers recommend replacing a defective nozzle. If you disassemble a nozzle, work carefully to avoid damaging the tip or enlarging the holes.

_____ 7. Servicing of the fuel-injection pump is a specialized job usually done by a shop that specializes in fuel-injection work. When a fuel-injection pump requires service, the technician usually will remove it and install a new or rebuilt pump.

JOB 19   MULTIPLE-CHOICE TEST

1. Black exhaust smoke may indicate
   a. water in the fuel
   b. a defective injection nozzle
   c. oil in the fuel
   d. excessive engine speed   1. ____

2. One purpose of the nozzle check valve is to
   a. shut off fuel flow rapidly and completely
   b. prevent dirt from entering the nozzle
   c. clean the fuel
   d. allow easy removal of the nozzle   2. ____

3. If the high-pressure spray from a nozzle hits your skin, the fuel may cause
   a. a fire
   b. an explosion
   c. dirty hands
   d. an infection   3. ____

4. When disassembling a nozzle, be careful to avoid
   a. scratching the housing
   b. damaging the tip or enlarging the holes
   c. cleaning the holes
   d. removing the lubricant   4. ____

5. A defective fuel-injection pump normally is serviced by
   a. the technician overhauling it
   b. the parts department overhauling it
   c. replacing it with a new or rebuilt pump
   d. disassembly and cleaning   5. ____

JOB 20
Changing Oil and Oil Filter

Objective: To learn how to change the engine oil and oil filter.

References: AM ♦20-20 to 20-25, SG Chap. 20, automotive manufacturers' service manuals.

Equipment: Various engines.
Tools: Oil-filter tool, oil-can spout, drain pan, basic hand tools.
Supplies: Oil, oil filter.

SHOP FACTS

Using up the oil additives and accumulating contaminants make oil changes necessary. To change the oil, you need as many quarts or liters of oil as listed in the manufacturer's specifications to replace the oil you drain from the engine. The oil must be the correct type and grade for the engine.

According to the manufacturer's recommendations, the oil filter should be changed the first time the oil is changed in a new engine. After that, the filter should be changed every other time the oil is changed on most engines. For some engines, the manufacturer specifies that the oil filter should be changed every time the oil is changed. Refer to the manufacturer's specifications for the recommended oil-change interval.

You can tell whether or not a filter is working by feeling it after the engine has been running. If the filter is hot, it has been passing oil. If it is only warm, it may be clogged and not allowing oil to filter through. On automotive engines, the filter element and container are replaced as a single disposable unit. Some heavy-duty oil filters have a separate cartridge-type filter element. The container remains on the vehicle while the filter element inside is replaced.

SHOP SKILLS

_____ 1. If the engine is cold, run it for about 5 minutes to warm up the oil. Then shut off the engine.

♦ **CAUTION** ♦ Operate the engine only in a well-ventilated area. Exhaust gas contains deadly carbon monoxide which can kill in closed areas.

_____ 2. Raise the car on a lift. Or you can use a jack to raise the front end of the car. Then place stands under the front end and let the car down onto the stands.

♦ **CAUTION** ♦ Do not go under the car with only the jack holding the front end up. If the jack slips, the car could fall and injure you.

_____ 3. With a wrench or socket, loosen the drain plug slightly until you can turn it with your fingers.

_____ 4. Place the drain pan under the plug (Fig. 20-1) to catch the oil. Be sure the drain pan is properly placed to catch the oil and is large enough to hold the amount of oil that is in the crankcase. The oil will flow outward at first rather than straight down. Remove the drain plug.

♦ **CAUTION** ♦ If the engine is hot, the oil can be hot enough to burn you.

_____ 5. While the oil is draining, look at the drain-plug gasket to make sure that it is in good condition. After the oil has drained, start the plug into the threads in the drain hole. Be careful not to cross-thread it. Then tighten the plug securely, but be careful not to overtighten it.

_____ 6. After draining the oil and installing the drain plug, move the drain pan under the oil filter. Using the oil-filter wrench (Fig. 20-2), loosen the filter one or two turns counterclockwise. Do not remove the filter until all the oil from it drains into the drain pan.

_____ 7. Then unscrew the filter and put it in the drain pan, gasket-end facing up. Make sure that the old filter gasket is not on the engine. Clean any sludge out of the filter-mount-

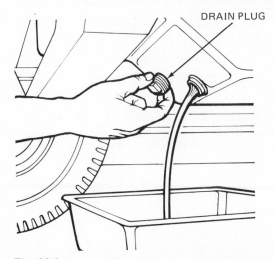

Fig. 20-1 Draining the oil from the engine. (Chrysler Corporation)

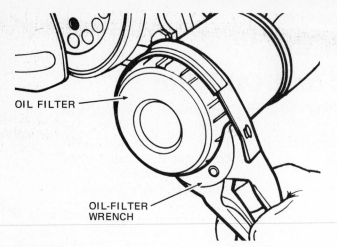

OIL FILTER

OIL-FILTER
WRENCH

Fig. 20-2 Replacing the oil filter. (Chrysler Corporation)

ing recess on the engine. Clean the engine oil-filter-gasket surface.

_____ 8. Compare the new filter with the old filter. If the new filter is a different size, make sure that it will have sufficient clearance from the frame and suspension after it is installed.

_____ 9. Check the gasket end of the new filter. It should be the same size as the one on the old filter. The threads for attaching the filter to the engine must be the same for both filters.

_____ 10. Coat the face of the gasket on the new filter with clean oil. If the filter mounts in a position that allows it to be filled with oil before it is installed, fill it with fresh oil. Make sure that the gasket is properly positioned on the filter. Then hand-tighten the filter until the gasket makes contact with the engine gasket surface. Be careful to avoid cross-threading the filter into the engine.

_____ 11. Now tighten the filter by hand an additional half-turn, or the amount specified, to make sure that it is securely tightened. Do not use the wrench to tighten the filter, unless specified to do so. Wipe the filter and mounting area clean.

_____ 12. Lower the car if it has been raised on a lift. Remove the oil-filter cap. Fill the crankcase to the required level with the proper type and grade of engine oil. Start the engine.

_____ 13. Watch the oil-indicator light or gauge on the instrument panel. It should glow or the gauge should show low

pressure for only a few seconds. Then the light should go out or normal oil pressure should be indicated in less than 30 seconds.

_____ 14. After running the engine for about 5 minutes, shut it off. Check around the drain plug and oil filter for leaks.

_____ 15. Fill out a new lubrication sticker and attach it to the vehicle.

_____ 16. Check the crankcase oil level with the dipstick to make sure that the crankcase is filled to the proper level. Add oil if necessary. The car is now ready to be returned to the customer.

JOB 20 MULTIPLE-CHOICE TEST

1. After the oil and filter have been changed, the oil light should go out in less than
   a. 1 minute
   b. 2 minutes
   c. 30 seconds
   d. 45 seconds   1. _____

2. To check for leaks after changing the oil and filter, run the engine for about
   a. 5 minutes
   b. 1 hour
   c. 1 minute
   d. 30 seconds   2. _____

3. When filling in a lubrication sticker, enter the date and the
   a. trip indicator reading
   b. time
   c. odometer reading
   d. flat-rate time   3. _____

4. Before putting oil into an engine, be sure the oil is the correct
   a. price and color
   b. weight and color
   c. type and grade
   d. grade and additive   4. _____

5. The drain plug is loosened and tightened with
   a. pliers
   b. a wrench
   c. a hacksaw
   d. a pipe and hammer   5. _____

JOB 21
Engine Cooling Systems

Objective: To learn the operation of the engine cooling system.

References: AM ♦21-1 to 21-17, SG Chap. 21, automotive manufacturers' service manuals.

Equipment: None.
Tools: Basic hand tools.

SHOP FACTS

The purpose of the cooling system (Fig. 21-1) is to keep the engine at its most efficient operating temperature at all speeds and under all operating conditions. During the combustion of the air-fuel mixture in the engine cylinders, temperatures of 4000°F [2200°C] or higher may be reached by the burning gases. Some of this heat is absorbed by the cylinder walls, cylinder head, and pistons. They, in turn, must be provided with some means of cooling so that they will not get too hot.

Cylinder-wall temperatures must not go higher than about 400 to 500°F [205 to 260°C]. Temperatures higher than this cause the lubricating-oil film to break down and lose its lubricating properties. However, the engine operates best at temperatures as close to the limits imposed by oil properties as possible. Removing too much heat through the cylinder walls and head lowers the thermal efficiency of the engine. Cooling systems are designed to remove about one-third (30 to 35 percent) of the heat produced in the combustion chambers by the burning of the air-fuel mixture.

The engine is very inefficient while cold. Therefore the cooling system includes devices that prevent normal cooling action during the engine warm-up. These devices allow the

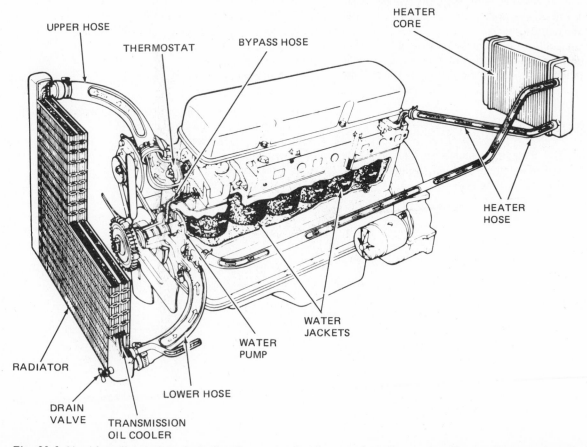

Fig. 21-1 Liquid cooling system, including the car heater, for an automotive engine. The small arrows show the direction of coolant flow. **(Chrysler Corporation)**

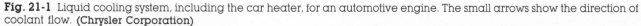

engine parts to reach their normal operating temperatures more quickly. This shortens the inefficient cold operating time. When the engine reaches its normal operating temperature, the cooling system begins to function. The cooling system cools the engine rapidly when it is hot and slowly or not at all when the engine is cold or warming up.

Two general types of cooling systems are used on automobile engines: air cooling and liquid cooling. Most automotive engines are liquid-cooled. Most engines for airplanes, snowmobiles, motorcycles, power lawn mowers, and chain saws are air-cooled.

In operation, the engine cooling system is really a temperature regulating system. It maintains the engine temperature within certain limits, neither too hot nor too cold. A cold engine is inefficient. Combustion of the air-fuel mixture is incomplete. The engine may run rough, have excessive fuel consumption and exhaust emissions, and contaminate the crankcase with excessive blowby and liquid fuel dripping into it. The job of the cooling system is to get the engine up to normal operating temperature as quickly as possible and then maintain it at that temperature. The cooling system should not allow overheating or overcooling.

In the liquid cooling system (Fig. 21-1), a liquid is circulated around the cylinders to absorb heat from the cylinder walls. The liquid is water to which an antifreeze solution is added to prevent freezing in cold weather. This mixture is called the *coolant*. The coolant is heated as it passes through the engine. The hot coolant flows through a radiator in which the heat in the coolant is passed on to air that is flowing through the radiator. The water jackets, radiator size, and coolant passages are designed to maintain the cylinder walls, head, pistons, and other working parts at efficient, but not excessive, temperatures.

When the coolant flows through the radiator, it loses heat. The cooled coolant then flows back through the engine and is kept in circulation by the water pump. This circulation of the coolant continually removes heat from the engine.

SHOP SKILLS

____ 1. Figure 21-1 shows the cooling system for an in-line engine. It is typical of automotive engine cooling systems. Identify each part of the cooling system.

____ 2. Using the references and Fig. 21-1, trace the flow of coolant from the top of the radiator through the engine and back to the top of the radiator. First do this assuming the thermostat is closed and then assuming the thermostat is open.

____ 3. Examine engine heads and blocks to locate the water jackets and coolant passages. Examine various water pumps, radiators and pressure caps. Referring to Fig. 21-1, trace the coolant flow from the radiator through the engine and heater and back to the radiator.

JOB 21   MULTIPLE-CHOICE TEST

1. The water pump is driven from the
   a. camshaft
   b. engine fan
   c. crankshaft timing gear
   d. crankshaft pulley   1. ____

2. The device in the cooling system that restricts coolant circulation with the engine cold is called the
   a. pump
   b. bypass
   c. thermostat
   d. pressure cap   2. ____

3. The pressure cap contains two valves—the pressure valve and the
   a. vacuum valve
   b. release valve
   c. atmospheric valve
   d. overflow valve   3. ____

4. Two types of antifreeze are alcohol base and
   a. heptane
   b. ethylene glycol
   c. tetraethyl
   d. octane   4. ____

5. The device in the cooling system that increases the boiling point of the coolant is called the
   a. radiator pressure cap
   b. water pump
   c. bypass valve
   d. atmospheric valve   5. ____

JOB 22-1
Thermostat Testing and Replacement

Objective: To learn how to test and install thermostats.

References: AM ♦22-1 to 22-15, SG Chap. 22, automotive manufacturers' service manuals.

Equipment: Various thermostats and engines.
Tools: Thermometer, pan of water, stove, basic hand tools.

SHOP FACTS

Different car manufacturers have different testing procedures for checking thermostats. Three different manufacturers' procedures are given below.

Figure 22-1 shows how the thermostat, when closed, blocks off the radiator from the engine. Note how, when the thermostat opens, it permits coolant to circulate between the engine and the radiator.

SHOP SKILLS

CHEVROLET PROCEDURE

____ 1. To remove the thermostat, partly drain the cooling system so that the coolant level is below the thermostat. If the cooling system contains good antifreeze, use a drain pan to catch the coolant as it is drained. The coolant can then be put back in the radiator after the thermostat is replaced.

____ 2. Remove the thermostat-housing bolts or nuts, and then remove the housing and gasket.

____ 3. Examine the thermostat for any damage, such as a cracked bellows or a sticking valve or valve plunger.

____ 4. Note the thermostat opening temperature, which is usually stamped on the thermostat, or get the specification from a service manual.

____ 5. Pour a mixture of ⅓ antifreeze and ⅔ water in a pan. Stick the thermometer into the mixture. Heat the mixture until it is 25°F [14°C] above the temperature stamped on the thermostat.

____ 6. Submerge the thermostat completely in the mixture (Fig. 22-2) and agitate the mixture with the thermostat. If the thermostat is good, the thermostat valve should open fully.

____ 7. Remove the thermostat and submerge it in a mixture of ⅓ antifreeze and ⅔ water that is heated to a temperature of 10°F [5.5°C] below the temperature stamped on the thermostat. If the thermostat is good, the valve should close completely.

____ 8. If the thermostat is good, reinstall it, using a new housing gasket. If the thermostat does not open and close as specified, replace it. Be sure that the old gasket is removed entirely and that the new gasket is properly installed. Put the thermostat in with the pellet end toward the engine. If you install the thermostat upside down, the engine will overheat. Do not overtighten the housing nuts or bolts. The thermostat housing may break if it is overtightened or not tightened evenly.

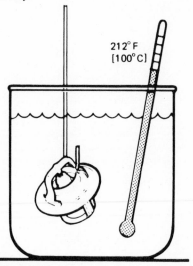

212°F [100°C]

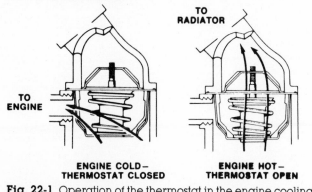

TO RADIATOR

TO ENGINE

ENGINE COLD— THERMOSTAT CLOSED

ENGINE HOT— THERMOSTAT OPEN

Fig. 22-1 Operation of the thermostat in the engine cooling system.

Fig. 22-2 Testing a cooling-system thermostat. **(Ford Motor Company)**

____ **9.** Refill the radiator, and start the engine. Check for leaks. Be sure that the radiator is full before returning the car to the customer.

PLYMOUTH PROCEDURE

____ **1.** Plymouth recommends testing the thermostat in the system. With the cooling system filled to the proper level, warm the engine by driving the car for about 10 minutes. Remove the radiator cap, observing proper safety precautions. Insert a thermometer into the coolant. Idle the engine with the hood raised. Coolant temperature should stabilize at no lower than 8°F [−13°C] below the thermostat opening temperature.

FORD PROCEDURE

____ **1.** Ford recommends immersing the thermostat in boiling water, as shown in Fig. 22-2. If the thermostat does not open, it is defective. If the problem is slow warm-up, the thermostat may be leaking.

____ **2.** Hold the thermostat up to the light to see whether the valve is closing completely. If there is a gap between the valve and valve seat with the thermostat at room temperature, replace the thermostat.

JOB 22-1   MULTIPLE-CHOICE TEST

1. When cold, the thermostat prevents circulation of coolant between
   a. the cylinder block and cylinder head
   b. the water pump and engine
   c. the engine and radiator
   d. none of the above   1. ____

2. When the thermostat is open, coolant flows from
   a. the engine to the radiator
   b. the water pump to the radiator
   c. the radiator to the heater core
   d. none of the above   2. ____

3. The number stamped on the top of a thermostat is its
   a. part number
   b. rating
   c. closing temperature
   d. none of the above   3. ____

4. To check thermostat operation, heat it
   a. in a mixture of antifreeze and water
   b. in an oven
   c. with a torch
   d. none of the above   4. ____

5. A thermostat installed upside down will cause an engine to
   a. run cold
   b. not stop
   c. not start
   d. overheat   5. ____

JOB 22-2

Checking, Flushing, and Cleaning Cooling Systems

Objective: To learn how to check, flush, and clean the engine cooling system.

References: AM ♦22-16 to 22-19, SG Chap. 22, automotive manufacturers' service manuals.
Equipment: Various automobiles and engines.

Tools: Antifreeze hydrometer, flushing equipment, basic hand tools.
Supplies: Cooling-system cleaning compounds.

SHOP SKILLS

____ 1. The radiator air passages should be blown out from back to front with compressed air to remove bugs and dirt. At the same time that this is done, inspect the radiator for leaks.

____ 2. A leaking radiator usually has rusty scale and stains on the radiator below the leak. A leaking radiator can be repaired by removal and soldering. If the radiator is in poor condition, a new core or radiator should be installed.

____ 3. To check the condition of the radiator hose, squeeze the hose (Fig. 22-3). A hose that is soft, hard, rotted, or swollen should be replaced. Drain the cooling system, catching and saving the coolant for reuse if it is fairly fresh and clean. Take off the hose clamps and remove the hose. If it sticks, twist it or use a hose remover to pry it loose.

____ 4. Install a new hose of the correct type, size, and length. Make sure that the hose clamps fit tightly to avoid leaks.

____ 5. The strength of the antifreeze solution may be tested with an antifreeze hydrometer. Draw up sufficient liquid from the radiator into the hydrometer to suspend the float. Note the reading on the float stem at the liquid level and the temperature of the liquid. Check the table on the hydrometer to determine the freezing temperature of the solution. A ball-type hydrometer can be used instead of the float type. The number of balls that float tells you the strength of the antifreeze solution.

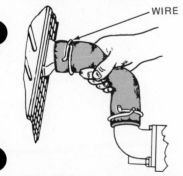

Fig. 22-3 To check the condition of a radiator hose, squeeze the hose. **(Chrysler Corporation)**

♦ CAUTION ♦ Never remove the radiator cap when the radiator is hot. Sudden release of the cooling-system pressure may cause the coolant to boil and blow out of the radiator. Wait for the engine to cool before removing the cap.

____ 6. The color of the coolant should be noted. Coolant that is rusty usually indicates deposits of rust or scale in the engine water jackets and radiator. This retards cooling and may permit the engine to overheat. Scale and rust may be cleaned out by flushing the engine and the radiator.

____ 7. Before the cooling system is flushed, the thermostat should be removed. Then reinstall the thermostat housing. Set the car-heater temperature control at the HOT position.

____ 8. A cooling-system cleaning compound can be used just before flushing to help remove rust, sludge, and other deposits from the cooling system. A typical cleaning procedure is as follows. Add the liquid part of the cleaner to the radiator. Then fill the cooling system with water to about 3 inches [75 mm] below the overflow pipe. Cover the radiator and run the engine until the temperature indicator reaches 180°F [82°C]. Remove the radiator cover and run the engine for an additional 20 minutes. Do not allow the water to boil. Then add the powder portion of the cleaner and run the engine for another 10 minutes. Finally, stop the engine and allow it to cool for a few minutes. Then drain the cooling system and flush it out with water.

Note Some engine manufacturers specify *reverse flushing*. This means that the flushing water is sent through the radiator and the engine in a direction reverse from that in which it usually travels. Other engine manufacturers specify straight flushing.

____ 9. For reverse flushing of the radiator, remove radiator hoses and attach a lead-away hose to the top of the radiator. Attach a new short length of hose to the lower end of the radiator. Apply the flushing gun to the lower hose, as shown in Fig. 22-4. When air and water are used, apply the air gradually and in short blasts to avoid excessive air pressure. Continue flushing until the water from the lead-away hose runs clean.

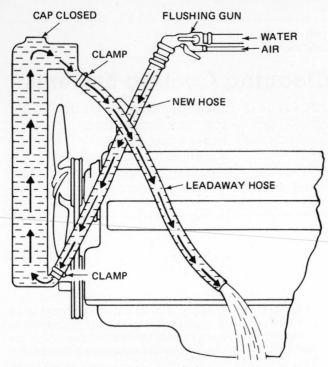

Fig. 22-4 Reverse-flushing a radiator.

_____ 10. To reverse-flush the engine, attach a lead-away hose to the water-pump inlet and a short length of new hose to the water outlet at the top of the engine. Apply the flushing gun to the upper hose and continue to flush the engine until the water runs clean.

_____ 11. To straight-flush the radiator and the engine, use the above procedure but reverse the position of the lead-away hoses and the flushing gun.

Note There is a popular fast-flush method which does not require the removal of the thermostat and cylinder-block drain plugs.

_____ 12. Check the thermostat following the procedure outlined in Job 22-1. Reinstall the thermostat and hoses. Refill the cooling system. Pressure-test the cooling system and radiator cap.

_____ 13. Manufacturers recommend that every two years the cooling system be drained and flushed with water. Then the cooling system should be filled with a fresh solution of antifreeze and water. Regardless of whether freezing temperatures are expected, the coolant should provide freeze protection to at least −20°F [−29°C]. This will provide adequate corrosion protection and proper temperature-indicator-light operation.

JOB 22-2 MULTIPLE-CHOICE TEST

1. Accumulations of rust and scale in the radiator will cause
   a. engine overheating
   b. slow warm-up
   c. damaged hose
   d. reduced heating capacity   1. _____

2. When you are reverse-flushing the radiator, the flushing gun is connected to the
   a. upper tank
   b. thermostat housing
   c. lower tank
   d. pump inlet   2. _____

3. If the thermostat is stuck open, the engine will
   a. overheat
   b. start hard
   c. warm up slowly
   d. warm up quickly   3. _____

4. Exhaust-gas leakage into the cooling system is most likely due to a defective
   a. manifold gasket
   b. cylinder-head gasket
   c. water pump
   d. hose connection   4. _____

5. Air will be drawn into the cooling system if there are leaks at any point between the
   a. radiator and block
   b. radiator and head
   c. pump and block
   d. radiator and pump   5. _____

JOB 23

Using Jumper Wires and Test Lights

Objective: To learn how to test electric circuits with jumper wires and test lights.

References: AM ♦23-1 to 23-20, SG Chap. 23, automotive manufacturers' service manuals.

Equipment: Any vehicle with wiring to be checked.

Tools: Various jumper wires, 12-volt test light, continuity tester.

SHOP SKILLS

USING THE JUMPER WIRE

____ 1. Technicians working on the automotive electric system need several jumper wires of various lengths and with a variety of terminals on the ends. There are three ways that a jumper wire can be used when you are diagnosing circuits:
    a. To check for poor grounds
    b. To supply current from a known source directly to the load
    c. To bypass a wire or any other part of the circuit.

____ 2. To use a jumper wire, select one that is of the right length and gauge. A jumper wire always should be as large as or larger than the wire in the circuit to be tested. Many jumper wires have "alligator clip" terminals on one or both ends. However, jumper wires with other types of terminals also are useful additions to your toolbox.

____ 3. Select a car with an underhood or trunk light, or use any other light on the vehicle that is readily accessible. With the light on, connect the jumper wire from the socket of the light to a good ground, such as the engine block or frame. If the light gets brighter when you do this, then the socket has a poor ground.

____ 4. Remove the jumper wire. Locate the wire that provides current to the light. Trace the wire back from the light socket until you locate the connector. Then disconnect the wire.

____ 5. Now, attach one end of the jumper wire to the metal terminal inside the connector from the light wire. Then touch the other end of the jumper wire to a known source of current, such as the positive terminal on the battery.

____ 6. This check shows you that the light, or any other load, will work properly when current is supplied to it. Also, this type of check can be made to bypass any suspected faulty wiring from the battery to the connector.

♦ **CAUTION** ♦ Never connect a jumper wire to a known source of current first. When you do this, the other end striking any metal ground causes the jumper wire to be a short across the battery terminals. Depending on how good a connection is made, sparks or a fire may result, and you can easily be burned. In addition, this abnormal current flow may damage other wiring and electronic parts.

USING THE TEST LIGHT

____ 1. There are two types of test lights. These are:
    a. The 12-volt test light, which is powered by the battery in the car
    b. The self-powered test light (sometimes called a *continuity tester*), which is powered by a small battery (usually 1½ volts) contained within it, usually in the handle or body of the test light.

____ 2. The 12-volt test light is used to check for current sources in a circuit. Before starting the test, place the sharp tip of the test light on one battery terminal and touch the test-light lead terminal to the other. The test light should glow.

Note This procedure checks both the test light and the battery. Knowing that both are good prevents you from wasting time working with a burned-out bulb or a dead battery.

____ 3. To use the test light, connect the alligator clip on the end of the lead wire to a good ground (Fig. 23-1). Then touch the test point you have selected in the circuit with the tip of the test light.

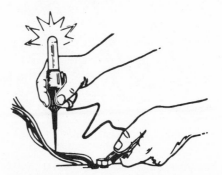

Fig. 23-1 Checking a circuit with a 12-volt test light. (**Lisle Corporation**)

____ 4. If attaching the test light across these two points completes a circuit, the light will glow. If the light does not glow, there is an open circuit between the battery and the test point you checked.

____ 5. To locate the actual open, move the tip of the test light along the circuit toward the positive terminal of the battery. Test as often as necessary until the bulb lights.

◆ **CAUTION** ◆ The purpose of the sharp tip on the test light is so that you can force the tip through the insulation of a wire to test for current. However, sometimes this is difficult, especially on small wires. Be very careful not to stab yourself while forcing the tip into the insulation. Wraparound test lights, which have a hooked end, are available for use behind the dash and in places where the sharp tip cannot be used safely.

USING THE CONTINUITY TESTER

____ 1. The self-powered test light, or continuity tester, has its own low-voltage battery. Never connect the continuity tester into a live circuit on the car or across the terminals of the car battery. Such a connection will instantly burn out the bulb in the continuity tester.

____ 2. Check the continuity tester by touching the clip on the end of the lead to the tip. The light should glow. If the light does not come on, check the bulb and the battery in the tester.

____ 3. To use the continuity tester, fasten or touch the clip to one end of the wire or device to be tested (Fig. 23-2). Then, with the tip of the tester, touch the other end. If the light comes on, there is continuity, and current will flow through that part of the circuit. If the light does not glow, the circuit is open, and no current can flow.

JOB 23 MULTIPLE-CHOICE TEST

1. Stranded wires (cables) are used mostly for
   a. low current and stiffness
   b. high current and flexibility
   c. both a and b
   d. neither a nor b   1. ____

2. A circuit protector is used to open the circuit when the
   a. wire begins to overheat
   b. engine begins to overheat
   c. battery begins to overheat
   d. alternator begins to overheat   2. ____

3. A circuit in which too much current is flowing is
   a. an open circuit
   b. a short circuit
   c. a grounded circuit
   d. none of the above   3. ____

4. When you use a continuity tester,
   a. current must be flowing in the circuit
   b. voltage must be available in the circuit
   c. the circuit must be connected to the car battery
   d. the circuit must be disconnected (isolated) from the car battery   4. ____

5. Before making a test with a 12-volt test light, Mechanic A checks the test light on the car battery. The light does not glow. Mechanic A says that the battery in the test light is dead. Mechanic B says that the battery in the car is dead. Who could be right?
   a. A only
   b. B only
   c. both A and B
   d. neither A nor B   5. ____

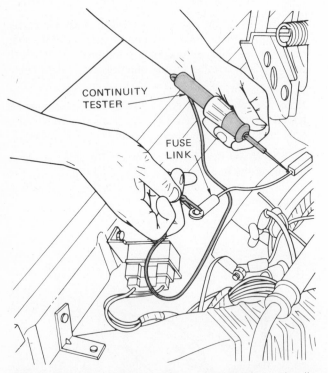

Fig. 23-2 Using a continuity tester to check part of a circuit. (Ford Motor Company)

JOB 24-1

Servicing and Charging Batteries

Objective: To learn how to service and charge automotive batteries.

References: AM ♦24-9 to 24-22, SG Chap. 24, battery-charger operating instructions, automotive manufacturers' service manual.

Equipment: Vehicles with batteries to be serviced and charged.

Tools: Slow charger, fast charger, thermometer, battery cleaning tool, battery carrier or heavy rubber gloves, basic hand tools.

Supplies: Baking soda, water, disposable towels, fender cover.

SHOP FACTS

♦ **SAFETY** ♦ *Always wear safety goggles when working on batteries. The sulfuric acid in battery electrolyte is very corrosive. If battery acid gets on clothes, it will eat holes in them. Battery acid can cause severe burns on your skin and blindness if it splashes into your eyes. Should this happen, immediately wash your eyes with water (Job 2). If electrolyte is spilled, wash it away with large amounts of water. Baking soda may be thrown on the spilled acid to neutralize it. Then the acid may be washed away harmlessly.*

SHOP SKILLS

SERVICING THE BATTERY

_____ 1. Raise the hood and cover the fender nearest the battery with a fender cover. Disconnect the grounded battery cable from its battery terminal. Then disconnect the positive battery cable from its battery terminal.

_____ 2. Remove the battery hold-down clamps. Make a quick check to see whether the battery case is cracked or leaking (Fig. 24-1). If leakage or heavy corrosion is found, do *not* lift the battery from the vehicle with your bare hands. Use a battery carrier or a pair of industrial rubber gloves (not the household type). Then remove the battery from the vehicle and set the battery in a suitable area for cleaning.

♦ **CAUTION** ♦ A battery is heavy. It weighs about 25 pounds (11 kg), and large batteries weigh even more. To prevent muscle strain, always lift a battery with your legs and not with your back. While lifting or carrying a battery, be careful not to drop it or to spill electrolyte.

_____ 3. Examine the battery for signs of leakage, a cracked case or top, corrosion, missing vent plugs, and corroded or

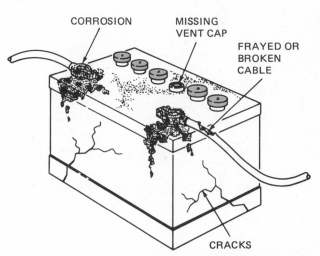

Fig. 24-1 Conditions to look for when visually inspecting a battery. **(Delco-Remy Division of General Motors Corporation)**

missing hold-down clamps. If a broken or cracked case or cover is found, the battery must be replaced.

_____ 4. If the top of the battery is covered with corrosion and the owner complains that it needs water frequently, the battery is being overcharged. A check of the charging system should be made. Follow the procedure outlined in Job 26-1 of this workbook.

_____ 5. Wash the entire outside of the battery—top, sides, and bottom—with a solution of baking soda and warm water. This solution is made by mixing two tablespoons of baking soda in a quart of water. Brush the solution on the battery, using a bristle brush. Do *not* brush over the top of the vent plugs. If any of the cleaning solution gets into the battery cells, it will be weaken the electrolyte.

_____ 6. Wait until the foaming stops. Then rinse off the battery with clean water. Do *not* dry the battery with compressed air. The compressed-air stream could cause electrolyte to spray out of the battery through the vent plugs.

_____ 7. Clean the battery posts with a battery-terminal cleaning tool (Fig. 24-2).

_____ 8. Remove the vent plugs and set them down on the top of the battery. If the condition or state of charge of the battery is to be checked, use the hydrometer to measure the specific gravity of the electrolyte in each cell. Follow the procedure outlined in Job 24-2 of this workbook.

_____ 9. Check the electrolyte level in each cell. If water is needed, it should be added until the electrolyte reaches the proper level. Many batteries have marks or rings in the cell covers which show whether or not the battery needs water. Some batteries have visual indicators that show whether water is needed.

CAREFUL Do *not* add too much water. Too much water causes the electrolyte to leak through the holes in the vent caps. This corrodes and eats away the battery tray and the hold-down clamps.

_____ 10. In the car, inspect the battery tray, battery cables, and hold-down clamps for corrosion damage. Any part that has been severely eaten away should be replaced.

_____ 11. Using a stiff brush, wash the battery cables, tray, and hold-down clamps in the solution of baking soda and water.

_____ 12. Rinse off the parts with clean water. Scrape off any excess corrosion or rust deposits. Open the water drain holes in the bottom of the battery tray. If acid-resistant paint is available, dry the tray and hold-down clamps with compressed air, and paint them.

_____ 13. Clean the terminals and the inside surfaces of the battery clamps with a battery-terminal cleaning tool (Fig. 24-2). Replace any damaged or frayed cables and broken terminal clamps.

_____ 14. Reinstall the battery in the car. Then install and tighten the hold-down clamps. Do not overtighten the hold-down clamps, as this may damage the battery case or cover.

Note The battery must not be installed backward. If it is, serious damage to the electric system may result. The larger battery terminal is the positive terminal.

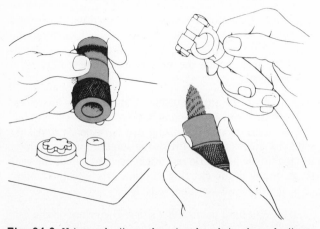

Fig. 24-2 Using a battery cleaning brush to clean battery posts and cable clamps. **(Buick Motor Division of General Motors Corporation)**

_____ 15. Install felt washers, if used, on the battery terminals. Check the battery polarity before connecting the cable clamps to the terminals. If the polarity is correct, install the clamps and tighten them securely. Then coat all connections with light grease, sealer, or an anticorrosion compound to retard corrosion.

SLOW-CHARGING THE BATTERY

Note Do not charge a maintenance-free battery if the charge indicator shows yellow or clear.

_____ 1. If the battery is to be charged in the vehicle, disconnect the battery ground cable from its battery post. This will protect the vehicle's electric system from high voltages during charge.

_____ 2. Visually inspect and clean the battery, as outlined in the first part of this job sheet. The electrolyte must be at the normal level before charging is attempted. Add water if necessary. Never attempt to charge a battery if the electrolyte is frozen. A battery with frozen electrolyte may explode during charging.

_____ 3. Explosive gases are given off by a charging battery. A spark or flame could ignite the gases and cause an explosion. Be sure that no one strikes a match or smokes around a charging battery. Turn off the charger when connecting or disconnecting the charger clamps at the battery posts. Otherwise, a spark will occur where the charging circuit is broken, and an explosion may result.

_____ 4. Several firms manufacture battery-charging equipment. Always follow the manufacturer's operating instructions when using a battery charger. There are two general types—slow chargers and fast chargers.

_____ 5. Slow charging is the preferred method of recharging a battery. Slow charging may be safely used on any battery, provided the electrolyte is at the proper level in all cells and is not frozen.

_____ 6. With the slow charger off, connect its clamps to the proper battery posts. Be sure to observe the correct polarity for each connection. Turn the charger on and adjust the charging rate. Follow the instructions of the charger manufacturer and the battery rating in setting the charging rate. If the charging rate cannot be determined, charge the battery at a 5-ampere rate.

_____ 7. The slow charge provides a relatively low charging rate for a long period of time. Charging rates in the 3- to 20-ampere range are common. Charging periods of 24 hours and more may be needed to bring a battery to full charge. The battery is fully charged when the cells are gassing freely at a low charging rate and no change in specific gravity occurs over a 2-hour period.

_____ 8. When charging is completed, turn the slow charger off before disconnecting the charger clamps from the battery.

_____ 9. If adequate time for a slow charge is not available, a fast charger may be used. A fast charger will give a sufficient

SPECIFIC GRAVITY READING†	CHARGE RATE, AMPERES	BATTERY CAPACITY, AMPERE-HOURS			
		36	41–45	53–54	63–68
1.125–1.150	35	50 minutes	65 minutes	80 minutes	115 minutes
1.150–1.175	35	40 minutes	50 minutes	65 minutes	95 minutes
1.175–1.200	35	30 minutes	40 minutes	50 minutes	70 minutes
1.200–1.225	35	25 minutes	30 minutes	35 minutes	50 minutes
Above 1.225	5	§	§	§	§

NOTE: Battery must be at a temperature of at least 40°F [4.4°C] before charging. At no time during the charging operation should the electrolyte temperature exceed 130°F [54.4°C].
† If the specific gravity is below 1.125, use the time indicated for the 1.125 specific gravity, then charge at 5 amperes until the specific gravity reaches 1.250 at 80°F [26.7°C].
§ Charge at 5-ampere rate only until the specific gravity reaches 1.250 at 80°F [26.7°C].

Fig. 24-3 Charging schedule for batteries with vent plugs.

charge in an hour to enable the battery and alternator to continue to carry the electric load. However, a battery cannot be fully charged by the fast-charge method (Fig. 24-3).

FAST-CHARGING THE BATTERY

Note Do not charge a maintenance-free battery if the charge indicator shows yellow or clear.

____ 1. Disconnect the battery ground cable. With the fast charger off, connect its clamps to the battery posts. Observe the proper polarity for each connection. Turn the charger on and adjust the charging rate and timer. Follow the instructions of the charger manufacturer and the battery rating in setting the charging rate and time period.

____ 2. If the charging rate and time cannot be determined, 12-volt passenger-car and light-truck batteries may be charged at a 35-ampere rate for 20 minutes. With a fast charger, a battery with vent plugs may be charged at any rate which does not cause the electrolyte temperature of any cell to exceed 125°F[51.7°C]. However, the charging rate must not be so high that it causes excessive gassing and loss of electrolyte. Figure 24-4 shows the charging schedule for maintenance-free batteries.

____ 3. When using a fast charger, follow the precautions listed by the manufacturer. Never ignore or bypass the safe-

OPEN CIRCUIT TERMINAL VOLTAGE	AMPERE-HOURS	CHARGE RATE, AMPERES*			
		5 AMPERES	10 AMPERES	20 AMPERES	30 AMPERES
Below 11.85	53	11 hours	5.5 hours	2.75 hours	1.75 hours
	62–68	13 hours	6.5 hours	3.25 hours	2 hours
11.85–12.00	53	8 hours	4 hours	2 hours	1.5 hours
	63–68	10 hours	5 hours	2.5 hours	1.5 hours
12.00–12.10	53	6 hours	3 hours	1.5 hours	1 hour
	63–68	8 hours	4 hours	2 hours	1.25 hours
12.10–12.25	53	5 hours	2.5 hours	1.25 hours	45 minutes
	63–68	6 hours	3 hours	1.5 hours	1 hour
12.25–12.35	53	3 hours	1.5 hours	45 minutes	0.5 hour
	63–68	4 hours	2 hours	1 hour	0.5 hour
Above 12.35	53	2 hours			
	63–68	2.5 hours			

* CAUTION: Do not exceed 30-ampere charge rate.
If gassing or spewing of the electrolyte occurs during charging, the charge rate must be reduced. Battery must be at a temperature of at least 40°F [4.4°C] before charging.

Fig. 24-4 Charging schedule for maintenance-free batteries. (Ford Motor Company)

guards built into the charger by its manufacturer. These safe-guards are intended to protect the battery from damage. Some chargers have thermostatic temperature- and time-limiting controls. Make sure that the instructions are followed.

_____ 4. The battery can be permanently damaged during fast charging unless certain precautions are taken. Here are a few important precautions:

    a. Battery electrolyte level must be at the normal level.

    b. Battery electrolyte temperature must never exceed 125°F[51.7°C]. If this temperature is reached, cool the battery by reducing the charging rate or by turning off the charger.

    c. Excessive gassing must not be allowed. If the battery begins to gas excessively, reduce the charging rate or turn off the charger.

    d. Do not fast-charge a battery for longer than 1 hour without checking the specific gravity. If the battery does not show a significant change in specific gravity after 1 hour of fast charging, then slow charging should be tried.

_____ 5. The fast charger provides a high charging rate for a short period of time. Charging rates of 40 to 70 amperes are common for batteries with vent caps. Charge periods vary up to 3 hours maximum, depending on the type and size of the battery. As the battery approaches full charge, the electrolyte in each cell will begin to gas or bubble.

_____ 6. When charging is completed, turn off the fast charger before removing the charger clamps from the battery.

JOB 24-1 MULTIPLE-CHOICE TEST

1. A car has a new battery that is fully charged but now has a bulge in the case. Mechanic A says to ignore the bulge and continue using the battery. Mechanic B says to replace the battery. Who is right?
   a. A only
   b. B only
   c. either A or B
   d. neither A nor B   1. ____

2. Some manufacturers stopped installing bolt-type battery-cable clamps on batteries with posts in new cars. The reason was to
   a. help prevent backward installation of the battery
   b. overcome the problem of battery clamps bolts working loose
   c. lower the internal resistance of the connection
   d. prevent cover damage by improper installation
        2. ____

3. On a battery with posts on the top, the positive post is always
   a. the smaller post
   b. the larger post
   c. the same size as the negative post
   d. closest to the starting motor   3. ____

4. A battery has been sitting in a car in storage for one year. To activate the battery, you should:
   I. Connect the battery to a fast charger at a 70-ampere charging rate.
   II. Dump out any liquid remaining and add new electrolyte.
   a. I only
   b. II only
   c. either I or II
   d. neither I nor II   4. ____

5. The maximum allowable charging rate for a maintenance-free battery is
   a. 5 amperes
   b. 20 amperes
   c. 30 amperes
   d. 70 amperes   5. ____

JOB 24-2

Testing Automotive Batteries

Objective: To learn how to test automotive batteries.

References: AM ♦24-23 to 24-29, SG Chap. 24, automotive manufacturers' service manuals.
Equipment: Various vehicles and batteries.

Tools: Hydrometer, battery-service tools, thermometer, clock or watch with a second hand, basic hand tools.
Supplies: Baking soda, water, disposable towels, fender cover.

SHOP FACTS

♦ **SAFETY** ♦ *Be careful when working on batteries. Wear safety goggles to protect your eyes while working with electrolyte and while testing batteries. The sulfuric acid in battery electrolyte is very corrosive. If battery acid gets on clothes, the acid will eat holes in them. Battery acid touching your skin can cause severe burns, and blindness if splashed into your eyes.*

If electrolyte is spilled, flush it away with large amounts of water. Baking soda may be thrown on the spilled acid to neutralize it. Then the acid may be washed away harmlessly. Do not let electrolyte drop on a car fender, because the paint will be damaged.

♦ **CAUTION** ♦ The gases given off by the battery during charging are very explosive. For this reason, there should be no open flames or electric sparks around a battery. A flame or spark could ignite the gases around the top of the battery, and a dangerous explosion could result. The battery might be blown apart, and anyone near the battery could be injured.

During a battery test, try to avoid sparking at the battery terminals. A battery can deliver a very high current on direct short. Use care to avoid shorting the battery or grounding the insulated battery cable.

TESTERS

A variety of battery-testing methods can be used to test batteries. Testers such as the 421 tester and the high-discharge, or battery-capacity, test can be used on any battery. But other testers which check individual cell conditions (such as the cadmium-tip tester, hydrometer, or refractometer) cannot be used on sealed "no-service" or maintenance-free batteries.

The first step in battery testing is to inspect the battery, as outlined in Job 24-1. If the battery has a cracked case or cover or loose parts, do not test it. Any of these defects requires replacement of the battery.

In a fully charged battery, the electrolyte is about 40 percent sulfuric acid and 60 percent water. The hydrometer test tells you the specific gravity of the electrolyte, which is a measure of the amount of sulfuric acid actually in the electrolyte. Under most conditions this is a good indication of the battery's state of charge (Fig. 24-5). But the hydrometer test does not tell you the actual battery condition. For example, the hydrometer does not tell if the plates and separators are in bad condition and the battery is about to fail. However, the hydrometer test is recommended by the battery manufacturers as a supplementary test for use with other tests.

A refractometer also can be used to check the specific gravity of the battery electrolyte. The refractometer reading is automatically adjusted for the temperature of the electrolyte. Enter the readings in the chart for step 6 below. The readings of a temperature-compensated ball-type hydrometer also are entered directly in step 6.

SHOP SKILLS

HYDROMETER AND REFRACTOMETER TEST

_____ 1. This test is made using a float-type hydrometer. Insert the short flexible tube of the hydrometer into the first cell. Squeeze the bulb so that enough electrolyte will be drawn into the tube to suspend the float. Do not draw in too much electrolyte. Make sure that the float is not bumping the top of the hydrometer or sticking to the side of the tube.

If the electrolyte level in the battery is too low, add water. Then charge the battery for 1 hour in order to mix the water with the electrolyte.

_____ 2. Read the hydrometer, keeping your eyes level with the top of the electrolyte. Keep the hydrometer tube in or slightly above the cell being checked. Do *not* let any electrolyte drip on the test bench, car, floor, or yourself. If any electrolyte does drip out, wipe it up with a throwaway rag or paper towel rinsed in a solution of baking soda and water.

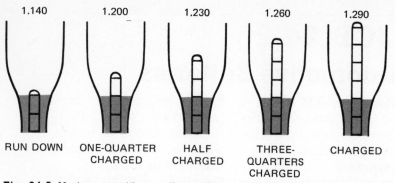

| 1.140 | 1.200 | 1.230 | 1.260 | 1.290 |
| RUN DOWN | ONE-QUARTER CHARGED | HALF CHARGED | THREE-QUARTERS CHARGED | CHARGED |

Fig. 24-5 Various specific-gravity readings. (Delco-Remy Division of General Motors Corporation)

_____ 3. After taking the reading, squeeze the bulb to return the electrolyte to the cell. Write the reading in the proper space in Fig. 24-6.

_____ 4. Repeat steps 1 to 3 for each cell in the battery.

_____ 5. Test two more batteries and write in the readings in the chart under step 3. Then rinse out the hydrometer with plain water and put it away.

_____ 6. Adjust the hydrometer readings for temperature. Add four points (0.004) to the reading for every 10°F [5.6°C] of electrolyte temperature above 80°F [26.7°C]. Subtract four points (0.004) for every 10°F [5.6°C] of electrolyte temperature below 80° [26.7°C]. Write the adjusted readings in the spaces of the chart in Fig. 24-7.

_____ 7. Based on the cell readings and the information in the references, write the condition of each battery in the space in Fig. 24-8. Then write down the service you recommend for each battery. A battery is defective and should be replaced if the difference in hydrometer readings between cells is more than 50 points (0.050).

HIGH-DISCHARGE, OR BATTERY-CAPACITY, TEST

_____ 1. The high-discharge, or battery-capacity, test measures the ability of a battery to deliver current. A load is ap-

plied to the battery for 15 seconds with a special tester. Then, while the battery is under load, the battery voltage is read. In a good battery, the voltage must not be below 9.6 volts at the end of the 15 seconds.

_____ 2. To make a capacity test of a battery, the temperature of the battery should be between 60 and 100°F [15.6 and 37.8°C]. If the battery temperature is not within this range, wait until the battery is at room temperature before making the test. Some manufacturers provide charts that list the minimum acceptable voltage at lower temperatures.

_____ 3. Find the specifications for the battery you are about to test. The load is the number of amperes of current that will flow from the battery during the test. The actual load you should use varies with the size of the battery. Some manufacturers' service manuals and shop bulletins contain the load, or "battery discharge rate," specifications. However, if the manufacturer's specifications are not available, you can use either of two optional load specifications:

    a. A load equal to one-half of the battery's cold cranking rate at 0°F [−17.8°C]

    b. A load equal to three times the battery's ampere-hour (A-H) rating

_____ 4. A battery-starter tester, or a _volt-ampere tester_ (VAT), is needed to make the battery-capacity test (Fig. 24-9). This tester combines a voltmeter with a high-range ammeter and a variable resistance, all built into the tester. Follow the

BATTERY NUMBER	CELL 1 SPECIFIC GRAVITY	CELL 2 SPECIFIC GRAVITY	CELL 3 SPECIFIC GRAVITY	CELL 4 SPECIFIC GRAVITY	CELL 5 SPECIFIC GRAVITY	CELL 6 SPECIFIC GRAVITY
1						
2						
3						

Fig. 24-6 Unadjusted hydrometer readings of battery specific gravity.

BATTERY NUMBER	CELL 1 SPECIFIC GRAVITY	CELL 2 SPECIFIC GRAVITY	CELL 3 SPECIFIC GRAVITY	CELL 4 SPECIFIC GRAVITY	CELL 5 SPECIFIC GRAVITY	CELL 6 SPECIFIC GRAVITY
1						
2						
3						

Fig. 24-7 Adjusted hydrometer readings of battery specific gravity.

BATTERY NUMBER	CONDITION	RECOMMENDED SERVICE
1		
2		
3		

Fig. 24-8 Condition and recommended service for each battery.

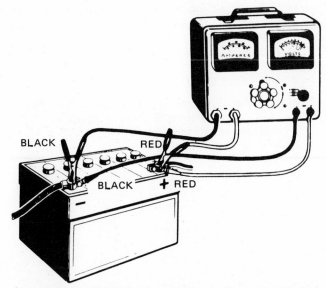

Fig. 24-9 Connections for making a battery-capacity test. (Chrysler Corporation)

tester operating instructions to make the test. A typical procedure is outlined in Fig. 24-10.

_____ **5.** Turn the load-control knob in the center of the tester to the OFF position.

_____ **6.** Turn the voltmeter scale-selector switch to the 20-volt position.

_____ **7.** The tester has four leads—one pair for the voltmeter and one pair for the ammeter and variable resistor. The ammeter leads are the larger cables. Usually the positive leads are red, and the negative leads are black. Identify the leads.

_____ **8.** Connect the positive leads to the positive battery post and the negative leads to the negative battery post. On the battery, each post will be marked POS and NEG, or there will be a plus sign (+) or a minus sign (−) on or near the post. For post-type batteries, the positive post is slightly larger than the negative post. Adapters must be attached to side-terminal batteries before the tester clamps can be installed.

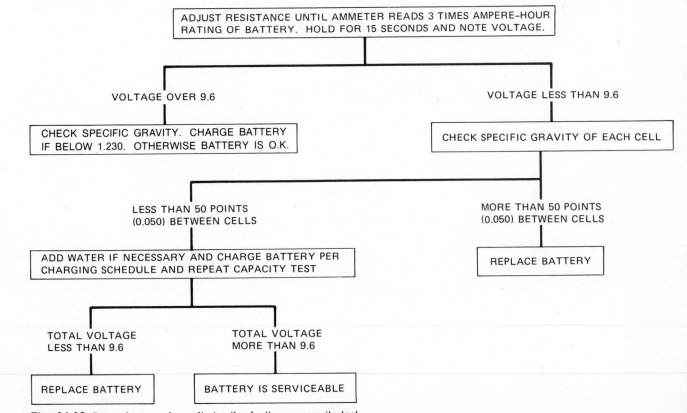

Fig. 24-10 Procedure and results for the battery-capacity test.

_____ 9. Check that the voltmeter-lead clips are connected to the battery posts, and *not* to the ammeter-lead clips.

_____ 10. Now turn the load control knob clockwise until the ammeter needle reaches the specified discharge rate, or load.

_____ 11. Keep the ammeter reading at the specified load for 15 seconds. At the end of 15 seconds, read the voltmeter. Then turn the control knob back to the OFF position. Do *not* allow the load to remain on the battery for longer than 15 seconds. This could damage the battery internally.

_____ 12. If the voltmeter reading at the end of 15 seconds is 9.6 volts or higher, the battery is good and can be charged if needed. If the battery voltage is below 9.6 volts, check the battery with a hydrometer as outlined in the first part of Shop Skills in this job sheet. The battery may be defective.

JOB 24-2 MULTIPLE-CHOICE TEST

1. In a fully charged battery, the electrolyte is
   a. all water
   b. all sulfuric acid
   c. 40 percent water
   d. 40 percent sulfuric acid   1. _____

2. Mechanic A says that a battery is defective if the hydrometer shows more than 50 points variation between cells. Mechanic B says that when there is more than 50 points variation between cells, there is no need to adjust the readings for temperature. Who is right?
   a. A only
   b. B only
   c. both A and B
   d. neither A nor B   2. _____

3. A car has a maintenance-free battery that goes dead overnight. The battery does not have a charge indicator. To test this battery, you should
   a. drill small holes in the top to check the electrolyte
   b. charge the battery and then make a capacity test
   c. check the voltage between the terminals
   d. replace the battery because there is no test for it
                                          3. _____

4. You want to make a capacity test on a battery, but cannot find any specifications for it. Inspecting the battery, you find "36 AMP HRS" on the cover. To make the test, you should apply a load of
   a. 108 amperes
   b. 18 amperes
   c. 300 amperes
   d. none of the above   4. _____

5. At the end of 15 seconds, during a capacity test, the battery voltage is 10.1 volts. The battery should be
   a. checked with a hydrometer
   b. checked with a refractometer
   c. charged
   d. discarded   5. _____

JOB 25-1
Testing the Starting System

Objective: To learn how to test starting systems.

References: AM ◆25-6 to 25-9, SG Chap. 25, automotive manufacturers' service manuals.

Equipment: Various engines and vehicles.
Tools: Starting-system tester (voltmeter and ammeter), basic hand tools.

◆ _____ ◆

SHOP FACTS

To check the starting system accurately, you must know the condition of the battery. If turning the key in the ignition switch produces only a click and no cranking, the cause could be a low battery or a problem in the starting system.

If a condition exists that could possibly be the fault of the battery, eliminate that possibility by first testing the battery (see Job 24-2 of this workbook).

SHOP SKILLS

ENGINE WILL NOT CRANK

Be sure that the battery has sufficient charge to crank the engine before trying to check the starting system.

_____ 1. Place the transmission lever in the NEUTRAL or PARK position. Make a quick check of the battery and cable connections.

_____ 2. Turn the key to START. If the battery is low, the solenoid will produce a clicking or a clattering noise. (On some cars with manual transmission, the clutch pedal must be depressed for the engine to crank.)

_____ 3. Listen for the noises from the starting motor. If the starting motors spins and the drive pinion engages the ring gear but the engine does not crank, the overrunning clutch is slipping. Remove the starting motor and replace the starting-motor drive.

_____ 4. If the starting motor does not spin, listen for a clicking noise as the key is turned to the START position. Ordinarily the solenoid plunger makes a loud click when it is pulled into the solenoid. If the plunger click is heard, the solenoid circuit is okay. The trouble is in the engine, solenoid contacts, starting motor, or starting-motor wiring.

_____ 5. If no click from the plunger is heard when the ignition switch is turned to START, the solenoid circuit is open or the solenoid is defective.

Note Be sure that the transmission lever is in the proper position for cranking the engine. No click from the solenoid may be the result of a defective or out-of-adjustment transmission neutral safety switch.

_____ 6. Touch a jumper wire between the solenoid battery terminal and the ignition-switch terminal on the solenoid. If the starting motor operates, the solenoid is okay. Look for the trouble in the ignition switch, in the neutral safety switch, or in the wires and connections between these units.

_____ 7. If the starting motor still does not operate, remove the starting motor from the car. Inspect and test the starting motor and the solenoid to determine why the motor is not cranking.

STARTING-SYSTEM TEST

_____ 1. A quick way to check the starting system is to measure the cranking voltage and starting-motor current draw as the engine is cranked. To begin the test, check that the battery is sufficiently charged to operate the starting motor at normal speed (Job 24-2).

_____ 2. Turn off all electrical equipment on the car, and close the doors to turn off the dome light and buzzer.

_____ 3. Connect a battery-starter tester or a volt-ampere tester to the battery, following the tester operating instructions (Fig. 25-1).

_____ 4. During the test the engine should not start. To prevent starting, disconnect the primary distributor lead from the ignition coil. On General Motors high-energy ignition systems, disconnect the ignition-switch lead from the distributor. On Ford cars, disconnect the push-on connector from the S terminal of the starter relay. Never allow the disconnected lead to touch ground.

_____ 5. Crank the engine for 10 seconds, while watching the voltmeter and ammeter and judging the cranking speed.

_____ 6. When the cranking speed is normal, compare the cranking voltage and current draw with the manufacturer's

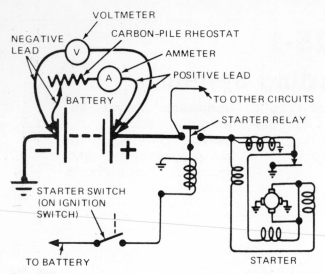

Fig. 25-1 Connections for making a starting-system test. (Ford Motor Company)

specifications. The cranking voltage should not be less than the manufacturer's specification. The current draw should not be more than the manufacturer's specification.

_____ 7. When the specifications are not available, the following general indicators of starting-system condition can be used. Cranking voltage should be 9 volts or higher during the test. Starting-motor current draw should be less than 250 amperes for large V-8 spark-ignition engines and less than 200 amperes for smaller spark-ignition engines.

_____ 8. Excessive current draw indicates a short circuit or a mechanical bind such as a dragging armature. Remove the starting motor for bench testing and service.

_____ 9. If the cranking voltage is low, this indicates excessive resistance in the circuit. Voltage-drop tests should be made of the wiring and components in the starting system to locate the source of trouble.

_____ 10. If the cranking speed is low (battery charged) and the voltage is above 9 volts, the starting motor needs service.

_____ 11. If the cranking speed is low and the voltage is below 9 volts, there probably is trouble in the starting motor.

However, the trouble may be in the engine, caused by a lack of oil, the wrong oil, or excessive friction as a result of worn or damaged parts.

JOB 25-1 MULTIPLE-CHOICE TEST

1. When the key is turned to START, a clicking sound is heard, but the engine does not crank. Which of the following is the *most probable* cause?
    I. The battery is low.
    II. The starter drive is defective.
    a. I only
    b. II only
    c. both I and II
    d. neither I or II   1. _____

2. When the key is turned to START, nothing happens, although the headlights are bright. Mechanic A says that the battery posts are corroded. Mechanic B says that the starting motor is jammed. Who is right?
    a. A only
    b. B only
    c. both A and B
    d. neither A nor B   2. _____

3. The starting-motor current draw on a full-size new car tests at 310 amperes. This indicates
    a. normal operation
    b. excessive resistance
    c. a short circuit
    d. an out-of-adjustment neutral safety switch   3. _____

4. An engine cranks abnormally slow, but the cranking voltage is 9.8 volts. Mechanic A says that the engine may have thick oil in it. Mechanic B says that the starting motor should be removed. Who is right?
    a. A only
    b. B only
    c. both A and B
    d. neither A nor B   4. _____

5. When a car has low cranking voltage but continues to start regularly, you should
    a. return the car to the customer
    b. charge the battery
    c. change the oil
    d. make voltage-drop tests   5. _____

JOB 25-2
Rebuilding Starting Motors

Objective: To learn how to check and rebuild starting motors.

References: AM ♦25-10, SG Chap. 25, automotive manufacturers' service manuals.

Equipment: Various starting motors.

Tools: Armature growler, armature lathe, basic hand tools

SHOP SKILLS

DISASSEMBLING THE STARTING MOTOR

____ 1. If the starting motor has a solenoid attached, disconnect the field leads from the solenoid starting-motor terminal. Remove the two solenoid-to-starting-motor attaching bolts. Rotate the solenoid about one-quarter turn to release its retaining lip from the starting motor. Remove the solenoid.

When you remove the solenoid, grasp it firmly because the solenoid is spring-loaded.

____ 2. Remove the brush cover band and the starting-motor drive-plunger-lever cover, if present.

____ 3. Remove the through bolts. Carefully observe the commutator brush-lead positions. Then disconnect the brush leads and remove the brushes.

Note You need to know the proper brush-lead positions to correctly reassemble the starting motor.

____ 4. Remove the starting-motor commutator end frame. Remove the field-frame assembly.

____ 5. Remove the shift-lever pivot bolt, plunger, shift lever, and armature from the drive housing.

____ 6. To remove the overrunning clutch from the armature, disengage the snap-ring retainer. Then slide the overrunning clutch off the armature shaft.

SERVICING THE STARTING MOTOR

____ 1. Use clean shop towels, a brush, and compressed air to clean the armature, field coil, and overrunning clutch. Wash all other parts in solvent and dry with compressed air. Do not clean the overrunning clutch in solvent.

____ 2. Check the end frame and drive-housing bearings for excess wear. Inspect all other parts for wear and defects.

____ 3. Inspect the armature for rubbing on the pole shoes, and the armature-shaft bearing surfaces for roughness and wear. Inspect the armature windings for broken and burned insulation and unsoldered connections. Check the armature for short circuits on a growler. Turn the commutator if required.

If the starting-motor armature is scored from rubbing on the pole shoes, the probable cause is a bent armature shaft or worn bearings.

____ 4. Check the brush holders for broken springs. Check the insulated brush holders for shorts. Tighten any rivets that are loose. Replace the brushes if they are worn to ¼ inch [6 mm] or less in length.

____ 5. Check the field coils for burned or broken insulation and continuity. Check the field brush connections and lead insulations.

____ 6. Examine the wear pattern on the overrunning-clutch teeth. Replace an overrunning clutch or a ring gear that has chipped, cracked, or excessively worn teeth or that shows a pattern of inadequate tooth engagement.

Note The overrunning-clutch pinion teeth must slide into the ring-gear teeth more than one-half the length of the ring-gear teeth.

____ 7. Check the overrunning clutch for locking. Grasp the overrunning clutch in one hand and rotate the drive pinion gear with the other hand. The gear should rotate freely in one direction and lock in the opposite direction.

ASSEMBLING THE STARTING MOTOR

____ 1. Begin the assembly by lubricating the armature shaft. Then install the overrunning clutch with the pinion outward. Install a new snap ring in the groove on the armature shaft. Use a block of hard wood and a hammer to start the snap ring onto the shaft.

____ 2. Move the snap-ring retainer up to the snap ring. Use pliers on opposite sides of the shaft to squeeze the retainer and thrust collar until the retainer is forced over the snap ring.

_____ 3. Lubricate the drive-housing bushing and shift-lever linkage. Install the shift-lever linkage in the drive housing.

_____ 4. Install the armature, with spacers, into the drive housing. Be sure the lever is in place on the drive assembly.

_____ 5. Install the brushes and leads in the brush holders. Position the brush holders and spring assemblies in the field frame and install the pivot pins. Be sure to center the brush springs on the brushes.

_____ 6. Lubricate the bushing in the commutator end frame. Assemble the field frame over the armature to the drive housing. Spread the brush holders far enough apart for the brushes to clear the commutator.

_____ 7. There are a locating pin and a matching recess in the drive housing and the field frame. Align the pin with the recess. Assemble the commutator end frame to the field frame. Install and tighten the through bolts.

_____ 8. Check the armature end play. Move the armature toward the commutator end frame. Use a thickness gauge to check the end-play clearance between the snap-ring retainer and drive housing. Typical end-play clearance should be 0.005 to 0.050 inch [0.13 to 1.3 mm]. If necessary, disassemble the starting motor and change the armature spacers as required to obtain the correct armature end play.

_____ 9. If a solenoid mounts on the starting motor, apply sealing compound to both sides of the solenoid flange that locks into the drive housing. Install the solenoid with a plunger return spring over the plunger. Depress the solenoid and rotate the lip into place. Install the two solenoid-to-drive end-frame bolts.

_____ 10. After installing the solenoid, install the bolt connecting the field leads to the solenoid starting-motor terminal. Install the brush cover band and the starting-motor drive-plunger-lever cover, if used.

_____ 11. Check the pinion clearance. On a starting motor with a solenoid attached, connect a 6-volt power supply between the solenoid S terminal and ground.

Note Whenever the starting motor is disassembled and assembled, the pinion clearance should be checked. If available, a 6-volt power supply should be used.

_____ 12. Energize the solenoid. Push the pinion as far away from the stop retainer as possible. Use a thickness gauge to check the clearance between the pinion and the retainer. A typical clearance is between 0.010 and 0.140 inch [0.25 and 3.5 mm].

_____ 13. If the clearance is not within specifications, the solenoid linkage or shift-lever mechanism is worn excessively. However, improper assembly of the linkage may also cause excess clearance. Disassemble the starting motor and replace the defective parts.

_____ 14. Before installing the starting motor, clean the starting-motor and flywheel-housing mounting surfaces. This will ensure good electrical contact.

JOB 25-2 MULTIPLE-CHOICE TEST

1. A starting-motor armature in a new car has been dragging and is scored. Mechanic A says that the most likely cause is a worn bearing. Mechanic B says that the most likely cause is a bent shaft. Who is right?
   a. A only
   b. B only
   c. both A and B
   d. neither A nor B   1. _____

2. The armature is placed in a growler to:
   I. Check for grounded circuits.
   II. Check for short circuits.
   a. I only
   b. II only
   c. both I and II
   d. neither I nor II   2. _____

3. New brushes should be installed
   a. anytime the old brushes are removed
   b. anytime the armature is turned
   c. when the old brushes are ¼ inch [6.35 mm] or less in length
   d. when the customer complains of slow cranking
                                                      3. _____

4. Chipped teeth on the starting-motor drive may be caused by
   a. shallow engagement with the ring-gear teeth
   b. excessive use of the starting motor
   c. the armature dragging
   d. worn bearings   4. _____

5. When the starting motor was removed, a shim was found between the starting motor and its mounting pad on the engine. Failure to reinstall this shim may cause
   a. the starting motor to lock up
   b. a vibration during cranking
   c. a short circuit in the starting motor
   d. a high-pitched whine during cranking   5. _____

JOB 26-1
Checking Charging Systems

Objective: To learn how to check charging systems and how to locate and correct various defects.

References: AM ♦26-10 to 26-14, SG Chap. 26, automotive manufacturers' service manuals.

Equipment: Various engines and alternators.
Tools: Basic hand tools.

♦ _____ ♦

SHOP SKILLS

Note Each car manufacturer recommends its own special charging-system testing procedure. Follow the checking procedure in the manufacturer's service manual for the charging system you are testing.

CHARGING-SYSTEM PRECAUTIONS

Note The following precautions must be observed when you work on charging systems. Failure to observe these precautions will result in serious damage to the electrical equipment.

____ 1. Do not polarize an alternator.

____ 2. Do not short across or ground any of the terminals in the charging system, except as specifically instructed in the manufacturer's testing procedure.

____ 3. Never operate the alternator with the output terminal disconnected.

____ 4. Make sure that the alternator and battery are of the same ground polarity.

____ 5. When connecting a charger or a booster battery to the vehicle battery, be sure to observe the polarity of the vehicle battery. Be careful not to cause any sparks around a battery.

VISUAL CHARGING-SYSTEM CHECKS

____ 1. Before making any electrical test, visually inspect all charging-system connections and slip-on connectors. Make sure all connections at the alternator, regulator, and engine are clean and tight.

____ 2. Inspect all wiring for cracked, frayed, and broken insulation.

____ 3. Check the fusible link located between the starting-motor solenoid and the alternator (on some vehicles). Replace the fusible link if it is burned.

____ 4. Check the battery posts and cable terminals for clean and tight connections. If they are corroded, remove the battery cables. Clean the battery posts and cable terminals, and reinstall all cables securely.

____ 5. Be sure that the alternator mounting bolts are tight and that the alternator is properly grounded.

____ 6. Check the alternator drive-belt tension; tighten to specifications if necessary.

____ 7. Check the state of charge of the battery with a hydrometer. The specific gravity must be at least 1.220 for the electrical tests of the charging system.

____ 8. Carefully note the customer's complaint about the charging system. This information will aid you in locating the part of the charging system causing the problem.

INDICATOR-LIGHT CHECK

Note Improper operation of the charging-system indicator light or ammeter (if used) indicates trouble in the charging system. The chart in Fig. 26-1 shows normal indicator-light operation, based on ignition-switch and engine conditions.

____ 1. If the indicator light operates normally and the battery is undercharged, check the battery with a battery tester. If the battery is okay, follow the charging-system testing procedure in the manufacturer's service manual. Be sure that an undercharged battery was not caused by vehicle accessories being left on for long periods.

____ 2. If the indicator light is off with the engine stopped and the ignition switch on, an open circuit is indicated.

IGNITION SWITCH	ENGINE	LIGHT
Off	Stopped	Off
On	Stopped	On
On	Running	Off

Fig. 26-1 Normal charging-system indicator-light operation.

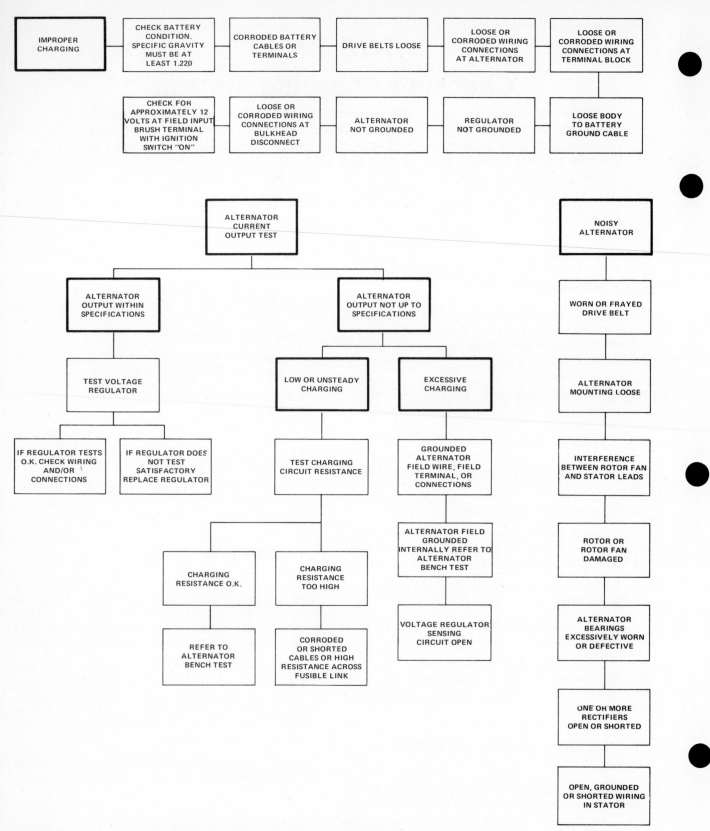

Fig. 26-2 Charging-system trouble-diagnosis chart. **(Chrysler Corporation)**

Check for a blown fuse or fusible link, a burned-out indicator-light bulb, a defective bulb socket, or an open circuit between the alternator or regulator and the ignition switch. If none of these conditions is found, follow the charging-system testing procedure in the manufacturer's service manual.

_____ 3. If the ignition switch is on with the engine running, and the indicator light is on, follow the charging-system testing procedure in the manufacturer's service manual. Figure 26-2 shows a typical charging-system trouble-diagnosis chart.

1. Mechanic A says that after installing an alternator, you must always polarize it. Mechanic B says that connecting a jumper wire between the stator terminal and the field terminal is a good way to check alternator output. Who is right?
   a. A only
   b. B only
   c. both A and B
   d. neither A nor B   1. ____

2. A burned-out fusible link indicates
   a. loose wires
   b. corroded terminals
   c. excess current flow
   d. high resistance   2. ____

3. Before the charging system can be checked, which of the following conditions must exist?
   I. The specific gravity of the battery must be at least 1.220.
   II. The indicator light must be off.
   a. I only
   b. II only
   c. both I and II
   d. neither I nor II   3. ____

4. All the following statements about indicator-light operation are true *except*
   a. ignition off, engine stopped, light off
   b. ignition on, engine running, light off
   c. ignition off, engine stopped, light on
   d. ignition on, engine stopped, light on   4. ____

5. A battery needs water every week. Mechanic A says that the cause is overcharging. Mechanic B says that the cause is undercharging. Who is right?
   a. A only
   b. B only
   c. both A and B
   d. neither A nor B   5. ____

JOB 26-2

Rebuilding Alternators

Objective: To learn to rebuild alternators.

References: AM ♦26-1 to 26-9, SG Chap. 26, automotive manufacturers' service manuals.

Equipment: Various engines and alternators.

Tools: Basic hand tools.

♦ _____ ♦

SHOP SKILLS

Alternators are devices that should operate for long periods without trouble. The only wearing parts in the alternator are the bearings, the brushes, and the slip rings. It is also possible for a diode to become defective. The exact disassembly and reassembly procedures depend on the type and model of alternator. This job sheet covers a general procedure for servicing a typical automobile alternator.

ALTERNATOR DISASSEMBLY

_____ 1. Tightly clamp the alternator mounting flange (on the drive end frame) in a vise.

_____ 2. Scribe a mark across the alternator end frames and stator ring. You will be able to reassemble them in the same position by aligning the marks.

_____ 3. Remove the through bolts. Separate the drive-end-frame-and-rotor assembly from the stator-and-slip-ring end-frame assembly. Use a screwdriver at the stator slot to pry off the drive end frame. The separation is made between the stator assembly and the drive end frame.

As the alternator separates, the brushes may drop into the grease on the rotor shaft. If the brushes are to be reused, wipe the grease from the brushes with a clean, dry cloth.

_____ 4. If the slip-ring end-frame bearing is not being removed, place a piece of tape over the bearing. This will prevent dirt from getting into the bearing.

_____ 5. Remove the drive end frame from the rotor. To do this, hold the end-frame mounting flange in a vise and remove the pulley retaining nut. Grasp the rotor, and slide the washer, pulley, fan, and spacer from the rotor shaft.

_____ 6. Remove the rotor and spacer from the drive-end-frame retainer, bearing, and slinger.

_____ 7. Remove the stator-lead attaching nuts. Pry the stator from the slip-ring end frame.

_____ 8. Remove the radio noise-suppression capacitor and the diode trio (if used) from the end frame. Remove the rectifier bridge and battery-terminal stud.

_____ 9. Remove the brush-holder assemblies and regulator assembly if the regulator is of the integral type.

_____ 10. To remove the slip-ring end-frame bearing, support the inside of the end frame. Press the seal and roller bearing out of the end frame.

CLEANING, INSPECTION, AND TESTING

_____ 1. Clean the rotor, stator, and bearings by wiping them with a clean cloth. Wash all other metal parts in solvent. A completely disassembled alternator is shown in Fig. 26-3.

_____ 2. Inspect and test the alternator components, following the procedure outlined in the manufacturer's service manual for the alternator you are servicing.

ALTERNATOR REASSEMBLY

_____ 1. Install the slip-ring end-frame bearing by placing a flat plate over the bearing. Press in from the outside of the housing until the bearing is flush with the outside of the end frame. Support the inside of the end frame around the bearing bore to prevent distortion. Use care to avoid misalignment during bearing installation.

Replace the bearing if its grease supply is used up. Do not relubricate or reuse the bearing.

_____ 2. Install a new bearing seal whenever the bearing is replaced. Lightly coat the seal lip with oil. Press the seal into the end frame, with the seal lip toward the inside of the end frame.

_____ 3. Position the regulator in the slip-ring end frame if the regulator is of the integral type.

_____ 4. Assemble the brush springs and brushes in the brush holder. Insert a toothpick or a piece of wire in the brush holder to hold the brushes out of contact with the rotor during assembly. Then install the brush holder in the slip-ring end frame.

_____ 5. Install the rectifier assembly, battery-terminal stud, radio noise-suppression capacitor, and diode trio (if used).

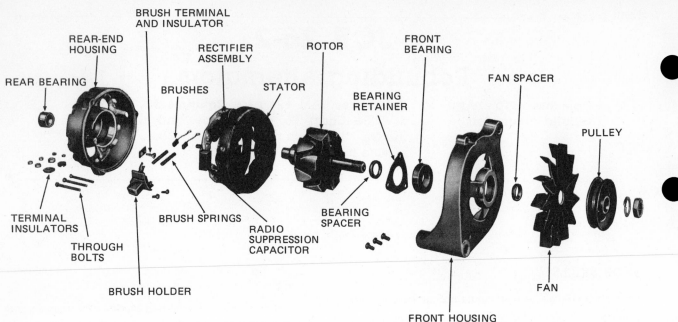

Fig. 26-3 A disassembled alternator. **(Ford Motor Company)**

_____ 6. Position the stator in the slip-ring end frame. Connect the stator leads and install the attaching nuts.

_____ 7. To install the drive-end-frame bearing, first refill the bearing one-quarter full with the proper grease. Do not overfill the bearing with grease. Press the assembled bearing and slinger into the end frame, using a piece of pipe on the outer race. Install the bearing retainer.

_____ 8. Install the rotor in the drive end frame. Assemble the fan spacer, fan, pulley, lock washer, and retaining nut on the rotor shaft. Tighten the nut to the specified torque.

_____ 9. Position the slip-ring end-frame-and-stator assembly on the rotor. Align the scribe marks made during disassembly.

_____ 10. Install the housing through bolts. Remove the toothpick or wire holding the brushes from contact with the slip rings. The alternator is now ready for final testing and installation on the vehicle.

JOB 26-2 MULTIPLE-CHOICE TEST

1. Mechanic A says that the parts that wear in an alternator are the bearings, brushes, and slip rings. Mechanic B says that bushings and diodes also can fail. Who is right?
   a. A only
   b. B only
   c. both A and B
   d. neither A nor B   1. _____

2. Before disassembling an alternator, the mechanic scratches a line across the end frames and stator ring. This is to
   a. find out whether any parts are made of aluminum
   b. provide alignment marks for reassembly
   c. both a and b
   d. neither a nor b   2. _____

3. The purpose of the capacitor in the alternator is to
   a. prevent excess arcing of the brushes
   b. aid in the collapse of the magnetic field
   c. limit the current output
   d. suppress noise in the radio   3. _____

4. Mechanic A says that greasy brushes from an alternator must be thrown away. Mechanic B says to wipe the brushes clean and reinstall them, if they are not worn too much. Who is right?
   a. A only
   b. B only
   c. both A and B
   d. neither A nor B   4. _____

5. Which of the following statements is true?
   I. A diode can fail by acting as an open in the circuit.
   II. A diode can fail by conducting in both directions.
   a. I only
   b. II only
   c. both I and II
   d. neither I nor II   5. _____

JOB 26-3

Checking Alternator Rotor, Stator, and Diodes

Objective: To learn how to check alternator rotor, stator, and diodes to trace various defects.

References: AM ♦26-1 to 26-16, SG Chap. 26, automotive manufacturers' service manuals.
Equipment: Various disassembled alternators, rotors, stators, and diodes.

Tools: Ammeter, ohmmeter, 12-volt test light, 12-volt battery, basic hand tools.

SHOP SKILLS

CHECKING THE ROTOR

Note The rotor should be checked for grounded, open, and short-circuited field coils. Any rotor that has defective field coils must be replaced. On some rotors, new field coils can be installed.

____ 1. To check the rotor for grounded field coils, connect the ohmmeter leads, in turn, from each slip ring to the rotor shaft (Fig. 26-4). The ohmmeter needle should not move. If the ohmmeter needle moves, the field coils are grounded.

A test light can also be used to check for grounded field coils. Make the same connections as above. If the test light glows at any time, the field coils are grounded.

____ 2. To check for an open field circuit in the rotor, connect the ohmmeter leads to the slip rings, as shown in Fig.

OHMMETER CHECK
FOR GROUNDS

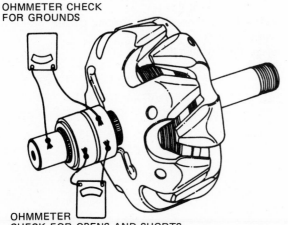

OHMMETER
CHECK FOR OPENS AND SHORTS

Fig. 26-4 Using an ohmmeter to check a rotor for grounded or open circuits. **(Chevrolet Motor Division of General Motors Corporation)**

26-4. If the ohmmeter needle does not move, the field circuit in the rotor is open and it should be replaced. (A test light can also be used to check the rotor for an open field circuit.)

____ 3. The field coils are checked for short circuits by measuring the internal resistance of the windings. With the ohmmeter leads connected to the slip rings (Fig. 26-4), read the resistance of the field coils on the ohmmeter. Typical field-coil resistance is between 2.4 and 3.5 ohms. Be sure to check the manufacturer's service manual for the specifications for the alternator you are servicing.

An ammeter can also be used to check the field winding for short circuits. Connect a 12-volt battery and an ammeter in series with the two slip rings. The specification for alternator field current is given in the manufacturer's service manual. Typical field current is about 4 amperes. An ammeter reading higher than specified indicates shorted field coils.

____ 4. Clean and inspect the rotor if it checks okay and is to be reinstalled. Wipe the rotor clean with a dry cloth. Do not clean the rotor in solvent.

____ 5. Inspect the slip rings for dirt and surface condition. If necessary, the slip rings can be cleaned with a small amount of solvent on a clean shop towel. On Chrysler-built vehicles, alternator slip rings can be replaced. Follow the procedure outlined in the manufacturer's service manual.

____ 6. If the slip rings are discolored and scored, polish them with a 400-grain or finer polishing cloth. Spin the rotor in a lathe, and hold the polishing cloth against the slip rings until they are clean.

Do not use sandpaper to clean the slip rings. Do not clean the slip rings by hand without spinning the rotor; otherwise flat spots will be left on the slip rings. This causes alternator noise after installation.

____ 7. Rough and out-of-round slip rings should be trued on a lathe. Remove only enough material to make the slip rings smooth and round. After turning, the slip rings must be round to within 0.002 inch [0.05 mm] of the maximum indicator reading. Finish the truing operation by polishing the slip rings with a 400-grain or finer polishing cloth. Then use compressed air to blow away all dust.

CHECKING THE STATOR

Note The stator is checked for grounded and open windings. A stator with either of these defects must be replaced.

_____ 1. To check the stator for grounded windings, connect the ohmmeter leads, in turn, from each stator lead to the stator frame. The ohmmeter needle should read infinity. If the ohmmeter needle moves toward zero, the stator windings are grounded to the frame.

A test light can also be used to check for grounded stator windings. Make the same connections as above. If the test light glows, the windings are grounded and the stator must be replaced.

_____ 2. To test for an open in the stator windings, connect the ohmmeter between each pair of stator leads, in turn. The ohmmeter needle should move close to zero and show the same reading for each pair of stator leads. If the ohmmeter needle does not move or remains close to infinity, there is an open circuit in the stator windings.

It is not practical to check the stator windings for short circuits because of the very low resistance of the windings. However, if all other electrical checks are normal and the alternator fails to supply its rated output, shorted stator windings are indicated.

CHECKING THE DIODES

Note Diodes are checked for short and open circuits, usually while their leads are disconnected. Defective diodes must be replaced. However, if you have the type of charging-system testers recommended by Chrysler and Ford, you can check the diodes without disconnecting the leads. Consult the manufacturer's service manual to find out how.

_____ 1. Disconnect all diode leads. Connect one ohmmeter lead to a diode lead. Touch the other ohmmeter lead to the metal diode case. Note the ohmmeter reading. Then reverse the leads. A good diode has a high resistance in one direction and a low resistance in the other. If both readings are low, the diode is short-circuited. If both are high, the diode is open.

Note Never test a diode with a 110-volt test light. The high voltage could burn out the diode. However, a test light of 12 volts or less can be used without danger of damaging the diode.

_____ 2. Repeat the preceding test for each diode. If any readings are not as specified, replace the diode.

Some alternators use a rectifier-bridge assembly and a diode-trio unit. Check the manufacturer's service manual for information on how to test the diodes in these devices.

JOB 26-3 MULTIPLE-CHOICE TEST

1. An alternator is disassembled because of excessive output. Mechanic A says to check for an open stator winding. Mechanic B says to check for a grounded field winding. Who is right?
   a. A only
   b. B only
   c. both A and B
   d. neither A nor B   1. ____

2. An alternator is noisy. All of the following could be the cause *except*
   a. defective rotor bearing
   b. defective diodes
   c. bent rotor fan
   d. regulator not grounded   2. ____

3. After rebuilding, an alternator fails to supply its rated output. The regulator is known to be good. The *most probable* cause of failure is
   a. a grounded field winding
   b. short-circuited stator windings
   c. a low battery
   d. none of the above   3. ____

4. Mechanic A says that a good diode will pass current in one direction only. Mechanic B says that a bad diode will pass current in both directions. Who is right?
   a. A only
   b. B only
   c. both A and B
   d. neither A nor B   4. ____

5. Burned slip rings are an indication of
   a. excessive current flow
   b. excessive resistance in the charging circuit
   c. worn bearings
   d. open stator windings   5. ____

JOB 27-1

Spark-Plug Service

Objective: To learn about spark plugs and how to service and replace them.

References: AM ♦27-22, SG Chap. 27, automotive manufacturers' service manuals.

Equipment: Various engines and spark plugs.

Tools: Spark-plug gap gauge, spark-plug thread chaser and seat-cleaning tool, spark-plug cleaner, basic hand tools.

SHOP SKILLS

_____ 1. Remove the spark-plug wire from each spark plug. Do not jerk or pull on the wire itself. Grasp the boot and rotate it slightly in each direction. Then pull the boot from the plug. Pulling on the wire might cause the fiber strands in the core of the wire to separate. Most spark-plug wires are of a special resistance type. The core is often carbon-impregnated linen. This type of wire is designed to eliminate radio and television interference. It has more resistance to cross-firing than does copper-core wire. However, it is more easily damaged than copper-core wire.

_____ 2. Use the correct size of spark-plug socket to loosen each plug one or two turns. Use care, when breaking the plug loose, to avoid cracking the spark-plug insulator. Most spark plugs have either a $\frac{5}{8}$-inch [16-mm] or $\frac{13}{16}$-inch [21-mm] hex shell.

_____ 3. If possible, use an air hose to blow any dirt from around the spark-plug threads.

_____ 4. Remove the spark plugs and gaskets (if used). Keep the spark plugs and gaskets in cylinder-number order or in engine-firing order. Having the plugs in order will help you analyze the condition of the spark plugs and the engine.

_____ 5. Inspect the insulator and electrodes of each spark plug. Any plug with a cracked or broken insulator must be replaced. Spark plugs that have burned or worn-away electrodes must also be replaced. Plugs that are in good condition except for carbon or oxide deposits can be cleaned and adjusted. Compare the plugs with the examples shown in Fig. 27-1.

The spark plugs used in contact-point ignition systems should be checked, cleaned, and regapped, or replaced, every 12 months or 12,000 miles [19,312 km]. Some manufacturers recommend replacing spark plugs at 15,000 to 50,000 miles [24,100 to 80,500 km] on certain late-model engines using electronic ignition systems and unleaded gasoline.

_____ 6. Clean the top insulator and terminal of each spark plug by wiping it with a shop towel moistened in solvent. Then wipe the plug with a dry shop towel.

_____ 7. If the lower end of a spark plug has an oily or wet deposit and the plug must be reused, brush the plug with solvent. Dry the plug thoroughly with compressed air. Then complete the remaining steps in the spark-plug service procedure. Brushing with solvent prevents the abrasive cleaning compound from gumming or caking within the plug.

_____ 8. Using a spark-plug gap gauge or needle-nose pliers on the side electrode, open the gap enough to permit cleaning and filing. Be careful not to press against the center electrode. Even a slight side force against the center electrode may crack the insulator.

_____ 9. Clean the spark plugs in a spark-plug cleaner. Blast each plug until the interior of the shell and the entire insulator are clean. However, avoid excessive blasting. Examine the interior of the plug in a good light. Remove any cleaning compound with compressed air. If traces of carbon remain in the plug, finish the cleaning with a light blast of abrasive cleaner.

_____ 10. File the center- and side-electrode surfaces to restore clean, sharp edges to the electrodes. Use a small, flat distributor-point file or the file that is part of some gap gauges.

The abrasive cleaner does not always remove all the oxide or scale deposits from the electrodes.

_____ 11. When the spark plugs have been thoroughly cleaned and filed, carefully inspect each plug again. Look for hairline cracks, small chips out of the insulator, and other defects which may not have been visible before cleaning.

Replace any plug with an electrode that is badly burned, pitted, or worn so thin that it might last only a short time. If the majority of plugs in an engine are worn out, replace the entire set.

_____ 12. After the spark plugs are cleaned, examine the threads for carbon and scale deposits. Clean any deposits from the threads by hand, using a small wire brush. A wire wheel mounted on a bench grinder can also be used. Be careful to brush only on the threads, and not on the electrodes or the insulator tip. Clean threads permit easier installation and proper seating of the plug when it is reinstalled. Plugs with badly nicked or damaged threads should be discarded.

NORMAL

Brown to grayish tan color and slight electrode wear. Correct heat range for engine and operating conditions.

RECOMMENDATION: Service and reinstall. Replace if over recommended mileage.

WORN

Center electrode worn away too much to be filed flat.

RECOMMENDATION: Replace with new spark plugs of proper heat range.

PREIGNITION

Improper heat range, incorrect ignition timing, lean air-fuel mixture, or hot spots in combustion chamber has caused melted electrodes. Center electrode generally melts first and ground electrode follows. Normally, insulators are white, but may be dirty due to misfiring or flying debris in combustion chamber.

RECOMMENDATION: Check for correct plug heat range, over-advanced ignition timing, lean air-fuel mixture, clogged cooling system, leaking intake manifold, and lack of lubrication.

DETONATION

Insulator has cracked and broken away as a result of the shock waves created by detonation.

RECOMMENDATION: Cause of detonation must be found and corrected. Check for use of low-octane fuel, improper air-fuel mixture, incorrect ignition timing, overheating, and increased octane requirement in the engine.

MECHANICAL DAMAGE

Something such as a foreign object in cylinder, or the piston, has struck the ground electrode. It has been forced into the center electrode, which has bent, and broken off the insulator.

RECOMMENDATION: Check that plug has the correct reach for the engine, that the gap was set properly, and that no foreign object remains in cylinder.

GAP BRIDGED

Deposits in the fuel have formed a bridge between the electrodes, eliminating the air gap and grounding the plug.

RECOMMENDATION: Sometimes plug can be serviced and reinstalled. Check for excess additives in fuel.

CARBON DEPOSITS

Dry soot, frequently caused by use of spark plug with incorrect heat range.

RECOMMENDATION: Carbon deposits indicate rich mixture or weak ignition. Check for clogged air cleaner, high float level, sticky choke or worn contact points. Hotter plugs will provide additional fouling protection.

OIL DEPOSITS

Oily coating.

RECOMMENDATION: Caused by poor oil control. Oil is leaking past worn valve guides or piston rings into the combustion chamber. Hotter spark plug may temporarily relieve problem, but correct the cause with necessary repairs.

SPLASHED DEPOSITS

Spotted deposits. Occurs shortly after long-delayed tuneup. After a long period of misfiring, deposits may be loosened when normal combustion temperatures are restored by tuneup. During a high-speed run, these materials shed off the piston and head and are thrown against the hot insulator.

RECOMMENDATION: Clean and service the plugs properly and reinstall.

ASH DEPOSITS

Poor oil control, use of improper oil, or use of improper additives in fuel or oil has caused an accumulation of ash which completely covers the electrodes.

RECOMMENDATION: Eliminate source of ash. Install new spark plugs.

OVERHEATED

Blistered, white insulator, eroded electrodes and absence of deposits.

RECOMMENDATION: Check for correct plug heat range, over-advanced ignition timing, low coolant level or restricted flow, lean air-fuel mixture, leaking intake manifold, sticking valves, and if car is driven at high speeds most of the time.

HIGH-TEMPERATURE GLAZING

Insulator has yellowish, varnish-like color. Indicates combustion chamber temperatures have risen suddenly during hard, fast acceleration. Normal deposits do not get a chance to blow off. Instead, they melt to form a conductive coating.

RECOMMENDATION: If condition recurs, use plug type one step colder.

Fig. 27-1 Appearance of spark plugs related to causes. (Champion Spark Plug Company)

_____ 13. Check the specifications chart to find the gap recommended by the engine manufacturer. Reset the gap to specifications. Use a round wire gauge for setting the gap on used spark plugs. Adjust the gap by bending only the side (ground) electrode. Never bend the center electrode, as any side pressure on it may crack or break the insulator.

A plain flat thickness gauge cannot accurately measure the true width of the gap in a used spark plug. Do not set spark-plug gaps to specifications other than those given by the engine manufacturer. All spark plugs, used or new, should be gapped prior to installation.

_____ 14. Test the spark plugs in a spark-plug tester, if available. Follow the manufacturer's instructions for the tester you are using.

_____ 15. Wipe each gasket seat in the cylinder head with a clean shop towel. Make sure that the cylinder-head threads are clean. If they are dirty, clean them with a spark-plug thread chaser and seat-cleaning tool.

_____ 16. Place a new gasket on the spark plug if the plug uses a replaceable compression-type gasket. The replaceable gasket must be screwed all the way onto the plug, until it makes complete contact with the plug seat. Then, screw the spark plug in, finger tight. Be careful not to cross-thread the plugs. Tighten the plugs to the torque recommended in Fig. 27-2. Note that some plugs can be installed without a torque wrench.

_____ 17. Reconnect the spark-plug wires to the plugs. Be sure to connect the correct plug wire to each plug.

| SPARK PLUG THREAD TYPE | WITH TORQUE WRENCH | | WITHOUT TORQUE WRENCH |
	CAST IRON HEADS	ALUMINUM HEADS	CAST IRON OR ALUMINUM HEADS
10 mm	12 lb ft	10 lb ft	¼ to ⅜ turn
12 mm	18 lb ft	16 lb ft	¼ turn
14 mm	25 lb ft	22 lb ft	½ to ¾ turn
14 mm taper seat	15 lb ft	15 lb ft	————
18 mm	35 lb ft	25 lb ft	½ to ¾ turn
18 mm taper seat	17 lb ft	15 lb ft	————
⅞ inch	40 lb ft	30 lb ft	½ to ¼ turn

The above values are applicable only when:
1 Both threads on spark plug and in cylinder head are clean, smooth, and dry.
2 Spark plug has been installed finger tight with a new replaceable seat gasket.
3 Spark plug with a solid gasket is installed only with a torque wrench.

Fig. 27-2 Chart showing spark-plug tightening specifications. (AC Spark Plug Division of General Motors Corporation)

JOB 27-1 MULTIPLE-CHOICE TEST

1. After pumping the throttle lever several times on a car with a stuck choke, the smell of gasoline is strong, and the engine cranks but will not start. Mechanic A says that the plugs are most likely fouled. Mechanic B says that the plugs are most likely wet with gasoline. Who is right?
   a. A only
   b. B only
   c. both A and B
   d. neither A nor B   1. ____

2. When unleaded gasoline is used in an engine
   a. spark plugs last longer
   b. spark plugs must be cleaned more often
   c. spark-plug "gap growth" is quicker
   d. none of the above   2. ____

3. A spark plug that is removed from an engine has a severely cracked insulator with pieces missing around the center electrode. Which of the following statements is *true?*
   I. The spark plug has experienced preignition.
   II. The spark plug has been running too hot.
   a. I only
   b. II only
   c. both I and II
   d. neither I nor II
                                         3. ____

4. A set of new spark plugs of the proper heat range are in an engine for only a few hundred miles. When the plugs are removed, they have an oily coating on the firing end. Mechanic A says that the plugs can be cleaned in solvent. Mechanic B says that the plugs can never be used again. Who is right?
   a. A only
   b. B only
   c. both A and B
   d. neither A nor B   4. ____

5. After cleaning a set of plugs from an engine with contact-point ignition, you cannot locate the specification for the gap setting. You should set the gap at
   a. 0.016 inch
   b. 0.019 inch
   c. 0.035 inch
   d. 0.080 inch   5. ____

JOB 27-2
Installing Contact Points and Condenser

Objective: To learn how to install points and condenser in contact-point distributors.

References: AM ♦27-24, SG Chap. 27, automotive manufacturers' service manual.
Equipment: Various cars and engines with contact-point distributors.

Tools: Point spring-tension gauge, point-aligning tool, thickness gauges, basic hand tools.

SHOP SKILLS

Note This job sheet covers the replacing and adjusting of distributor points and condenser without removing the distributor from the engine. The procedure for removing and installing a distributor and for timing the distributor to the engine is covered in Job 27-3.

_____ **1.** Release the distributor-cap retainers or hold-down screws and remove the cap. Position the cap out of the work area (away from the distributor).

The distributor cap on a Delco window-type distributor is removed as follows. Place a screwdriver in the slotted head of the latch, press down, and turn the latch one-quarter turn in either direction.

_____ **2.** Remove the rotor. Some rotors are held in place with screws, so the screws must be removed.

_____ **3.** Remove the radio-frequency-interference shield from the distributor (if used). Disconnect the primary and condenser leads from the points.

_____ **4.** Remove the screw(s) holding the contact points to the breaker plate. Lift out the points. Remove the condenser clamp screw. Then remove the clamp and condenser.

_____ **5.** Wipe the breaker plate clean of oil and dirt. If a round-wick type of cam lubricator is mounted on the breaker plate, rotate the wick one-half turn.

_____ **6.** Attach the clamp to the new condenser, and fasten the condenser to the breaker plate. Place the new set of points in position on the breaker plate. Install the attaching screw(s). (There may be a small pilot pin in the breaker-plate side of the point set. This pin must engage and seat in the matching hole in the breaker plate.)

_____ **7.** Connect the primary and condenser lead wires to the terminal on the point set. Check the point-spring tension with a point-spring tension gauge.

Note Many point sets are factory-assembled; their point-spring tension cannot be adjusted. Be sure that the primary

and condenser leads are properly positioned. Improper installation may cause the leads to ground against the breaker plate.

_____ **8.** If necessary, align the points by bending the fixed contact-point support. Figure 27-3 shows correct and incorrect point alignment. Use an aligning tool, if available. Do not bend the movable point breaker lever. Used points cannot be aligned and should be replaced if seriously misaligned.

_____ **9.** Turn or crank the distributor shaft until the breaker-arm rubbing block is on the high point of the cam lobe. This provides maximum point opening. Loosen the contact-point lockscrew.

Note The point opening of new points can be checked with a thickness gauge (Fig. 27-4). However, a thickness gauge will not give an accurate measurement on rough or uncleaned used points.

_____ **10.** Use a screwdriver to move the point support to obtain the specified point opening. Tighten the contact-point lockscrew. Then recheck the point opening.

Note Many manufacturers recommend a 0.019-inch [0.48-mm] gap for new points, and a 0.016-inch [0.41-mm] gap for used points. Contact points must be set to the proper opening. Points set too close tend to burn and pit rapidly. Points

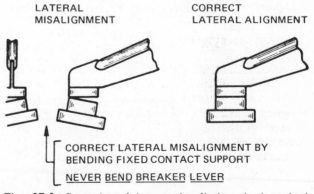

LATERAL MISALIGNMENT   CORRECT LATERAL ALIGNMENT

CORRECT LATERAL MISALIGNMENT BY BENDING FIXED CONTACT SUPPORT
NEVER BEND BREAKER LEVER

Fig. 27-3 Correct and incorrect adjustment of contact points.

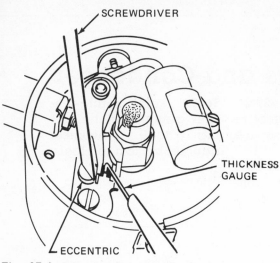

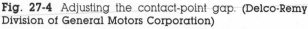

Fig. 27-4 Adjusting the contact-point gap. (Delco-Remy Division of General Motors Corporation)

set too wide tend to cause a weak spark at high speed. New points are set with a larger gap because the rubbing block wears slightly in seating to the cam. Always clean used points before adjusting them.

_____ 11. Wipe the cam clean. Then apply a light film of distributor-cam lubricant to the cam. Do not use engine oil to lubricate the distributor cam.

_____ 12. Install the ignition-point shield (if used). Then install the rotor.

On the Delco window-type distributor, the bottom of the rotor has two locating pins—one round and one square. These fit into matching openings in the cam weight base. Therefore, the rotor only fits one way.

_____ 13. Position and lock the distributor cap on the distributor housing. Be sure the cap is fully seated in its proper position. A notch or locating tang on the edge of the cap or distributor housing is often used to position the cap.

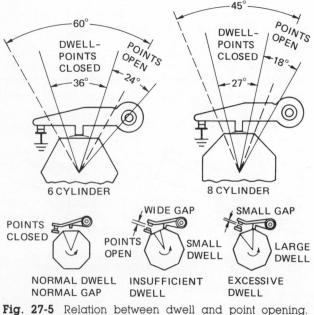

Fig. 27-5 Relation between dwell and point opening. (Ford Motor Company)

Note Improper positioning of the distributor cap causes the rotor blade to strike the contacts inside the cap. The result is a broken rotor, and sometimes also a broken cap.

_____ 14. Start the engine. Check the point dwell with a scope or dwell meter (Fig. 27-5). Reset the ignition timing to specifications before returning the car to the customer.

JOB 27-2 MULTIPLE-CHOICE TEST

1. Which of the following statements is _true_ about contact-point wear?
   I. As points wear, gap decreases, dwell increases, and timing retards.
   II. As points wear, gap increases, dwell decreases, and timing retards.
   a. I only
   b. II only
   c. both I and II
   d. neither I nor II   1. ____

2. Mechanic A says that dwell should be adjusted before setting the timing. Mechanic B says that the order is not important. Who is right?
   a. A only
   b. B only
   c. both A and B
   d. neither A nor B   2. ____

3. If the point-spring tension is low, the engine may miss because of
   a. point bounce
   b. point arcing
   c. point sticking
   d. point float   3. ____

4. When installing new points, you cannot find the specification for point opening. You should adjust the point gap to
   a. the same as that of the old points
   b. 0.016 inch [0.41 mm]
   c. 0.019 inch [0.48 mm]
   d. none of the above   4. ____

5. During installation of the condenser, the mechanic unknowingly grounds the condenser lead. Which of the following is the _most likely_ to occur?
   a. the coil will burn up
   b. the points will arc severely
   c. the engine will not start
   d. after the engine starts, the timing will be off   5. ____

JOB 27-3
Distributor Removal and Installation

Objective: To learn how to remove and install ignition distributors.

References: AM ♦27-26, SG Chap. 27, automotive manufacturers' service manuals.

Equipment: Various engines and distributors.

Tools: Basic hand tools.

♦ ——————————————————————————————————————— ♦

SHOP SKILLS

DISTRIBUTOR REMOVAL

___ **1.** Remove the air cleaner, if necessary. Disconnect the vacuum hose(s) at the distributor.

___ **2.** Disconnect the primary wire running from the coil to the distributor.

___ **3.** Unfasten the distributor-cap retainers, and remove the cap. Place the cap and wires to one side, out of the way.

___ **4.** Scratch aligning marks on the distributor housing and the cylinder block (Fig. 27-6). The marks locate the position of the distributor housing in the block.

___ **5.** Scribe another mark on the distributor housing beneath the tip of the rotor. This mark locates the position of the rotor in the distributor housing.

___ **6.** Remove the distributor hold-down bolt and clamp. Lift the distributor out of the block.

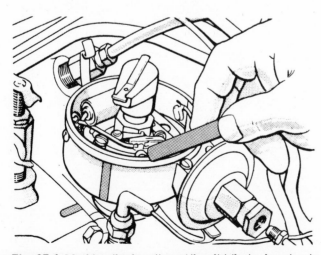

Fig. 27-6 Marking the location of the distributor housing in the engine block. If the rotor does not line up with the marks, make an extra mark on the distributor housing to show the location of the rotor tip. **(Ford Motor Company)**

Note If the engine is not cranked while the distributor is removed, the distributor may be installed in the correct position by aligning the marks made during removal.

DISTRIBUTOR INSTALLATION

Note If marks were not made during distributor removal or if the engine was cranked while the distributor was removed, the engine must be timed. This is necessary to establish the proper relationship between the distributor rotor and the number 1 piston.

___ **1.** Remove the number 1 spark plug from the cylinder head. Place a shop towel over your finger, and cover the spark-plug hole.

___ **2.** Crank the engine until you feel compression pressure.

___ **3.** Bump the engine with the starting motor until the timing marks on the crankshaft pulley and the timing cover are aligned.

Note When the timing marks are properly aligned, the number 1 cylinder is in firing position.

___ **4.** Check that the distributor gasket or rubber O-ring seal is in place on the distributor housing. Position the distributor in the block with the rotor at the number 1 firing position.

You may have to turn the rotor slightly to engage the distributor drive. When the distributor is properly positioned, the rotor will line up with the marks made on the housing during removal. If these marks are not being used, check the manufacturer's shop manual for the position of the rotor and distributor housing.

___ **5.** Check that the distributor housing is seated fully against the cylinder block. If the distributor housing is not seated fully against the cylinder block, the oil-pump shaft is not engaged. To engage the oil-pump shaft, press down firmly on the distributor housing with your hand. Bump the engine a few times with the starting motor until the distributor housing drops into place. Keep your hand clear of the rotor while doing this.

_____ 6. Install, but do not tighten, the distributor-housing retaining clamp and bolt. The bolt should be just loose enough to allow you to turn the distributor with your hand.

_____ 7. Rotate the distributor until the breaker points are beginning to open to fire the number 1 cylinder. This step must be done very carefully, or the engine will not start.

_____ 8. Place the distributor cap in position on the distributor. Check that the tip of the rotor lines up with the distributor-cap terminal for the number 1 spark plug.

_____ 9. Install the distributor cap and, if removed, the wires. Check that the spark-plug wires are correctly installed in the distributor cap. You should feel the spark-plug wires snap firmly into place in the distributor-cap tower.

Note The spark-plug wires in the Hall-effect distributor cap are secured by clips on the ends of the wires. To remove them, take off the cap and use needle-nose pliers to pinch the clips together so the wires can be pulled out. To install them, pinch the clips together and push them through the holes in the terminals. Then replace the boots.

_____ 10. Connect the primary wire from the coil to the distributor. Do not connect the distributor vacuum hose(s).

_____ 11. Start the engine. Set the ignition timing. Connect the vacuum hose(s) at the distributor. Install the air cleaner if removed.

If the engine does not start, recheck the location of the spark-plug wires in the distributor cap. If the reason for failure to start is not found, repeat the distributor-installation timing procedure—steps 1 through 10, above.

JOB 27-3 MULTIPLE-CHOICE TEST

1. After the distributor is reinstalled and the engine started, the oil light will not go out. Which of the following is the *most probable* cause?
   a. the oil pump has failed
   b. the oil light has short-circuited
   c. the distributor gear has stripped
   d. the oil-pump drive has not engaged   1. ____

2. A distributor is removed without its position in the block being marked. Mechanic A says that the timing cover must be removed to time the distributor during installation. Mechanic B says that the valve cover must be removed before the distributor can be retimed. Who is right?
   a. A only
   b. B only
   c. both A and B
   d. neither A nor B   2. ____

3. After the distributor is installed and the engine cranked, the engine backfires loudly and will not run. Which of the following is the *most probable* cause?
   I. The distributor has been installed 180° off.
   II. The engine has jumped timing.
   a. I only
   b. II only
   c. both I and II
   d. neither I nor II   3. ____

4. The distributor has been installed in the block, but the mounting flange on the housing remains about ⅜ inch above the block. Mechanic A says that the oil-pump drive is not engaged. Mechanic B says that the camshaft is out of position. Who is right?
   a. A only
   b. B only
   c. both A and B
   d. neither A nor B   4. ____

5. When the distributor is installed, the mechanic finds that both primary wires have been disconnected from the coil. Which of the following is the *most probable* connection?
   I. Connect the distributor lead to the positive terminal of the coil.
   II. Connect the distributor lead to the negative terminal of the coil.
   a. I only
   b. II only
   c. both I and II
   d. neither I nor II   5. ____

JOB 27-4
Adjusting Ignition Timing

Objective: To learn how to check and adjust ignition timing.

References: AM ♦27-20, SG Chap. 27, automotive manufacturers' service manuals.

Equipment: Various engines.

Tools: Timing light, tachometer, basic hand tools.

♦ **SAFETY** ♦ *When connecting a timing light, always connect the leads to the battery first. Then make the connection to the number 1 spark plug. When disconnecting the timing light, always disconnect the timing-light lead from the number 1 spark plug first. Then disconnect the battery leads. If you disconnect the battery leads first, you can get a high-voltage shock when you touch the battery connections.*

SHOP FACTS

There are several methods of timing the engine and various timing devices that can be used. The spark must occur at the spark-plug gap as the piston reaches some definite position in the compression stroke. Adjusting the distributor on the engine so that the spark occurs at this correct instant is called *ignition timing.*

You adjust the timing by turning the distributor in its mounting (Fig. 27-7). If you rotate the distributor in the direction opposite to normal distributor-shaft rotation, you move the timing ahead. Then the contact points open earlier (or the voltage signal from the pickup coil occurs earlier).

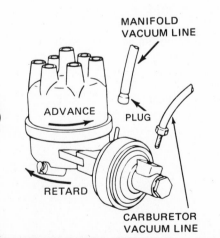

Fig. 27-7 Turning the distributor in the direction of distributor-shaft rotation retards ignition timing. Turning the distributor in the opposite direction advances ignition timing. **(Champion Spark Plug Company)**

This advances the spark so that the sparks appear at the spark plugs earlier.

Turning the distributor in the direction of distributor-shaft rotation retards the sparks. The sparks appear at the plugs later.

Magnetic, or monolithic, timing is a timing method that requires a special timing probe and a probe receptacle on the front of the engine. When the probe is in the receptacle with the engine running, a digital readout shows the ignition timing on the advance meter. The timing is then adjusted as in the method using a timing light.

One advantage of magnetic timing is that the timing is done on the crankshaft, not on a pulley that is driven through a rubber ring. Here is how it operates. The crankshaft pulley includes a torsional-vibration damper to reduce crankshaft vibrations. This damper works through a rubber ring between the driving flange on the crankshaft and the pulley itself. The rubber ring can reduce the accuracy of the setting because it allows the pulley to shift away from normal alignment with the crankshaft. Since the triggering device in the magnetic timing system is on the crankshaft itself, the timing is more accurate. Also, any variation resulting from where the technician stands and the angle at which the timing light is held is eliminated.

SHOP SKILLS

_____ 1. With the engine running, you cannot see the timing marks on the rapidly rotating crankshaft pulley in normal light. You must use a timing light (Fig. 27-8). The timing light is a stroboscopic light. It is connected to the number 1 spark plug. When the spark plug fires, the high-voltage surge causes the timing light to flash. This short, brilliant flash of light makes the timing marks appear to be standing still.

_____ 2. To adjust the ignition timing, locate and clean the timing marks on the pulley and on the timing indicator. If you cannot see the marks clearly, rub chalk on the proper lines on the pulley and the indicator. Check the ignition-timing and engine-idle-speed specifications on the engine decal or in the shop manual.

_____ 3. Disconnect the distributor vacuum-advance line and plug it (Fig. 27-7). There may be more than one vacuum line

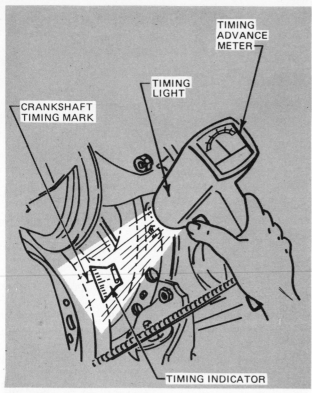

Fig. 27-8 The timing light flashes every time the number 1 spark plug fires.

attached to the distributor. If so, then disconnect and plug all the lines before adjusting the ignition timing (Fig. 27-7).

_____ 4. Connect a tachometer and a timing light to the engine. Start the engine and run it at the specified idle speed. To connect the timing light, place the trigger-pickup clamp around the spark-plug wire. Ice picks, pins, or wires should never be forced through the spark-plug nipple to connect the timing light.

_____ 5. With the engine at normal operating temperature aim the timing light at the timing marks (Fig. 27-8). The 0 mark is TDC. All before-top-dead-center (BTDC) settings fall on the "before" or "advance" side of 0. On most engines, the greatest number of lines are on the BTDC side of 0. Each line represents 2 degrees.

_____ 6. Adjust the timing to specifications by loosening the distributor clamp screw that holds the distributor in its mounting. Then turn the distributor one way or the other (Fig. 27-7). As you turn the distributor, the marking on the pulley will move ahead or back. Turning the distributor in the

direction of normal cam rotation retards the timing. Turning the distributor in the opposite direction of cam rotation advances the timing.

_____ 7. When the ignition timing is correct, the markings will align with a timing pointer, or timing mark, as shown in Fig. 27-8.

_____ 8. After the timing is set, tighten the distributor clamp screw. Then recheck the timing.

_____ 9. Recheck the idle speed and adjust it if necessary. Stop the engine and remove the tachometer and timing light. Connect the vacuum lines to the distributor.

JOB 27-4 MULTIPLE-CHOICE TEST

1. To advance the ignition timing, you should turn the distributor
   a. in the same direction that the rotor turns
   b. in the opposite direction from the direction that the rotor turns
   c. always clockwise
   d. always counterclockwise   1. ____

2. Before setting the timing, you should always
   a. check and adjust the reluctor air gap
   b. check and adjust the point gap
   c. check and adjust the air-fuel mixture
   d. none of the above   2. ____

3. A distributor has two vacuum lines connected to the vacuum-advance unit. Mechanic A says that before setting the timing, the carburetor vacuum line must be disconnected and plugged. Mechanic B says that before setting the timing, the manifold vacuum line must be disconnected and plugged. Who is right?
   a. A only
   b. B only
   c. both A and B
   d. neither A nor B   3. ____

4. In a contact-point ignition system, changing the timing has what effect on dwell?
   a. dwell increases at high speed
   b. dwell decreases at low speed
   c. dwell increases at low speed
   d. none of the above   4. ____

5. On all new cars, the ignition-timing specification is
   a. stamped on the distributor
   b. shown on the engine decal
   c. listed in the owner's manual
   d. listed in the service manual   5. ____

JOB 28

Electronic Ignition Systems

Objective: To learn the construction and operation of the basic electronic ignition system.

References: AM ♦28-1 to 28-14, SG Chap. 28, automotive manufacturers' service manuals.

Equipment: Various engines equipped with electronic ignition systems.
Tools: None.

SHOP FACTS

BASIC OPERATION OF ELECTRONIC IGNITION

The distributor housing, advance mechanisms, rotor, and distributor cap are similar for the electronic ignition and the distributor with points (Fig. 28-1). Both systems use the same type of ignition coil and spark plugs. Some electronic ignition systems also use a resistor in the primary circuit. However, except for the drive and advance mechanisms, the components inside the electronic distributor are different.

A pickup coil and a reluctor (or armature) replace the distributor cam and breaker points. While the job of the points and cam is done by the pickup coil and reluctor, they do the job quite differently. A condenser is no longer required. The reluctor and pickup coil do electrically the job that the points and cam did mechanically.

In the distributor shown in Fig. 28-2, the pickup-coil assembly consists of a small permanent magnet and a coil that is wound around a pole piece. The pole piece is an extension of the mounting bracket and is attached to the permanent magnet.

The reluctor looks like a gear. It is attached to the distributor shaft in place of the cam. The reluctor is not a magnet. Its job is to provide—at the right time—a better magnetic path than air by providing reduced reluctance (reluctance is resistance to magnetic flow). That is why it is called a *reluctor*.

The permanent magnet in the pickup-coil assembly provides a magnetic field from the pole piece to the permanent magnet itself. This magnetic field passes through the coil that is wound around the pole piece. The magnetic field is relatively weak. The air gap between the pole piece and the magnet does not provide a good magnetic path.

As a tooth of the reluctor approaches the pickup coil, the tooth provides a better magnetic path than the air gap. The strength of the magnetic field in the pickup coil is increased. Increasing the field strength at the pickup coil induces a positive voltage at one terminal of the pickup coil. This positive voltage continues to build until the reluctor tooth is exactly opposite the pole piece.

In electronic ignition, battery current flows through the primary winding of the ignition coil and then through the control unit, which is grounded. This is similar to the action in a breaker-point ignition system when the points are closed. The control unit remains on, and the current flows through the primary-coil windings, as long as a negative voltage from the pickup coil is *not* applied to it.

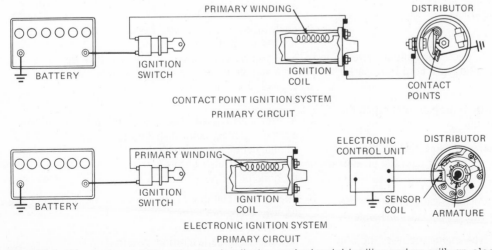

Fig. 28-1 Comparison of the primary circuit of a contact-point ignition system with an electronic ignition system.

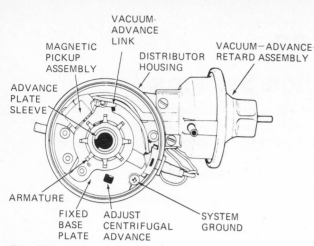

Fig. 28-2 Ignition distributor for an electronic ignition system using a rotating armature and a magnetic-pickup assembly. (Ford Motor Company)

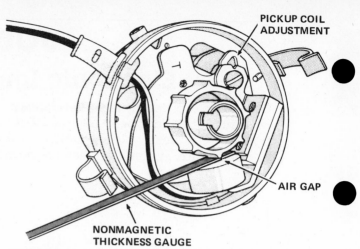

Fig. 28-3 Measuring the air gap in an electronic distributor with a nonmagnetic brass thickness gauge. (Chrysler Corporation)

When the reluctor passes the pole piece and the pickup voltage turns negative, it turns off the control unit. Now current cannot flow through the control unit. Therefore, the current flow through the ignition-coil primary winding is interrupted. This interruption of the current flow in the primary induces a voltage in the secondary winding of the ignition coil. The induced voltage is large enough to fire the spark plug.

The control unit determines electronically how long the ignition-coil primary current is allowed to flow before it is interrupted. In this way, the control unit determines dwell. The control unit is sealed and has no moving parts, so the dwell cannot be adjusted. The reluctor and pickup coil determine ignition timing. However, it takes both the control unit and the reluctor and pickup coil, working together, to time the interruption of the ignition-coil primary circuit. Changing the air gap between the reluctor and the pole piece does not change either dwell or timing.

In many Chrysler electronic ignition systems, the dual-ballast resistor contains two resistors, each performing a different job. One side is a ½-ohm ignition-compensating resistor. It maintains a constant primary current regardless of changes in engine speed. It is bypassed during cranking, to allow full battery voltage to the coil. The other side of the dual-ballast resistor is a 5-ohm auxiliary resistor that protects the electronic control unit by limiting the current flow.

SHOP SKILLS

_____ 1. Locate a car with a basic electronic ignition system, such as a Chrysler electronic ignition or a Ford Duraspark I or II system.

_____ 2. Trace the current flow from the battery through the components of the primary circuit.

_____ 3. Remove the distributor cap. Note the air gap between the tip of the armature, or reluctor, and the pickup-coil assembly (Fig. 28-3).

_____ 4. Using a nonmagnetic thickness gauge, measure the air gap. Then note how the adjustment is made to change it.

_____ 5. Locate a car with a V-type engine that uses the GM high-energy ignition (HEI) system. Remove the cover and note how the coil is attached.

_____ 6. Remove the distributor cap, and notice the construction of the rotor and how it is attached. When removing and installing the distributor cap, be careful not to loosen the center contact from the cap.

_____ 7. Examine a variety of other electronic ignition systems. Determine the name and purpose of each part.

_____ 8. If necessary, look in the manufacturer's service manual to find the location of the timing marks. Also find the specifications for ignition timing and the procedure for adjusting it.

JOB 28   MULTIPLE-CHOICE TEST

1. The spark at the spark plug occurs immediately after
   a. the primary circuit is opened
   b. the primary circuit is closed
   c. both a and b
   d. neither a nor b   1. ____

2. In a comparison of electronic and contact-point ignition systems
   a. the secondary circuits are basically the same
   b. different types of switches are used to open and close the primary circuits
   c. secondary voltages may be higher in electronic ignition systems
   d. all of the above   2. ____

3. Each time an armature tip passes through the magnetic field of the pickup coil
   a. a voltage is produced in the armature tip
   b. a voltage is produced in the pickup coil
   c. both a and b
   d. neither a nor b   3. ____

4. A rotor with curved plates called _shutters_ is used in
   a. some contact-point distributors
   b. magnetic-pickup distributors
   c. Hall-effect distributors
   d. none of the above   4. ____

5. The ignition coil mounts in the top of the distributor cap on V-type engines with a
   a. Hall-effect distributor
   b. Ford Duraspark ignition system
   c. GM HEI system
   d. detonation control system   5. ____

JOB 29

Scope-Testing Electronic Ignition Systems

Objective: To learn how to use the oscilloscope to diagnose electronic ignition systems.

References: AM ♦29-1 to 29-17, SG Chap. 29, automotive manufacturers' service manuals.

Equipment: Various engines equipped with electronic ignition systems.

Tools: Electronic ignition testers, oscilloscopes, 12-volt test light, ohmmeter, basic hand tools.

SHOP SKILLS

TESTING THE CHRYSLER ELECTRONIC IGNITION

____ 1. A dwell meter is not used in diagnosing or servicing the Chrysler electronic ignition. The dwell is always correct, unless the electronic control unit has been damaged. The tachometer and timing light are connected and used in the normal manner.

The Chrysler electronic ignition tester must be used to test the primary circuit of the Chrysler electronic ignition system.

____ 2. Problems in the secondary circuit should be diagnosed with an oscilloscope, as in the contact-point ignition system. Figure 29-1 shows a contact-point oscilloscope pattern (top) and the pattern for the Chrysler electronic ignition system (bottom).

____ 3. Before testing any part of the Chrysler electronic ignition, be sure that the battery voltage is at least 12 volts. If the special tester is not available, components of the electronic ignition system may be tested with a voltmeter and an ohmmeter. For the complete procedure, see the service manual for the vehicle you are servicing. The manual contains diagrams showing the test points and the test specifications.

____ 4. There are two cautions to observe while working on the Chrysler electronic ignition:

Whenever you remove or install the wiring-harness connector to the control unit, the ignition switch must be in the OFF position. This prevents possible damage to the control unit.

Do *not* touch the switching transistor on the electronic control unit while the ignition is on. The switching transistor will give you a shock if you touch it.

____ 5. To correct the problem of no spark, visually inspect the distributor cap, rotor, and spark-plug wires for cracks and tightness. Check the primary wire at the ignition coil and ballast resistor for tightness.

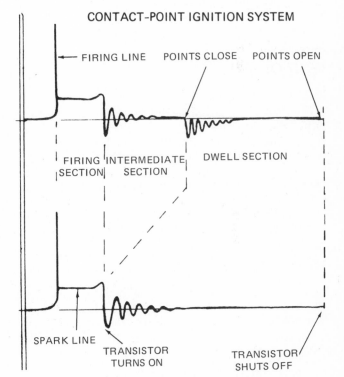

Fig. 29-1 Comparison of contact-point system pattern (top) with Chrysler electronic system pattern (bottom). **(Chrysler Corporation)**

____ 6. Check the air gap between the reluctor tooth and the pickup coil. To set the air gap, loosen the pickup-coil hold-down screw. Insert a 0.008-inch [0.20-mm] nonmagnetic thickness gauge between the reluctor tooth and the pickup coil. Adjust the pickup coil so that the thickness gauge is snug.

____ 7. Check the dual-ballast resistor with the ohmmeter. One side should read from 0.5 to 0.6 ohm, and the other side should read from 4.75 to 5.75 ohms. If the readings are not within specifications, replace the dual-ballast resistor.

___ 8. Unplug the connector on the pickup-coil leads at the distributor. Check the pickup coil by placing the ohmmeter leads on the pickup-coil terminals. The resistance should be between 150 and 900 ohms. Test the pickup coil for grounding by connecting the ohmmeter leads between either terminal on the pickup-coil leads and the distributor housing. The ohmmeter should show an open circuit. If the coil resistance is not within the given values, or if the pickup coil is grounded, replace the pickup-coil assembly in the distributor.

___ 9. The ignition coil used in the Chrysler electronic ignition system is the same type of ignition coil used in the contact-point ignition system. The coil can be checked on an oscilloscope, with a coil tester, or with an ohmmeter. The primary resistance should be between 1.41 and 1.79 ohms at 70 to 80°F [21 to 27°C]. If the coil is not within specifications, replace it.

___ 10. If all other units check okay, check the ignition secondary by removing the coil wire from the center tower of the distributor. Hold the wire approximately 3/16 inch [5 mm] from the engine, and crank the engine. If a spark does not occur, replace the electronic control unit. It is a sealed unit which cannot be serviced or adjusted.

GENERAL MOTORS HIGH-ENERGY IGNITION(HEI)

General Motors introduced the HEI system as standard equipment on its passenger-car engines in 1975. This system includes a magnetic-pulse distributor and a high-energy ignition coil (35,000 volts) in one unit (Fig. 29-2). On some in-line engines, the high-energy ignition coil is separately mounted. Both operate in basically the same way as the system described in Job 28.

Trouble in the high-energy ignition system will show up as either "engine will not start" or "engine starts but runs roughly."

ENGINE WILL NOT START

___ 1. Connect a voltmeter between the BAT-terminal lead on the distributor connector and ground. Turn on the ignition switch. If the voltmeter reads zero, there is an open cir-

cuit in the wire between the distributor and the bulkhead connector, the wire between the bulkhead connector and the ignition switch, or the wire between the ignition switch and the starting-motor solenoid. Locate the open wire and repair it.

___ 2. If the voltmeter reads battery voltage when connected as in step 1 above, remove one spark-plug wire from its spark plug. With insulated pliers, hold the wire approximately 1/4 inch [6.35 mm] away from the cylinder block. Then crank the engine. If sparking occurs, the trouble is not in the distributor. Check the spark plugs. If they are okay, perform a diagnosis of the fuel system. If no spark occurs while the engine is cranked, the components of the ignition system should be checked with a special high-energy ignition analyzer.

Note The General Motors HEI system uses special 8-mm-diameter spark-plug wires. The spark-plug-wire boots seal more tightly to the spark plugs. Twist the boot one-half turn in either direction to break its seal. Then pull on the boot to remove the wire from the spark plug.

♦ CAUTION ♦ Never remove a spark-plug wire from an engine using HEI when the engine is running! The HEI system can deliver up to approximately 35,000 volts to the spark plugs. This high secondary voltage can jump a great distance. It can cause an electric shock and serious injury to the mechanic holding the wire.

ENGINE STARTS BUT RUNS ROUGHLY

___ 1. Check for proper fuel delivery. If it is okay, check all vacuum hoses for leakage. With the engine running, look and listen for sparks jumping to ground or to other plug wires. Check the ignition timing and the distributor centrifugal-advance mechanism. If no fault is located, remove all the spark plugs and check for defects such as improper gap, fouling, and cracked insulators. If no defects are found, the components of the ignition system should be checked with the special HEI system analyzer or an oscilloscope.

___ 2. Figure 29-2 shows the oscilloscope connections for HEI distributors. Note that when the coil is mounted in the top of the distributor, a special HEI pickup adapter must be used instead of the regular pattern-pickup end on the scope lead.

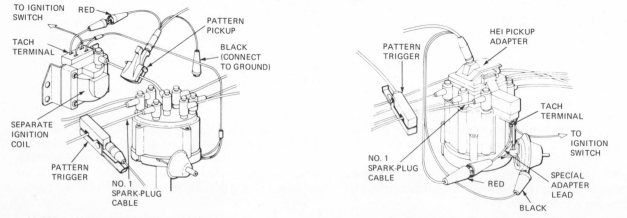

(a) OSCILLOSCOPE CONNECTIONS—IN-LINE ENGINES

(b) OSCILLOSCOPE CONNECTIONS—V-TYPE ENGINES

Fig. 29-2 Oscilloscope connections for testing the General Motors HEI system. A special HEI pickup adapter that is needed when the coil is mounted in the top of the distributor cap. **(Sun Electric Corporation)**

_____ 3. Figure 29-3 shows the normal secondary patterns of the HEI system. Compare these to the patterns shown on the scope when it is attached to a car with HEI.

_____ 4. Some V-6 engines have irregular firing intervals. As a result, the spacing between the firing lines is not always the same length.

FORD ELECTRONIC IGNITION

The Ford electronic ignition is similar to the system discussed in Job 28. However, large 8-mm silicone spark-plug wires indicate a Duraspark high-energy ignition system which can deliver up to 47,000 volts. Ford recommends a different method of testing the electronic-amplifier module on the car.

_____ 1. If the electronic-amplifier module is suspected of being defective, unplug the connectors from the module without removing the module from the vehicle. Connect a known good module to the connectors. The substitute mod-

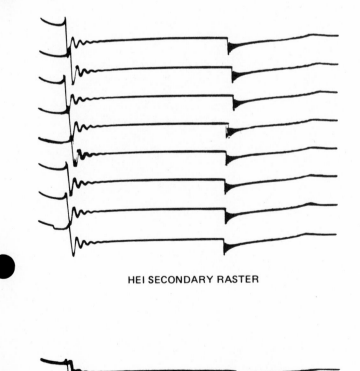

HEI SECONDARY DISPLAY

HEI SECONDARY RASTER

HEI SECONDARY SUPERIMPOSED

Fig. 29-3 Normal secondary patterns for the GM HEI system. (Sun Electric Corporation)

ule does not have to be fastened to the vehicle in order to operate properly.

_____ 2. Attempt to start the engine. If the engine starts and accelerates properly, proceed to step 3. If the engine still does not start, the fault is in the wiring or other vehicle systems. Inspect and repair them as necessary.

_____ 3. Reconnect the original module. Again attempt to start and run the engine. Now, if the engine will not start, remove the original module and replace it with a new one. If the engine now starts and runs on the original module, the module is not defective.

_____ 4. With the engine running, check all connections in the primary wiring of the ignition system for such faults as poor wire crimps to terminals. The faulty connection will spark when the engine misfires or stops. Correct it as necessary.

_____ 5. With the engine running, and the scope connected, compare the patterns with those shown in Figs. 29-1 and 29-3.

JOB 29   MULTIPLE-CHOICE TEST

1. In the electronic distributor, the air gap must be checked with
   a. a dwell meter
   b. a dial indicator
   c. a brass thickness gauge
   d. none of the above   1. _____

2. All the following parts of the scope pattern are nearly the same for contact-point and electronic ignition systems *except*
   a. the firing line
   b. the spark line
   c. the dwell section
   d. none of the above   2. _____

3. A car has large (0.320-inch [8-mm]) silicone spark-plug wires. Mechanic A says that the maximum voltage available from the coil may be up to 35,000 volts. Mechanic B says that the maximum voltage available from the coil may be up to 47,000 volts. Who is right?
   a. A only
   b. B only
   c. either A or B
   d. neither A nor B   3. _____

4. When you are watching the scope pattern of an HEI system, the length of the dwell line varies with engine speed. Which of the following statements is true?
   I. This is normal operation.
   II. The module in the distributor is defective.
   a. I only
   b. II only
   c. both I and II
   d. neither I nor II   4. _____

5. On a scope showing the display pattern for a four-cylinder engine, the firing line for the number 1 cylinder appears at the
   a. top of the screen
   b. bottom of the screen
   c. left of the screen
   d. right of the screen   5. _____

JOB 30

Headlight Aiming

Objective: To learn how to aim and adjust head-lights.

References: AM ◆30-1 to 30-23, SG Chap. 30, auto-motive manufacturers' service manuals.

Equipment: Vehicles with headlights to be aimed.
Tools: Headlight aimer, basic hand tools.

SHOP FACTS

Headlights are made in two types and four sizes (two round and two rectangular). The round sizes are 5¾ inches [146 mm] in diameter and 7 inches [178 mm] in diameter. The rectangular headlights are 6½ by 4 inches [165 by 100 mm] and 7.9 by 5.6 inches [200 by 142 mm]. Round and rectangular headlights are shown in Fig. 30-1.

The type of headlight is identified by the number "1" or "2" molded into the glass at the top of the lens. A type 1 headlight has only one filament. A type 2 headlight has two filaments—one for the high beam and the other for the low beam. The high beam is for driving on the highway when there is no car approaching from the other direction. The low beam is for city driving and for passing a car coming in the opposite direction. The use of the low beam for passing prevents the oncoming driver from being temporarily blinded by the high beam.

Some vehicles have only one pair of headlights. These are both type 2 headlights. Other vehicles have two pairs of head-lights—one pair of type 1 and one pair of type 2.

SHOP SKILLS

PREPARATION FOR HEADLIGHT AIMING

_____ 1. To prepare a vehicle for headlight aiming, check for the following:
   a. Excess ice and mud should be removed from under the fenders.
   b. Tires must be inflated to the proper pressure.

   c. The only load should be the driver in the normal position.
   d. The lenses should be clean, and both high and low filaments in all headlights should operate. Head-lamps with burned-out filaments or cracked or bro-ken aiming buttons on the lens should be replaced.

_____ 2. If all the above are okay, then make sure that the front wheels are pointed straight ahead.

_____ 3. Check the suspension to ensure that the vehicle is not leaning to one side or the other. If it seems to be leaning, rock the vehicle sideways to equalize the suspension. If the vehicle still leans, the suspension should be checked further.

INSPECTING HEADLIGHT AIM

_____ 1. Headlights must be aimed correctly. If they are aimed too high or to the left, they might blind an oncoming driver. This could cause a serious accident. Incorrect aiming can also reduce the driver's ability to see the road properly. This could also lead to an accident.

_____ 2. All headlights have three aiming pads on the front lens. Adjustments are made by turning two spring-loaded screws. The screw at the top is for up-and-down adjustment. The screw at the side is for left-to-right adjustments (Fig. 30-1).

_____ 3. There are several methods of checking the aiming of headlights. The simplest method uses a headlight-aiming screen. The screen is placed 25 feet [7.6 m] in front of the vehicle, on a perfectly level floor. With the vehicle directly in front of the screen, the low beam and high beam are checked separately.

_____ 4. Position the vehicle so that it is square with the screen (Fig. 30-2). The front of the headlamps should be di-rectly over a reference line that is painted on the floor.

_____ 5. Next locate the middle tape on the aiming screen so that it is in line with the center of the vehicle. This can be done as shown in Fig. 30-2. Sight through the center of the rear window of the vehicle and over the hood ornament. Have the tape moved until it is in line with these two points. If there is no center hood ornament, mark the center of the

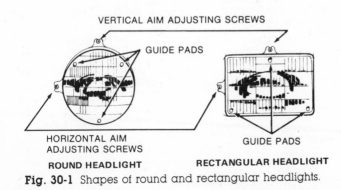

VERTICAL AIM ADJUSTING SCREWS

GUIDE PADS

HORIZONTAL AIM ADJUSTING SCREWS

GUIDE PADS

ROUND HEADLIGHT   **RECTANGULAR HEADLIGHT**

Fig. 30-1 Shapes of round and rectangular headlights.

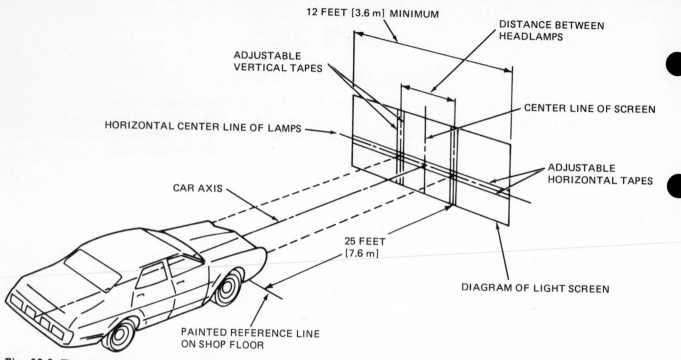

Fig. 30-2 Floor-type headlight-aiming screen.

front and rear windows with narrow strips of masking tape. Use these "sights" to locate the center tape of the aiming screen directly in line with the vehicle axis.

_____ 6. With the vehicle properly located and loaded, switch the headlamps to high beam. Observe the center of the high-intensity zone on the aiming screen (Fig. 30-3).

Note Always inspect the following headlamps on low beam only: 5¾ inch [146 mm], type 2; 7 inch [178 mm], type 2; and 6½ by 4 inch [165 by 100 mm], type 2. All other headlamps are inspected on high beam.

_____ 7. The headlights require aiming if the center of the high-intensity zone on the screen is:
  a. More than 4 inches [102 mm] to the right or left of the vertical centerline for each headlamp
  b. More than 4 inches [102 mm] above or below the horizontal centerline for each headlamp

_____ 8. With the vehicle properly located and loaded, switch the headlamps to low beam. Observe the left and top edges of the high-intensity zone on the aiming screen (Fig. 30-3).

_____ 9. The headlights require aiming if:
  a. The left edge of the high-intensity zone is more than 4 inches [102 mm] to the right or left of the vertical centerline for each headlamp
  b. The top edge of the high-intensity zone is more than 4 inches [102 mm] above or below the horizontal centerline for each headlamp

HEADLIGHT AIMING WITH MECHANICAL AIMER

_____ 1. A variety of headlight-aiming devices are used. Each requires a special procedure, as outlined by the manufacturer. One type, the optical aimer, reduces the size of the headlight beam. It shows the reduced beam on a small screen in the aimer. By looking in the aimer, you see the same type of pattern as would be shown on an aiming screen. However, the pattern is very small.

_____ 2. Some manufacturers, in their aiming instructions, call for a full fuel tank and an empty vehicle. Others call for a partly full tank and two people in the front seat.

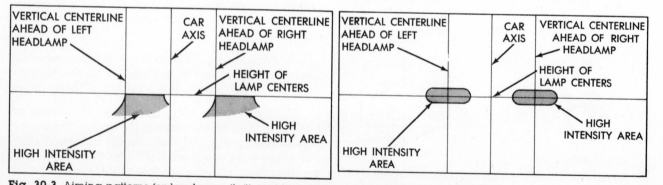

Fig. 30-3 Aiming patterns for low beam (left) and high beam (right). **(Chrysler Corporation)**

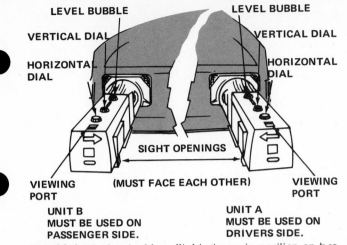

LEVEL BUBBLE LEVEL BUBBLE

VERTICAL DIAL VERTICAL DIAL

HORIZONTAL DIAL HORIZONTAL DIAL

SIGHT OPENINGS

VIEWING PORT (MUST FACE EACH OTHER) VIEWING PORT

UNIT B MUST BE USED ON PASSENGER SIDE. UNIT A MUST BE USED ON DRIVERS SIDE.

Fig. 30-4 Mechanical headlight aimers in position on two headlights. (Chrysler Corporation)

_____ 3. The tires must be inflated to the specified pressure. Just before checking the aim, after the vehicle is positioned, bounce each corner of the vehicle a couple of times. This will equalize the suspension system.

_____ 4. One type of mechanical headlight aimer is shown in Fig. 30-4. Two of these devices (one right-side and one left-side) are required.

_____ 5. Figure 30-5 shows the two aimers being calibrated to correct for the floor slope. Here is the checking and adjusting procedure.

_____ 6. Remove any large amounts of mud or ice from under the fenders. Drive the vehicle onto a flat surface. It does not have to be exactly level.

_____ 7. The tire pressure should be checked and corrected. The vehicle should be loaded with an average weight; this should include the driver and a normal amount of weight in the rear. Rock the vehicle from side to side to equalize the springs. Make sure the automatic level control (where present) is working.

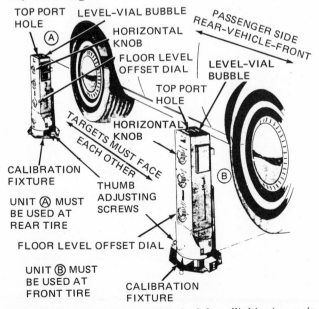

TOP PORT HOLE LEVEL-VIAL BUBBLE PASSENGER SIDE REAR-VEHICLE-FRONT

A

HORIZONTAL KNOB

FLOOR LEVEL OFFSET DIAL LEVEL-VIAL BUBBLE

TOP PORT HOLE

TARGETS MUST FACE EACH OTHER

HORIZONTAL KNOB

B

CALIBRATION FIXTURE

UNIT A MUST BE USED AT REAR TIRE

THUMB ADJUSTING SCREWS

FLOOR LEVEL OFFSET DIAL

UNIT B MUST BE USED AT FRONT TIRE

CALIBRATION FIXTURE

Fig. 30-5 Calibrating mechanical headlight aimers to compensate for the slope of the floor. (Chrysler Corporation)

_____ 8. Clean the headlamp lenses and aiming pads.

_____ 9. Attach the floor compensation and calibration adapters to the aimers. Put the aimers at the centerline of each wheel, on one side of the vehicle (Fig. 30-5). Unit A of the pair must be at the rear wheel, and unit B at the front wheel. The targets must face each other. Now level each unit by adjusting the compensation knob on each adapter. Turn the knob one way or the other until the bubble is centered.

_____ 10. Now look into the top portholes of unit A (at the rear wheel). Turn the horizontal knob to align the split image (Fig. 30-6).

_____ 11. Transfer the plus or minus reading on the horizontal dial to the floor-level dial on the aimer. Then set the horizontal dial to zero.

_____ 12. Repeat the procedure at the other aimer. Then remove the adapters from the two aimers.

_____ 13. If you use the same floor area to aim all vehicles, you don't have to perform steps 9 to 12 every time. Instead, use paint or tape to mark off a centerline for the rear wheels of all vehicles. Then check the floor level (steps 9 to 12) for several vehicles with varying wheelbase measurements. On the floor, mark a front-wheel centerline for each wheelbase; also mark plus and minus readings for the floor-level dial for that position.

_____ 14. If your floor slopes abnormally, you may have to check each side of the vehicle for floor slope. Then use an average figure (split the difference) to set the floor-slope offset dials on the two aimers.

_____ 15. You are now ready to check the headlight aiming. Remove the headlight trim, if required. Vehicles made before 1970 usually require removal of the trim. On later vehicles, the headlights can be adjusted without removing the trim.

_____ 16. Attach the correct adapter for the headlights being checked. Install the aimers on the headlamps. The three aiming pads on the lamp must touch the three steel inserts in the adapter. Secure the aimers by pushing the piston handles forward and engaging the rubber suction cups. Then pull the piston handles back to lock the aimers in position (Fig. 30-4).

_____ 17. Adjust the horizontal aim by setting the horizontal dial to zero. Make sure the split-image target lines are visible in the viewing port. Rotate the aimer, if necessary, to locate the target. Now turn the horizontal adjusting screw on the headlight until a split image of the target line appears in the mirrors as one solid line. To remove backlash, make the final adjustment by turning the screws in a clockwise direction. Repeat these steps with the other aimer and headlamp.

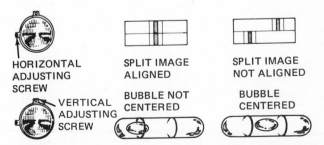

HORIZONTAL ADJUSTING SCREW SPLIT IMAGE ALIGNED SPLIT IMAGE NOT ALIGNED

VERTICAL ADJUSTING SCREW BUBBLE NOT CENTERED BUBBLE CENTERED

Fig. 30-6 Split-image and bubble alignment, and headlamp adjusting screws. (Chrysler Corporation)

____ **18.** Adjust the vertical aiming by setting the vertical dial of one aimer to zero. Special settings may be required for some vehicles. Check the law in your state.

____ **19.** Turn the vertical adjusting screw at the top of the headlamp until the level bubble is centered between the lines.

____ **20.** Adjust the other headlight in the same way.

____ **21.** Recheck the horizontal alignments, and readjust them as necessary.

____ **22.** For a four-headlight system, repeat the aiming procedure with the second set of headlights.

____ **23.** Remove the aimers by holding the aimer securely and pressing the VACUUM RELEASE button.

Note Headlight aimers should be checked for calibration periodically, as outlined in the manufacturer's service manual.

JOB 30 MULTIPLE-CHOICE TEST

1. The number "2" molded into the lens of a headlight means the headlight
   a. has two filaments (high beam and low beam)
   b. fits only a 1972-model car
   c. is defective
   d. is a quartz-halogen unit   1. ____

2. Mechanic A says there are two types of headlights. Mechanic B says there are four sizes of headlights. Who is right?
   a. A only
   b. B only
   c. both A and B
   d. neither A nor B   2. ____

3. Headlights with the number "1" molded on the lens are:
   I. Checked on high beam only.
   II. Checked on low beam only.
   a. I only
   b. II only
   c. either I or II
   d. neither I nor II   3. ____

4. To adjust the vertical (up-and-down) aim of a headlight, you should
   a. turn the screw on the side of the headlight
   b. turn the screw at the top of the headlight
   c. replace the headlight
   d. none of the above   4. ____

5. The three small glass bumps on the lens of most headlights are
   a. examples of poor quality control in manufacturing
   b. part of the focusing system in the light
   c. guide pads for mounting a mechanical aimer
   d. none of the above   5. ____

JOB 31

Air Pollution, Smog, and the Automobile

Objective: To learn about how the automobile contributes to the air-pollution problem and the systems used on the automobile to help control it.

References: AM ♦31-1 to 31-34, SG Chap. 31, automotive manufacturers' service manuals.

Equipment: Various cars.
Tools: Basic hand tools.

SHOP FACTS

This job is concerned with how the automobile contributes to air pollution. Select a car for examination. As you work through the job sheet, identify the sources of air pollution on the car. As you identify each source, review the reference and the job sheet until you know which pollutants come from each source.

The word "smog" comes from the words "smoke" and "fog." Smog is a sort of fog mixed with other substances. Smog, and the chemicals and substances in it, can be harmful, even deadly. Along with smoke, smog is the most visible evidence of atmospheric pollution. But some atmospheric pollution is not visible; it does not become visible until it is mixed with moisture or sunlight. Lead compounds from leaded gasoline, hydrocarbons (unburned gasoline), carbon monoxide, and other gases may pollute the air without being seen.

All air is polluted to some extent. Much of the air pollution is from natural causes, such as dust stirred up by wind, and gases given off by rotting animal and vegetable matter. People add to this natural pollution by burning coal, oil, gas, gasoline, and many other things. Most fuels, such as coal, wood, and gasoline, contain hydrogen (H) and carbon (C). During combustion, oxygen in the air unites with the hydrogen and carbon to form water (H_2O), carbon monoxide (CO), and carbon dioxide (CO_2). In addition, many fuels contain sulfur, which burns to form sulfur oxides (SO_x).

During the combustion process in the combustion chamber, some of the nitrogen in the air combines with oxygen to form nitrogen oxides (NO_x). All the fuel may not burn completely, so smoke and ash are also formed. Smoke is simply particles of unburned fuel and soot, called *particulates*, mixed with air. Altogether, it is estimated that about 200 million tons of people-made pollutants enter the air every year in the United States alone. This is about a ton for every man, woman, and child in the country. Clean-air laws have been passed to reduce this 200 million tons of people-made pollution.

The automobile can give off pollutants from four places (Fig. 31-1). Atmospheric pollutants can come from the fuel tank, the carburetor, the crankcase, and the tail pipe. Pollu-

tants from the fuel tank and carburetor consist of gasoline vapors (HC). Pollutants from the crankcase consist of partly burned air-fuel mixture that has blown by the piston rings. Blowby gases are mostly HC. Pollutants from the tail pipe consist of unburned gasoline (HC), carbon monoxide (CO), nitrogen oxides (NO_x), and—if there is sulfur in the gasoline—sulfur oxides (SO_x).

SHOP SKILLS

____ 1. Raise the hood of the vehicle, and identify the two sources of pollutants in the engine compartment: the carburetor and the crankcase. If you can smell gasoline in the engine compartment, unburned gasoline vapor (HC) is escaping into and polluting the air.

____ 2. Locate and identify the positive crankcase ventilation (PCV) valve.

____ 3. Walk around the car, and locate the fuel-tank filler cap (the "gas cap"). Note whether there is a sign, on or close to the cap, saying "Unleaded Gasoline Only." This indicates the car is equipped with a catalytic converter; the converter will be damaged if the engine burns fuel that contains lead. Gasoline can evaporate from the fuel tank and escape into the atmosphere. This is one source of the pollutant HC in the air. Vapor loss from the fuel tank and carburetor is almost completely controlled by the evaporative-control system.

____ 4. Locate the tail pipe at the rear of the car. It is from this source that unburned gasoline (HC), carbon monoxide (CO), nitrogen oxides (NO_x), and sulfur oxides (SO_x) enter

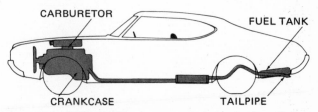

Fig. 31-1 Four possible sources of atmospheric pollution from the automobile.

and pollute the air. To clean up the exhaust gas coming from the tail pipe, many emission control devices have been added and engine changes have been made. The exhaust gas can be cleaned up in three ways: (1) by controlling the air-fuel mixture, (2) by controlling combustion, and (3) by treating the exhaust gas. Each of these methods is discussed in the references.

JOB 31   MULTIPLE-CHOICE TEST

1. The word "smog" comes from the words
   a. "smoke" and "bog"
   b. "sand" and "fog"
   c. "smarting" and "fog"
   d. "smoke" and "fog"   1. ____

2. Along with smoke, the most visible evidence of atmospheric pollution is
   a. storm
   b. lightning
   c. fading paint
   d. smog   2. ____

3. Particles of unburned fuel and soot mixed with air are most commonly referred to as
   a. smog
   b. haze
   c. smoke
   d. carbon monoxide   3. ____

4. The automobile can give off pollutants from
   a. four places
   b. three places
   c. two places
   d. one place   4. ____

5. Pollutants from the fuel tank and carburetor consist of
   a. partly burned air-fuel mixture
   b. gasoline vapors
   c. carbon monoxide
   d. nitrogen oxides   5. ____

JOB 32-1

PCV-System Testing and Service

Objective: To learn how to test and service PCV systems.

References: AM ♦32-3 and 32-4, SG Chap. 32, automotive manufacturers' service manuals.

Equipment: Various engines equipped with crankcase emission control systems and PCV valves.
Tools: PCV tester, basic hand tools.

♦ _____ ♦

SHOP FACTS

Proper operation of the PCV system depends on the valve being free and not sticking or plugging. With mileage, deposits accumulate in the valve and passages. Several engine troubles can result from defective conditions in the PCV system. These troubles can also result from faults in other systems.

Rough idle and frequent stalling could result from a plugged or stuck PCV valve or from a clogged PCV air filter. With either condition, replace the PCV valve or filter.

Vapor flow into the air cleaner and oil in the air cleaner can result from backflow. Instead of filtered air flowing into the crankcase, vapors from the crankcase are flowing into the air cleaner. The cause is a plugged PCV valve or a plugged or leaking condition somewhere in the PCV system. It could also be caused by worn piston rings or cylinder walls which allow more blowby than the PCV system can handle.

Sludge or oil dilution in the crankcase can result from a plugged PCV valve or hose. Either condition prevents normal circulation of the ventilating air and blowby gases.

SHOP SKILLS

QUICK CHECKS OF THE PCV SYSTEM

____ 1. A quick check of the PCV system can be made with the engine idling at normal operating temperature. Pull the PCV valve from the valve cover (Fig. 32-1). A hissing sound should be heard from the valve. This indicates that the valve and the line to it are not plugged.

____ 2. Next, shake the valve (Fig. 32-1). A rattle should be heard. This indicates that the valve is not stuck.

____ 3. Place your thumb over the opening in the end of the valve, and feel for vacuum (Fig. 32-1). If no vacuum is felt or if you can feel a pressure forcing air out, the system is not operating properly. Check the PCV valve, hoses, and connections for free flow.

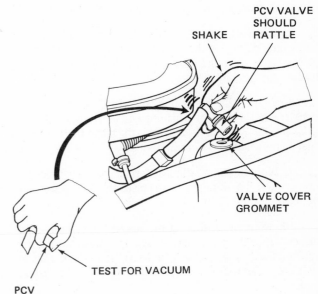

Fig. 32-1 Making a quick check of the PCV valve. (**Chrysler Corporation**)

____ 4. Toyota recommends making a quick flow check of the PCV valve. Remove the valve from the system and blow through the valve from each end. Air should pass freely in the direction of the intake manifold and should be restricted (but not blocked) in the opposite direction.

TESTING THE PCV SYSTEM

Two types of test can be made to check for proper operation of the PCV system. These are the *rpm-drop test* and the *crankcase-vacuum test*.

____ 1. To make an rpm-drop test, connect a tachometer to an engine that is at normal operating temperature. Note the engine idle speed.

____ 2. With your hand, pinch the PCV hose closed, or remove the PCV valve from the engine and place your thumb over the end of the valve, as shown to the lower left in Fig. 32-1. Be sure that the hose from the intake manifold remains attached to the PCV valve.

____ 3. Now, note the change in engine speed, or rpm drop, on the tachometer. If the system is operating properly, the engine speed will drop a minimum of 50 rpm. If engine speed does not change or changes less than 50 rpm, clean or replace the PCV valve and hoses.

____ 4. In an engine equipped with a PCV system, there should be a vacuum in the crankcase at idle. A simple crankcase-vacuum test can be made with the PCV valve in place. Remove the oil-filter cap, and hold a piece of stiff paper over the opening.

____ 5. In less than 1 minute, the vacuum in the crankcase should be attempting to pull the paper into the opening. If the PCV system does not pass these tests, replace the PCV valve and try the test again.

____ 6. If the system still does not pass the test, the hose may be clogged. It should be cleaned out or replaced.

____ 7. If neither the hose nor the PCV valve is the problem, the vacuum passage in the carburetor may be plugged. Clean the passage by twisting a ¼-inch [6.35-millimeter (mm)] drill through it with your fingers.

____ 8. Figure 32-2 shows one type of PCV tester used to check crankcase vacuum. This tester is sometimes called an *inclined-ramp-and-ball tester.* Inside the tester there is a circular ramp which has a vacuum-sensitive ball rolling on it.

____ 9. With the engine idling at normal operating temperature, remove the oil-filler cap and place the PCV tester over the opening (Fig. 32.2).

____ 10. Note the position of the ball. If the ball settles in the GOOD (green) area, crankcase vacuum is adequate and the system is functioning properly. If the ball settles in the REPAIR (red) area, there is pressure in the crankcase. The system needs service.

____ 11. Clean the hoses, install a new PCV valve, and retest.

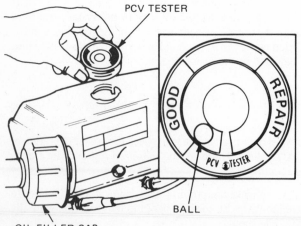

Fig. 32-2 Using a PCV tester to check for crankcase vacuum. (ATW)

SERVICING THE PCV SYSTEM

The PCV valve must be replaced at regular intervals and whenever it clogs or sticks.

____ 1. When you install a new PCV valve, inspect and clean the PCV system thoroughly. This includes all hoses, grommets, and connectors. Clean the insides of the hoses with a brush, and wash the outsides in solvent. Thoroughly clean all connectors, especially the elbow connection. On vented crankcase systems, wash the oil-filler cap in solvent and shake it dry. Some types of oil-filler cap must not be dried with compressed air.

____ 2. After all parts of the PCV system are clean, inspect them carefully. Replace any component that shows signs of damage, wear, or deterioration. Be sure that the grommet that the PCV valve fits into is not damaged or torn (Fig. 32-1).

____ 3. Replace any cracked or brittle hose with hose of a similar type. Replace any component, hose, or fitting that does not allow a free flow of air after cleaning.

____ 4. Whenever the PCV system is serviced, the PCV filter must also be checked. Remove the air-cleaner cover, and take out the PCV filter.

____ 5. Check the filter for damage, dirt buildup, and clogging. If the filter is clean, reinstall it in the air cleaner. A dirty or damaged PCV filter must be replaced.

JOB 32-1   MULTIPLE-CHOICE TEST

1. A quick check of the PCV system is to pull the valve and
   a. stick your finger over the end of the valve
   b. stick your finger in the hole in the valve cover
   c. "rev" the engine and look for smoke
   d. replace the valve   1. ____

2. A quick check of a PCV valve is to
   a. clean the valve
   b. shake the valve
   c. blow through the valve
   d. replace the valve   2. ____

3. PCV valves should be replaced at least every
   a. 2 years
   b. 1 year
   c. 6 months
   d. 3 months   3. ____

4. The check for crankcase vacuum is made with the engine
   a. stopped
   b. running at high speed
   c. running with a heavy load
   d. idling   4. ____

5. A PCV tester checks
   a. intake-manifold vacuum
   b. crankcase vacuum
   c. crankcase compression
   d. intake-manifold pressure   5. ____

JOB 32-2

Evaporative-Control-Systems Service

Objective: To learn how to service evaporative control systems.

References: AM ♦32-4 and 32-5, SG Chap. 32, automotive manufacturers' service manuals.

Equipment: Various vehicles with evaporative control systems.
Tools: Basic hand tools.

SHOP FACTS

Evaporative control systems require little service. About the only service required by some systems is to replace the filter located in the bottom of some canisters at specified intervals. American Motors recommends replacing the filter every 30,000 miles [48,280 km]. Chevrolet requires filter replacement every 24 months or 30,000 miles [48,280 km], whichever comes first. This is typical of General Motors recommendations. Chrysler calls for replacing the filter every 15,000 miles [24,140 km]. Ford schedules an inspection of the charcoal canister every 20 months or 20,000 miles [32,187 km], whichever comes first.

No testers are needed to check evaporative control systems. Almost all problems can be found by visual inspection. Problems are indicated by a strong odor of fuel. Some technicians use an infrared exhaust-gas analyzer to quickly detect small vapor losses from around the fuel tank, canister, air cleaner, lines, or hose. Any loss will register on the HC meter of the exhaust-gas analyzer.

Most problems with evaporative control systems can be noted during the visual inspection. Typical defects are damaged lines, liquid-fuel and vapor leaks, and missing parts. The filler cap can be damaged or corroded so that its valves fail to work properly. A problem with the fuel-tank cap could result in deformation of the tank. This could also occur if the wrong cap is installed on the tank. Be sure that the fuel-tank filler cap is the type specified by the manufacturer for the vehicle and that the cap seals the fuel tank.

Many different engine-idling problems can result from faulty or improper connections of a hose. A plugged canister, vapor-line restrictor missing, or high-volatility fuel can also cause poor idle.

Fuel odor or loss of fuel could be caused by several conditions in the evaporative control system. These include:

1. Overfilled fuel tank
2. Leaks in fuel, vapor, or vent line
3. Wrong or faulty fuel-tank cap
4. Faulty liquid-vapor separator
5. Excessively high fuel volatility
6. Vapor-line restrictor missing.
7. Canister drain cap or hose missing.

A collapsed fuel tank can result if the wrong fuel tank cap is installed or if the vacuum valve in the cap sticks. In either case, no air can enter to replace fuel being withdrawn by the fuel pump. The result could be a vacuum in the fuel tank great enough to allow atmospheric pressure to crush the tank.

Excessive pressure in the fuel tank could result from a combination of high temperatures and a plugged vent line, liquid-vapor separator, or canister. Pressure can be released by turning the tank filler cap just enough to allow the pressure to escape slowly.

SHOP SKILLS

____ 1. To service the evaporative control system (Fig. 32-3), inspect the fuel-tank cap. Check the condition of the sealing gasket around the cap. If the gasket is damaged, replace the cap. Check the filler neck and tank for stains resulting from fuel leakage. Usually, you can trace a stain back to its origin. Then fix the cause of the leak. This may require replacing a gasket, clamp, or hose, or replacing the tank

____ 2. Inspect all lines and connections in the fuel and evaporative control systems for damage and leakage. Perform any necessary repairs. Check all clamps and connections for tightness.

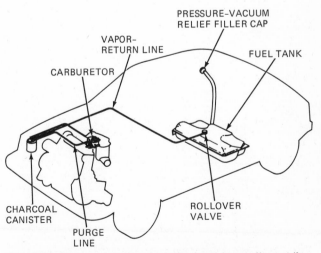
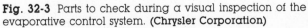

Fig. 32-3 Parts to check during a visual inspection of the evaporative control system. **(Chrysler Corporation)**

Note The hoses used in evaporative control systems are specially made to resist deterioration from contact with gasoline and gasoline vapor. When you replace a hose, make sure that the new hose is specified by the manufacturer for use in evaporative control systems. Sometimes this type of hose is marked EVAP.

____ 3. Check the charcoal-canister lines for liquid fuel. If any is present, replace the liquid-vapor separator or the liquid check valve.

____ 4. Some types of charcoal canister require replacement of the canister filter (Fig. 32-4). To replace the canister filter, remove the canister and turn it upside down, and remove the bottom cover. Pull out the old filter with your fingers, and put the new filter inside.

____ 5. If the canister itself is cracked or internally plugged, a new canister assembly should be installed.

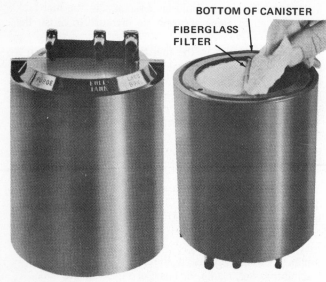

BOTTOM OF CANISTER

FIBERGLASS FILTER

Fig. 32-4 Replacing the air filter in the charcoal canister.

JOB 32-2 MULTIPLE-CHOICE TEST

1. Servicing evaporative control systems requires
   a. many special tools
   b. an exhaust-gas analyzer
   c. a PCV tester
   d. no special tools   1. ____

2. Collapsing of the fuel tank may be caused by
   a. the use of the wrong fuel-tank cap
   b. overfilling the fuel tank
   c. freezing weather
   d. unseasonably hot weather   2. ____

3. A fuel odor noticeable in the passenger compartment indicates
   a. normal operation
   b. an overheated engine
   c. a liquid-fuel or vapor leak
   d. that the air filter needs cleaning   3. ____

4. Some canisters have
   a. replaceable filters
   b. replaceable charcoal
   c. replaceable floats
   d. water traps   4. ____

5. A cracked charcoal canister must be
   a. patched with epoxy
   b. cleaned
   c. replaced with a new canister
   d. checked for contamination   5. ____

JOB 32-3

Servicing Air-Injection Systems

Objective: To learn how to service the air-injection-reactor (AIR) system of exhaust emission control.

References: AM ♦32-7, SG Chap. 32, automotive manufacturers' service manuals.

Equipment: Various engines equipped with the AIR system.
Tools: Belt-tension gauge, basic hand tools.
Supplies: Can of soapy water.

♦ _____ ♦

SHOP FACTS

Troubles related to the air-injection system (Fig. 32-5) include noise, no air supply, backfire, and high HC and CO levels in the exhaust gas.

Noise from the belt or air pump could result from a loose belt, loose air-pump mounting bolts, worn pump bearings or other internal trouble, or air leaks from the system. On many cars, the pump is not repairable. It must be replaced if damaged. The air pump should be adjusted to give the belt the correct tension. Do not pry on the pump housing, because this can ruin the pump. If you have to use a pry bar, pry as close to the pulley end as possible. Some manufacturers recommend using a belt tensioner and a belt-tension gauge.

Air leaks should be stopped by tightening hose connections and replacing any hose that is defective.

If no air is getting to the air manifold, the exhaust gas will probably be high in HC and CO. Causes of no or inadequate air include a loose belt, frozen pump, leaks in the hoses or connections, and failure of the diverter or check valve. A defective pump or valve must be replaced. They usually are not repairable.

Backfire is usually caused by a defective diverter valve which fails to block off the air supply when the accelerator pedal is suddenly released. The same thing happens if the vacuum hose becomes disconnected or blocked.

No routine service is required on the air-injection system except to replace the air filter every 12,000 miles [19,312 km] on those systems using a separate air filter. All late-model air pumps use a centrifugal filter which requires no separate service.

The air-injection system should be checked and serviced during an engine tuneup. The air-injection system should also be checked whenever a customer complaint indicates that the cause could be the AIR system.

There are various procedures for checking the antibackfire valve. Check the manufacturer's service manual for the proper procedure for the engine you are servicing.

SHOP SKILLS

_____ 1. With the engine stopped, inspect the air-pump drive belt for wear, cracks, and deterioration. Replace if necessary. Check the belt tension with a belt-tension gauge. Adjust the belts to the manufacturer's specifications.

Note Do not pry out on the air-pump housing while trying to tighten the belt. The air-pump housing will distort or break and damage the pump.

_____ 2. Inspect the installation of the air pump. All connections to the air-bypass valve, check valves, and air manifolds must be tight. Check the condition and location of all hoses, especially the small signal hoses that carry intake-manifold vacuum. Look for deterioration, cracking, and small holes. All hoses must be secure, without any kinks, and not leaking. The various types of antibackfire valves are also known as *gulp valves* and *air-bypass*, or *diverter, valves*. Regardless of the name, they all work in about the same way. They help prevent backfires in the exhaust system during deceleration.

_____ 3. Check all hose and tube connections and positions. Hoses that burn or rub through against other engine parts cause the air-injection system to fail. If you suspect a leak on the pressure side of the air system, run the engine at idle. Slowly cover the area of the suspected leak with soapy water. If there is a leak, bubbles will form at the hole. If a hose must

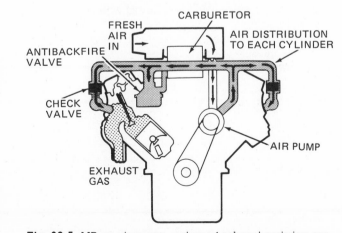

Fig. 32-5 AIR, or air-pump, system of exhaust emission control. **(Motor Vehicle Manufacturers Association)**

be replaced, use only the proper type of replacement hose on air-injection systems.

_____ 4. Inspect the check valve whenever its hose is disconnected or whenever check-valve failure is suspected. To make a quick test of the check valve, blow through the check valve toward the air manifold with your mouth. Then attempt to blow through the check valve in the other direction. Air should flow in one direction only, toward the air manifold. An inoperative air pump, along with signs of exhaust gases in the pump, indicates check-valve failure.

_____ 5. Inspect the air-manifold assemblies and the air-injection tubes in the cylinder heads or exhaust manifolds. Examine carefully for cracks and tight connections. The air-injection tubes do not require periodic service. However, whenever the cylinder heads or exhaust manifolds are removed from an engine, inspect the outlet end of each tube. Common problems are carbon buildup around and inside the tubes and warped or burned-away tubes. Remove any carbon buildup from the tubes by turning a small drill with your fingers until the passage is open. Warped or burned-away tubes require replacement of the air manifold.

_____ 6. Remove one of the outlet hoses from the back of the air pump. Accelerate the engine to approximately 1500 rpm. With your hand, feel the airflow from the pump (Fig. 32-6). If the airflow increases as the engine speeds up, the pump is okay. If the airflow does not increase, or if no air comes out, the pump needs further diagnosis, service, or replacement.

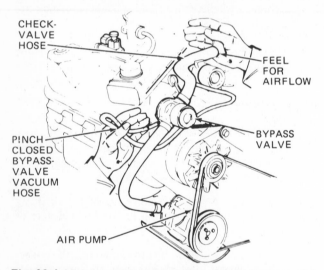

CHECK-VALVE HOSE

FEEL FOR AIRFLOW

PINCH CLOSED BYPASS-VALVE VACUUM HOSE

BYPASS VALVE

AIR PUMP

Fig. 32-6 Make a quick check of the air-injection pump by removing the hose from the check valve and feeling the airflow from the hose. **(Ford Motor Company)**

Clean or replace the inlet air filter for the air pump, if used. The air-pump filter may be a separate, small filter-and-housing assembly. The air-injection system is not completely noiseless. Under normal conditions, noise rises slightly in pitch as engine speed increases. To determine whether excessive noise is the fault of the air-injection system, run the engine briefly with the drive belt removed. Never attempt to oil a noisy pump.

_____ 7. Disconnect the small intake-manifold-vacuum signal hose at the air-bypass valve. A vacuum should be felt at the end of the hose when the engine is running.

_____ 8. Reconnect the vacuum signal hose. With the engine idling, no air should be felt escaping through the air-pump muffler. Open and quickly close the throttle. A momentary blast of air should discharge through the air-pump muffler for at least 1 second. If no air discharge is felt, the air-bypass valve is defective and must be replaced.

JOB 32-3 MULTIPLE-CHOICE TEST

1. Different names for antibackfire valves are
   a. PCV, diverter, and air bypass
   b. gulp, diverter, and exhaust bypass
   c. gulp, diverter, and air bypass
   d. PCV, EGR, and CCS   1. _____

2. Leaks in hoses that carry pressurized air can be located with
   a. soapy water
   b. water
   c. compressed air
   d. solvent   2. _____

3. Periodic service of the air-injection tubes is
   a. required every 3 months
   b. required every 6 months
   c. never required
   d. required every year   3. _____

4. The letters AIR stand for
   a. automotive industry research
   b. automotive ignition range
   c. air-injection reactor
   d. automotive injection reactor   4. _____

5. Drive-belt tension should be adjusted with a
   a. ruler
   b. belt-tension gauge
   c. tape measure
   d. crowbar   5. _____

JOB 32-4
Servicing EGR Systems

Objective: To learn how to service exhaust-gas recirculation (EGR) systems.

References: AM ♦32-11, SG Chap. 32, automotive manufacturers' service manuals.

Equipment: Various engines equipped with the EGR system.
Tools: Hand vacuum pump, basic hand tools.

SHOP SKILLS

____ 1. On some EGR valves, the valve stem is visible under the diaphragm, or vacuum actuator. A quick check of this type of valve can be made with the engine warmed up and idling. With the transmission in neutral, abruptly open the throttle until the engine accelerates to about 2000 rpm. If the EGR valve is operating, you will see the stem (and the groove in it) move up as the valve opens. If the stem does not move, check the EGR valve further, as explained below.

____ 2. Figure 32-7 shows the setup Ford recommends for a quick check of the EGR valve on the car. Check all hose connections in the EGR system. Then, with the engine warmed up and idling, connect the vacuum tester to the EGR valve. Apply 8 inches [203 mm] of vacuum to the valve. If there is no change in idle condition or rpm, the EGR valve is restricted and should be cleaned. If the valve is not dirty, it is defective and must be replaced. However, if the engine idle roughens when the vacuum is applied, and the rpm drops or the engine stalls, the EGR valve is okay.

____ 3. General Motors recommends checking the EGR valve in a similar manner by connecting a hose from the intake manifold to the EGR valve. The engine must be warmed up and running at fast idle. If the valve is good, the engine speed should drop at least 100 rpm on a car with automatic transmission. Otherwise, clean or replace the valve.

____ 4. The thermal vacuum switch is called a *ported vacuum switch (PVS)* by Ford. To check it, remove both hoses from the valve. Connect a vacuum tester to the lower port

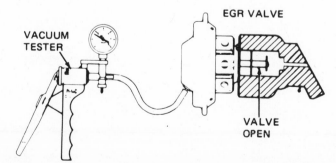

Fig. 32-7 Testing the EGR valve. **(Ford Motor Company)**

and a vacuum gauge to the upper port. With the engine cold (coolant temperature 60°F [15.6°C] or less), apply vacuum to the valve. If the valve is working properly, no reading should appear on the vacuum gauge. (This closed position of the PVS valve prevents exhaust-gas recirculation on a cold engine.) If the gauge shows a vacuum reading, the PVS valve is defective and must be replaced.

____ 5. Next, operate the engine until it warms up. Then apply vacuum to the valve. The vacuum gauge should register. If the gauge does not register a vacuum, replace the PVS valve.

Note Chevrolet points out that leakage of up to 2 inches [51 mm] of vacuum in 2 minutes through the thermal vacuum switch is okay. It does not indicate that the switch is defective.

____ 6. The different manufacturers recommend various service intervals for EGR systems. When the engine is operated on leaded gasoline, the EGR system should be checked for proper operation every 12 months or 12,000 miles [19,312 km], whichever comes first. Engines operated on unleaded gasoline require an EGR-system check only every 24 months or 24,000 miles [38,624 km].

____ 7. Some cars have an EGR maintenance light on the instrument panel. The light comes on automatically at 15,000 miles [24,140 km], to remind the driver to have the EGR system checked. Many late-model cars do not require regular service of the EGR system. Instead, the EGR system is diagnosed when a trouble develops. Then the needed test or service is performed.

____ 8. A sticking EGR valve should be inspected for deposits. If there is more than a thin film of deposits, clean the EGR valve. Remove any deposits from the mounting surface and from around the valve and seat. The method of cleaning depends on the type of valve (Fig. 32-8).

____ 9. General Motors recommends cleaning an EGR valve from a V-type engine as follows. Hold the valve assembly in your hand, and tap the protruding valve lightly with a plastic hammer. Then lightly tap the sides of the valve. Shake out the loose particles. If you are not certain of the type of valve or how to clean it, refer to the manufacturer's service manual.

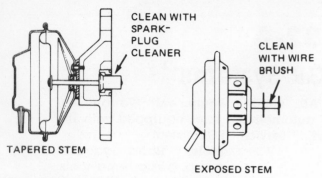

CLEAN WITH SPARK-PLUG CLEANER

CLEAN WITH WIRE BRUSH

TAPERED STEM

EXPOSED STEM

Fig. 32-8 Two different types of EGR valves and how to clean them. **(Ford Motor Company)**

Note Do not clamp the EGR valve in a vise or wash an EGR valve in solvent. Damage to the valve and diaphragm may result.

____ 10. A buildup of deposits in any passage of an EGR system should be cleaned out. Deposits can be loosened with a round wire brush, such as a valve-guide cleaning brush. Passages (such as the exhaust-gas entry port) that are completely blocked by hard deposits can be opened with a small drill. Hold the drill between your fingers, and turn it into the deposit to cut it out.

____ 11. When cleaning passages in the manifold, cover the holes with rags or masking tape. This will keep dirt from falling into the manifold.

____ 12. For the EGR system to operate properly, it must be completely free of vacuum leaks. Any cracked, brittle, or broken hoses may leak and must be replaced. Sometimes you will find hoses that are too short. These will not stay connected, as they tend to pull away from their connectors. Hoses that are too long may interfere with the throttle link-age. Also, long hoses may bend or kink, preventing the vacuum signal from passing through. Short hoses must be replaced. Long hoses must be cut to the correct length.

JOB 32-4 MULTIPLE-CHOICE TEST

1. Exhaust-gas recirculation does not occur at
   a. idle or part throttle
   b. part throttle or wide-open throttle
   c. idle or wide-open throttle
   d. part throttle   1. ____

2. If there is no change in idle rpm when vacuum is applied to the EGR valve, the valve is
   a. operating normally
   b. defective
   c. the wrong type
   d. none of the above   2. ____

3. The purpose of the thermal vacuum switch is to prevent exhaust-gas recirculation
   a. during wide-open throttle
   b. at idle
   c. when the engine is warmed up
   d. when the engine is cold   3. ____

4. When the engine is operated on leaded gasoline, the EGR system should be checked every
   a. 24 months or 24,000 miles [38,624 km]
   b. 15,000 miles [24,140 km]
   c. 30 days
   d. 12 months or 12,000 miles [19,312 km]   4. ____

5. A sticking EGR valve should be
   a. replaced
   b. soaked in carburetor cleaner
   c. inspected for deposits
   d. washed with soap and water   5. ____

Name _____ Date _____

JOB 33-1
Engine-Testing Instruments

Objective: To learn how to use engine-testing instruments.

References: AM ♦33-1 to 33-16, SG Chap. 33, automotive manufacturers' service manuals.
Equipment: Various vehicles and engines.

Tools: Tachometer, cylinder compression tester, cylinder leakage tester, ignition timing light, dynamometer, cooling-system testers, PCV tester, fuel-system testers, electric-system testers, basic hand tools.

♦ _____ ♦

SHOP FACTS

When you are assigned a job requiring the use of a testing instrument that is new to you, follow these general steps. First, read the references and the instructions on how to hook up and calibrate the instrument. Then take the instrument to a vehicle, and follow the instructions step by step.

Ask your instructor about any steps that you don't understand. Also ask for advice when you cannot locate the connecting points on the vehicle that are illustrated in the instructions. Below are orientation steps for some of the most frequently used basic engine-testing instruments.

SHOP SKILLS

TACHOMETER

____ 1. The tachometer measures engine speed in revolutions per minute. It is a necessary instrument because the idle speed must be adjusted to a specific rpm. Also, many tests must be made at specific engine speeds. On the spark-ignition engine, the tachometer is connected to the ignition system and operates electrically.

____ 2. Obtain a copy of the instructions for hooking up and calibrating the tachometer used in your shop. Take the tachometer and the instructions to a vehicle. Then hook up and calibrate the tachometer.

COMPRESSION TESTER

____ 1. The cylinder compression tester (Fig. 33-1) measures the ability of the cylinders to hold compression. Pressure operates on a diaphragm in the tester. This causes the needle on the face of the tester to move around to indicate the pressure being applied.

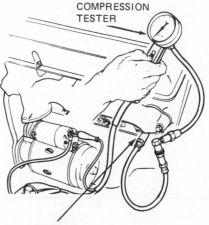

Fig. 33-1 Using a cylinder compression tester. (Sun Electric Corporation)

____ 2. Read the references in your AM textbook on how to perform a cylinder compression test and how to prepare the engine for testing. Take the compression tester to an engine, and go through the steps necessary to perform the test. If the tester is the type that uses screw-in adapters in the spark-plug hole, select the proper adapter for the engine you are working on.

VACUUM GAUGE

____ 1. The vacuum gauge (Fig. 33-2) is important for tracking down troubles in a spark-ignition engine that does not run well. This gauge measures intake-manifold vacuum, which changes with different operating conditions and with different engine defects. The way the vacuum varies from normal shows you what is wrong inside the engine.

____ 2. Read the references in your AM textbook on how to hook up an engine vacuum gauge and interpret its readings. Take a vacuum gauge to a vehicle. Locate places where it can

READING		DIAGNOSIS
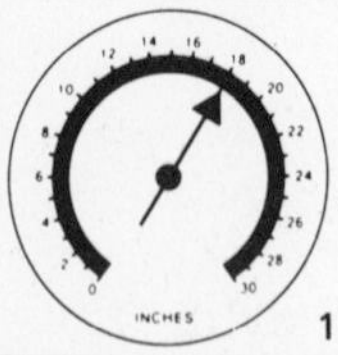 1	Average and steady at 17–21.	Everything is normal.
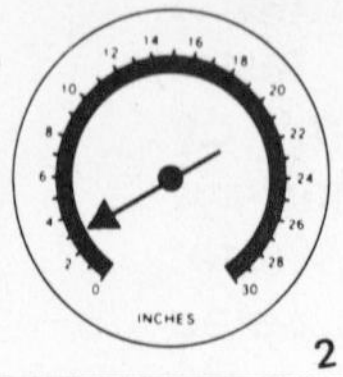 2	Extremely low reading—needle holds steady.	Air leak at the intake manifold or throttle body; incorrect timing.
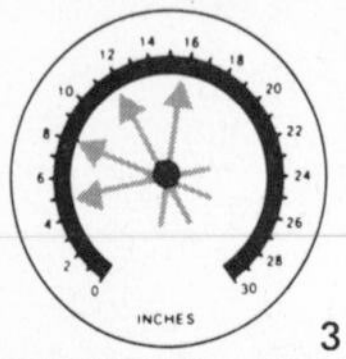 3	Needle fluctuates between high and low reading.	Blown head gasket between two side-by-side cylinders. (Check with compression test.)
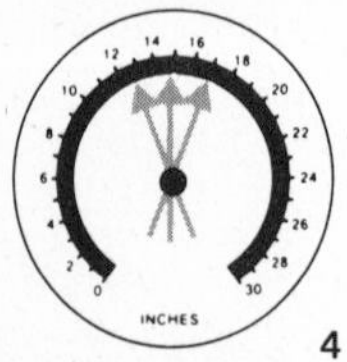 4	Needle fluctuates very slowly, ranging 4 or 5 points.	Idle mixture needs adjustment, spark-plug gap too narrow, sticking valves
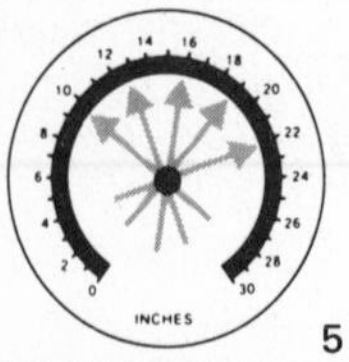 5	Needle fluctuates rapidly at idle—steadies as RPM is increased.	Worn valve guides.
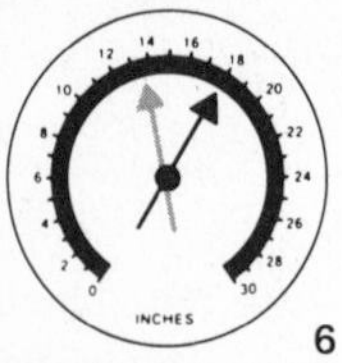 6	Needle drops to low reading, returns to normal, drops back, etc., at a regular interval.	Burned or leaking valve.
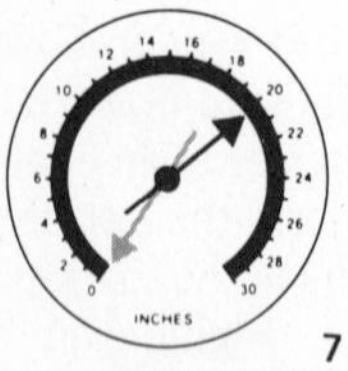 7	Needle drops to zero as engine RPM is increased.	Restricted exhaust system.
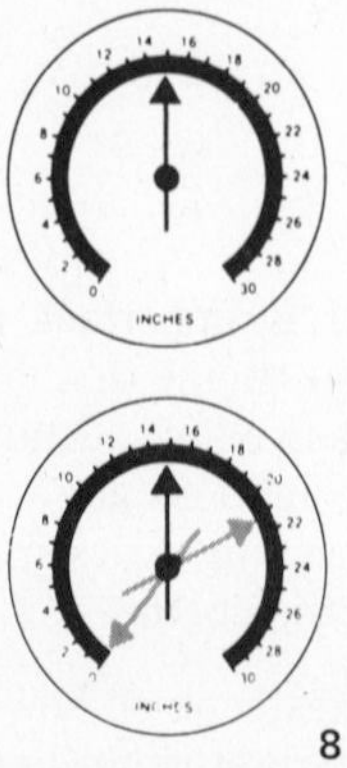 8	Needle holds steady at 12 to 16—drops to 0 and back to about 21 as you open and release the throttle.	Leaking piston rings. (Check with compression test.)

Fig. 33-2 Vacuum-gauge readings and their meaning. (Champion Spark Plug Company)

be hooked into the engine vacuum system. Be sure you locate sources of intake-manifold vacuum, and not ported vacuum lines that close off at idle speed. Measure the intake-manifold vacuum. Then compare the readings you obtain with Fig. 33-2.

TIMING LIGHT

____ 1. The ignition timing light is used to check ignition timing on spark-ignition engines. Sparks must reach the spark plugs in the cylinders at exactly the right time. They must arrive a specific number of degrees before TDC on the compression stroke. Adjusting the distributor to make the sparks arrive at the right time is called *ignition timing*.

____ 2. To time the ignition, you check the markings on the crankshaft pulley, with the engine running. Since the pulley turns rapidly, you cannot see the markings in normal light. But by using the timing light, you can make the pulley appear to stand still.

____ 3. Read the instructions on how to hook up and use an ignition timing light. Locate the timing marks and specifications for the vehicle you are working on. Take the timing light to the vehicle, connect the light, start the engine, and check the ignition timing marks.

JOB 33-1 MULTIPLE-CHOICE TEST

1. The two types of cylinder compression test are
   a. wet and dry
   b. slow and fast
   c. intake and compression
   d. odd and even   1. ____

2. A fuel-pump tester checks
   a. fuel octane number
   b. carburetor action
   c. pressure and capacity
   d. fuel consumption   2. ____

3. The tachometer is used to measure
   a. road speed
   b. dwell
   c. engine speed
   d. point gap   3. ____

4. The timing-light leads are connected to the battery and to
   a. a 110-volt wall outlet
   b. the number 1 spark-plug wire
   c. the ignition coil
   d. the alternator   4. ____

5. A vacuum gauge must be connected directly to
   a. carburetor vacuum
   b. air-cleaner vacuum
   c. exhaust-system vacuum
   d. intake-manifold vacuum   5. ____

Name _____ Date _____

JOB 33-2
Testing Automotive Exhaust Emissions

Objective: To learn how to use the exhaust-gas analyzer.

References: AM ♦33-1 to 33-16, SG Chap. 33, automotive manufacturers' service manuals.

Equipment: Various vehicles and engines.
Tools: Exhaust-gas analyzer, basic hand tools.

SHOP FACTS

The procedures for calibrating and using exhaust-gas analyzers vary with the make and model of tester. A typical exhaust-gas analyzer is shown in Fig. 33-3. Be sure to read the operating instructions for the analyzer you are using.

SHOP SKILLS

_____ 1. Plug the exhaust-gas-analyzer line cord into the regular 110-volt wall socket. Turn the analyzer on. Depending on the type of analyzer, the warm-up time is 5 minutes to 1 hour. Check the operating instructions for the analyzer to find the warm-up time.

Note Exhaust-gas analyzers should never be turned off while in use. If the analyzer is turned off even momentarily, it should be warmed up and recalibrated before use.

_____ 2. After warm-up is completed, calibrate the HC and CO meters (Fig. 33-4). This is done by first pushing the SET button on the analyzer. In this position, both the HC and CO meter needles should be exactly on the zero line at the left edge of the meter faces. If the needles are not in their proper positions, turn the knobs marked HC SET and CO SET until the needles are lined up with their zero lines.

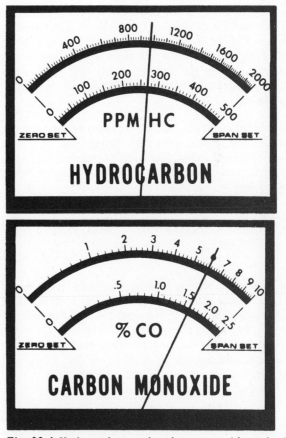

Fig. 33-4 Hydrocarbon and carbon monoxide meter faces. (Sun Electric Corporation)

Note Some exhaust-gas analyzers require a sample from a bottle of special gas for calibration. Other analyzers can be calibrated without the use of bottled gas. The following steps are for an exhaust-gas analyzer that calibrates without bottled gas. Procedures for calibrating other analyzers differ slightly.

_____ 3. Locate the push button marked SPAN. Push in on the SPAN button and hold it depressed. In a few seconds, the meter needles will swing up the scale to the right side of the meter faces. Now use the SPAN SET knob under each meter to align each needle with the SPAN SET line on the right of the meter face.

_____ 4. Release the SPAN push button. In a few seconds, the meter needles should swing back to the left. If the meters are

Fig. 33-3 Using an exhaust-gas analyzer to check the exhaust emissions from the tail pipe of an automobile engine.

properly calibrated, the needles will again be aligned with the zero line. If the meter needles are not on zero, repeat the calibration procedure.

Note If the exhaust-gas analyzer is left on continuously, it need be calibrated only once a day.

____ 5. Check the vehicle exhaust system to be sure that it is free of leaks. A quick check is to block the tail pipe and listen for exhaust leaks anywhere in the system. If no leaks are heard, insert the exhaust-gas pickup probe at least 18 inches [0.46 m] into the tail pipe (Fig. 33-3). Be sure that the probe is securely in place. The engine to be tested should be at normal operating temperature. If the vehicle is equipped with dual exhausts, insert the probe into the side opposite the exhaust-manifold heat valve.

____ 6. To measure the amount of CO, run the engine at fast idle (1500 to 2000 rpm) for about 30 seconds. This will clear any excess fuel out of the engine. Then run the engine at its specified idle speed. Use the idle-speed adjustment screw as necessary to obtain the specified speed. After each adjustment, allow 10 seconds for the meter to stabilize before taking a reading.

____ 7. Read CO at idle on the CO meter. Be sure that you are reading the correct scale on the meter. Write the reading in the proper space below. Then run the engine at 2500 rpm. Read the CO meter again, and write the reading in the proper space below.

_____   _____   _____
% CO @ idle   % CO @ 2500   % CO specs
                     rpm

Note A good CO reading is within specifications at idle and equal to or lower than specifications (specs) at 2500 rpm. A bad CO reading is higher than specified at idle or increases at 2500 rpm. In general, the higher the CO reading, the richer the air-fuel mixture. For tuneup testing, most vehicles with exhaust emission controls should have less than 2.5 percent CO at idle. Vehicles without exhaust emission control should have less than 5 percent CO at idle.

____ 8. To measure HC, run the engine at fast idle (1500 to 2000 rpm) for about 30 seconds. This will clear any excess fuel out of the engine. Then run the engine at its specified idle speed.

____ 9. Read HC at idle on the HC meter. Be sure that you are reading the correct scale on the meter. Write the reading in the proper space below. Then run the engine at 2500 rpm. Read the HC meter again, and write the reading in the proper space below (ppm means *parts per million*).

_____   _____   _____
HC ppm @ idle   HC ppm @   HC ppm specs
                 2500 rpm

Note A good HC reading is within specifications at idle and equal to or less than specs at 2500 rpm. A bad HC reading is higher than specified at idle or increases at 2500 rpm. In general, the higher the HC reading, the more unburned air-fuel mixture is passing out the tail pipe. For tuneup testing, most vehicles with exhaust emission controls should have fewer than 300 ppm HC at idle. Vehicles without exhaust emission controls should have fewer than 500 ppm HC at idle.

JOB 33-2 MULTIPLE-CHOICE TEST

1. Exhaust-gas analyzers measure
   a. HC and HO
   b. HC and CO
   c. CO and HO
   d. H_2O and CO_2 1. ____

2. HC stands for
   a. Harry Clark
   b. helium chloride
   c. heavy car
   d. hydrocarbon   2. ____

3. CO stands for
   a. carbon dioxide
   b. car obsolete
   c. Commanding Officer
   d. carbon monoxide   3. ____

4. The higher the CO reading, the
   a. less unburned gasoline in the exhaust
   b. cleaner the air-fuel mixture
   c. richer the air-fuel mixture
   d. more unburned gasoline in the exhaust   4. ____

5. The lower the HC reading, the
   a. less unburned gasoline in the exhaust
   b. leaner the air-fuel mixture
   c. richer the air-fuel mixture
   d. more unburned gasoline in the exhaust   5. ____

JOB 33-3

GM CCC-System Trouble Diagnosis

Objective: To learn how to perform a trouble diagnosis of the General Motors Computer Command Control (CCC) system.

References: AM ♦33-1 to 33-19, SG Chap. 33, automotive manufacturers' service manuals.
Equipment: Various engines equipped with the General Motors CCC system.

Tools: Digital volt-ohmmeter, dwell meter, tachometer, 12-volt test light, hand vacuum pump, jumper wires, basic hand tools.

SHOP FACTS

On an engine equipped with the General Motors CCC system, troubles are relatively easy to diagnose because of the built-in self-diagnostic capability. A test light must be used, instead of a voltmeter, where indicated in the test procedures. Also, not all dwell meters will work, so always use the type specified by the vehicle manufacturer. If connecting a dwell meter causes engine operation to change, do not use it.

CAREFUL Never attempt to measure the oxygen-sensor voltage. The current drain of a conventional voltmeter is great enough to permanently damage the sensor. No jumper leads, test leads, or other electrical connections should ever be made to the sensor. Before using any such device, first disconnect the harness from the sensor.

The self-diagnostic system lights a CHECK ENGINE light on the instrument panel when a problem is detected in the system (Fig. 33-5). Then, when the technician grounds a trouble-code TEST terminal (Fig. 33-6) under the instrument panel, the CHECK ENGINE light will flash a trouble code or codes indicating the problem locations. Figure 33-7 lists the code numbers that could flash and the meaning of each.

For example, if trouble code 14 flashes on, it indicates a problem in the engine-coolant-sensor circuit. Note in Fig. 33-7 that the engine must run for up to 2 minutes before the code will set. In the manufacturer's service manual, there is a diagnostic chart for trouble code 14. Follow the steps in the chart to locate the cause of the problem, and correct it.

The self-diagnostic system will not detect all possible

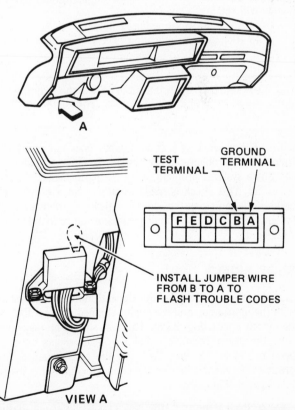

A

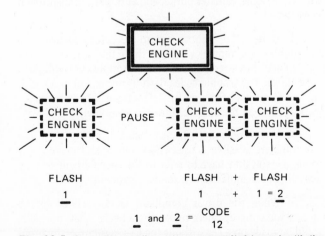

Fig. 33-5 Operation of the CHECK ENGINE light used with the GM CCC system. When the technician grounds the TEST terminal under the instrument panel, the CHECK ENGINE light will start to flash.

TEST TERMINAL   GROUND TERMINAL

F E D C B A

INSTALL JUMPER WIRE FROM B TO A TO FLASH TROUBLE CODES

VIEW A

Fig. 33-6 Location of the trouble-code TEST terminal in the under-dash connector. **(Buick Motor Division of General Motors Corporation)**

CCC-SYSTEM TROUBLE CODES

12 No reference pulses to the ECM. This code is not stored in memory and will only flash when the fault is present. Normal code with ignition ON, engine not running.

13 Oxygen-sensor circuit. The engine must run up to five minutes at part throttle, under road load, before this code will set.

14 Shorted coolant-sensor circuit. The engine must run up to two minutes before this code will set.

15 Open coolant-sensor circuit. The engine must run up to five minutes before this code will set.

21 Throttle-position-sensor circuit. The engine must run up to 25 seconds, at specified curb idle speed, before this code will set.

23 Open or grounded M/C-solenoid circuit.

24 Vehicle-speed-sensor (VSS) circuit. The car must operate up to five minutes at road speed before this code will set.

32 Barometric-pressure-sensor (BARO) circuit low.

34 Manifold-absolute-pressure (MAP) or vacuum-sensor circuit. The engine must run up to five minutes, at specified curb idle speed, before this code will set.

35 Idle-speed-control (ISC) switch circuit shorted. (Over 1/2 throttle for longer than two seconds.)

41 No distributor reference pulses at specified engine vacuum. This code will store.

42 Electronic-spark timing (EST) bypass circuit grounded or open.

43 ESC retard signal for too long; causes a retard in EST signal.

44 Lean-oxygen-sensor indication. The engine must run up to five minutes, in Closed Loop, at part throttle before this code will set.

44 AND 55 (At same time) Faulty oxygen-sensor circuit.

45 Rich-system indication. The engine must run up to five minutes, in closed loop, at part throttle before this code will set.

51 Faulty calibration unit (PROM) or installation. It takes up to 30 seconds before this code will set.

54 Shorted M/C-solenoid circuit and/or faulty ECM.

55 Grounded voltage-reference (ECM terminal 21), faulty oxygen sensor or ECM.

EXPLANATION OF ABBREVIATIONS

ALCL Assembly line communications link (under-dash connector)
BAT+ Battery positive terminal
BARO Barometric pressure
C.E. Check engine
CONV. Catalytic converter
ECM Electronic control module
EFE Early fuel evaporation
EGR Exhaust gas recirculation
ESC Electronic spark control
EST Electronic spark timing
HEI High energy ignition
ISC Idle speed control
MAP Manifold absolute pressure
M/C Mixture control
P/N Park/Neutral
PCV Positive crankcase ventilation
PORT Exhaust ports
PROM ECM calibration unit (Programmable read-only memory)
TCC Torque converter clutch
TPS Throttle position sensor
VAC Vacuum
VIN Vehicle identification number
VSS Vehicle speed sensor

Fig. 33-7 Left, CCC-system trouble codes and their meanings. Right, explanation of abbreviations frequently used in diagnosis and service of the CCC system. **(Pontiac Motor Division of General Motors Corporation)**

---

faults. The absence of a code number does not mean that there are no problems in the system. To determine whether there is a systems problem, a system performance check is necessary. This check is made when the CHECK ENGINE light and self-diagnostic system do not indicate a problem but the system is suspected and no other reason can be found for the complaint.

SHOP SKILLS

____ **1.** On a car that has the General Motors CCC system, with the ignition on and the engine stopped, make a diagnostic circuit check (Fig. 33-8). This test should be made anytime the driver complains that the CHECK ENGINE light has been on, or is on now. To begin the test sequence, first ground the TEST terminal in the connector under the instrument panel (Fig. 33-6).

____ **2.** If all is normal, the CHECK ENGINE light will flash a code 12 (Fig. 33-5), send a 30 degree dwell signal to the mixture-control (MC) solenoid in the carburetor, and energize all ECM-controlled solenoids. These include the AIR control, AIR switch, EGR, canister purge, and automatic-transmission converter clutch.

____ **3.** If the self-diagnostic system has detected a problem, the trouble-code number will flash three times. If more than one problem has been detected, each trouble code will flash three times. The trouble codes flash in numerical order with the lowest number flashing first. The trouble-code series repeats as long as the TEST terminal is grounded.

____ **4.** If a trouble code flashes, locate it in Fig. 33-7 and determine its possible causes. Then check and correct any problems. You may have to refer to the specific trouble-code chart in the manufacturer's service manual.

____ **5.** When the driver complaint is not related to the CHECK ENGINE light, then make the checks that normally would be made on a car without the CCC system. Many problems will not cause the CHECK ENGINE light to flash or remain on. To help locate these problems, use the driver complaint chart supplied by the manufacturer (Fig. 33-9). The CCC sys-

1. ALWAYS CHECK PROM FOR THE CORRECT APPLICATION AND INSTALLATION BEFORE REPLACING AN ECM.
2. REMOVE TERMINAL(S) FROM ECM CONNECTOR FROM CIRCUIT INVOLVED, CLEAN TERMINAL CONTACT AND EXPAND SLIGHTLY TO INCREASE CONTACT PRESSURE AND RECHECK TO SEE IF PROBLEM IS CORRECTED.

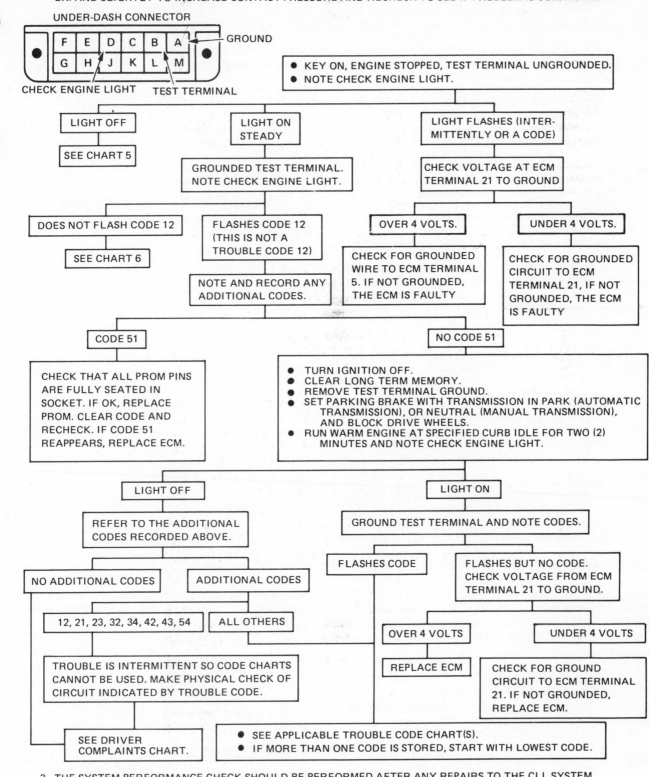

3. THE SYSTEM PERFORMANCE CHECK SHOULD BE PERFORMED AFTER ANY REPAIRS TO THE CLL SYSTEM HAVE BEEN MADE.
4. IT IS POSSIBLE TO SET A FALSE CODE 42 ON STARTING, BUT THE CHECK ENGINE LIGHT WILL NOT BE ON. NO CORRECTIVE ACTION IS NECESSARY.

Fig. 33-8 Chart for making a diagnostic circuit check. (Buick Motor Division of General Motors Corporation)

1. IF THE CHECK ENGINE LIGHT IS NOT ON, NORMAL CHECKS THAT WOULD BE PERFORMED ON CARS WITHOUT THE SYSTEM SHOULD BE DONE FIRST.

2. IF GENERATOR OR COOLANT LIGHT IS ON WITH THE CHECK ENGINE LIGHT, THEY SHOULD BE DIAGNOSED FIRST.

3. INSPECT FOR POOR CONNECTIONS AT COOLANT SENSOR, MIXTURE-CONTROL SOLENOID, AND OTHER COMPONENTS, AND POOR OR LOOSE VACUUM HOSES AND CONNECTIONS. REPAIR AS NECESSARY.

    a. INTERMITTENT CHECK ENGINE LIGHT BUT NO TROUBLE CODE STORED.
       (1) CHECK FOR INTERMITTENT CONNECTION IN CIRCUIT FROM:
          (a) IGNITION COIL TO GROUND AND ARCING AT SPARK PLUG WIRES OR PLUGS.
          (b) BATTERY TO ECM TERMINALS C AND R.
          (c) ECM TERMINALS A AND U TO ENGINE GROUND.
       (2) LOSS OF LONG-TERM MEMORY.
          (a) GROUNDING DWELL LEAD FOR 10 SECONDS WITH TEST LEAD UNGROUNDED SHOULD GIVE CODE 23. IT SHOULD BE RETAINED AFTER ENGINE IS STOPPED AND IGNITION TURNED TO RUN POSITION.
          (b) IF NOT, ECM IS DEFECTIVE. REPLACE IT.
       (3) EST WIRES SHOULD BE KEPT AWAY FROM SPARK PLUG WIRES, DISTRIBUTOR HOUSING, COIL AND GENERATOR. WIRES FROM ECM TERMINAL 13 TO DISTRIBUTOR AND THE SHIELD AROUND EST WIRES SHOULD BE A GOOD GROUND.
       (4) OPEN DIODE ACROSS AIR-CONDITIONING-COMPRESSOR CLUTCH.

    b. STALLING, ROUGH IDLE, OR IMPROPER IDLE SPEED.
       (1) CHECK IDLE-SPEED CONTROL.

    c. DETONATION (SPARK KNOCK)
       (1) CHECK: ESC PERFORMANCE, IF APPLICABLE.
                         MAP OR VACUUM SENSOR OUTPUT.
                         EGR OPERATION.
                         TPS ENRICHMENT OPERATION.
                         HEI OPERATION.

    d. POOR PERFORMANCE AND/OR FUEL ECONOMY.
       (1) MAKE EST DIAGNOSIS.
       (2) MAKE ESC DIAGNOSIS IF APPLICABLE.

    e. POOR FULL-THROTTLE PERFORMANCE.
       (1) SEE CHART 4 IF EQUIPPED WITH TPS.

    f. ALL OTHER COMPLAINTS.
       (1) MAKE SYSTEM PERFORMANCE CHECK ON WARM ENGINE (UPPER RADIATOR HOSE HOT).

4. THE SYSTEM PERFORMANCE CHECK SHOULD BE PERFORMED AFTER ANY REPAIR TO THE SYSTEM HAS BEEN MADE.

Fig. 33-9 Driver complaint chart. (Buick Motor Division of General Motors Corporation)

tem should be considered as a possible source of trouble for engine performance, fuel economy, and exhaust emission complaints *only after* a normal engine diagnosis. This means following the procedures that apply to a car without the CCC system.

_____ 6. After any trouble is located and corrected, make a system performance check of the CCC system. The procedure is shown in Fig. 33-10. The system performance check should also be made after any repairs to the CCC system.

JOB 33-3 MULTIPLE-CHOICE TEST

1. To ground the TEST terminal, you need
   a. a jumper wire
   b. a dwell meter
   c. a 12-volt test light
   d. all of the above   1. _____

2. If a spark-plug cable becomes disconnected from the spark plug, the CHECK ENGINE light will flash trouble code
   a. 21
   b. 42
   c. 55
   d. none of the above   2. _____

3. The sensor that reports intake-manifold vacuum is the
   a. BARO sensor
   b. MAP sensor
   c. PROM
   d. vehicle-speed sensor (VSS)   3. _____

4. If the CHECK ENGINE light is on steady, you should
   a. turn the ignition switch off
   b. apply battery voltage to the TEST terminal
   c. ground the TEST terminal
   d. check the voltage at ECM terminal 21   4. _____

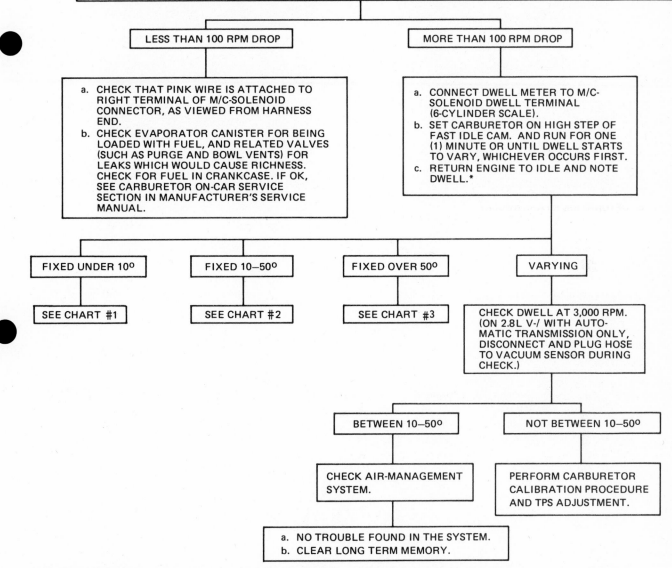

1. START ENGINE.
2. GROUND TEST TERMINAL (MUST BE GROUNDED BEFORE ENGINE IS STARTED.)
3. DISCONNECT PURGE HOSE FROM CANISTER AND PLUG IT. ON E2SE CARBURETORS, DISCONNECT BOWL VENT AT CARBURETOR.
4. CONNECT TACHOMETER.
5. DISCONNECT MIXTURE-CONTROL (M/C) SOLENOID AND GROUND M/C-SOLENOID DWELL TERMINAL.
6. RUN ENGINE AT 3,000 RPM AND, WHILE KEEPING THROTTLE CONSTANT, RECONNECT M/C SOLENOID AND NOTE RPM. IF CAR IS EQUIPPED WITH AN ELECTRIC COOLING FAN, IT MAY LOWER RPM WHEN IT ENGAGES.
7. REMOVE GROUND FROM M/C SOLENOID DWELL TERMINAL BEFORE RETURNING TO IDLE.

LESS THAN 100 RPM DROP

a. CHECK THAT PINK WIRE IS ATTACHED TO RIGHT TERMINAL OF M/C-SOLENOID CONNECTOR, AS VIEWED FROM HARNESS END.
b. CHECK EVAPORATOR CANISTER FOR BEING LOADED WITH FUEL, AND RELATED VALVES (SUCH AS PURGE AND BOWL VENTS) FOR LEAKS WHICH WOULD CAUSE RICHNESS. CHECK FOR FUEL IN CRANKCASE. IF OK, SEE CARBURETOR ON-CAR SERVICE SECTION IN MANUFACTURER'S SERVICE MANUAL.

MORE THAN 100 RPM DROP

a. CONNECT DWELL METER TO M/C-SOLENOID DWELL TERMINAL (6-CYLINDER SCALE).
b. SET CARBURETOR ON HIGH STEP OF FAST IDLE CAM. AND RUN FOR ONE (1) MINUTE OR UNTIL DWELL STARTS TO VARY, WHICHEVER OCCURS FIRST.
c. RETURN ENGINE TO IDLE AND NOTE DWELL.*

FIXED UNDER 10°

SEE CHART #1

FIXED 10—50°

SEE CHART #2

FIXED OVER 50°

SEE CHART #3

VARYING

CHECK DWELL AT 3,000 RPM. (ON 2.8L V-/ WITH AUTOMATIC TRANSMISSION ONLY, DISCONNECT AND PLUG HOSE TO VACUUM SENSOR DURING CHECK.)

BETWEEN 10—50°

CHECK AIR-MANAGEMENT SYSTEM.

a. NO TROUBLE FOUND IN THE SYSTEM.
b. CLEAR LONG TERM MEMORY.

NOT BETWEEN 10—50°

PERFORM CARBURETOR CALIBRATION PROCEDURE AND TPS ADJUSTMENT.

*OXYGEN SENSORS MAY COOL OFF AT IDLE AND THE DWELL CHANGE FROM VARYING TO FIXED. IF THIS HAPPENS, RUN THE ENGINE AT FAST IDLE TO WARM IT UP AGAIN.

Fig. 33-10 Chart for making a system performance check. (**Buick** Motor Division of General Motors Corporation)

5. The driver complains that the engine "pings," or detonates, under almost all driving conditions. Mechanic A says to check the MAP sensor. Mechanic B says to check the EGR operation. Who is right?
   a. A only
   b. B only
   c. both A and B
   d. neither A nor B

5. ____

JOB 33-4
Engine Tuneup

Objective: To learn how to perform an engine tuneup.

References: AM ♦34-17 to 34-19, SG Chap. 33, automotive manufacturers' service manuals.
Equipment: Various engines and vehicles.

Tools: Compression tester, spark-plug cleaner and tester, belt-tension gauge, battery-starter tester, volt-ampere tester, oscilloscope, vacuum gauge, fuel-pump tester, tachometer, timing light, exhaust-gas analyzer, basic hand tools.

♦ _____ ♦

SHOP FACTS

Engine tuneup means different things to different people. To some, it means a quick check of the engine that takes in only the obvious trouble spots. To others, it means use of test instruments to do a careful, complete analysis of all engine components. In addition, it means adjusting everything to specifications and repairing or replacing all worn parts.

The tuneup procedure restores drivability, power, performance, and economy that have been lost through wear, corrosion, and deterioration of engine parts. These changes take place gradually in many parts during normal car operation. Because of federal and state laws limiting automotive emissions, the tuneup procedure should include checks of all emission controls.

An engine tuneup follows a procedure. Many mechanics use a printed form supplied by automotive or test-equipment manufacturers. By following the form and checking off the items listed one by one, the mechanic is sure of not overlooking any part of the procedure. However, not all tuneup forms are the same. Different companies have different ideas about what should be done and the order in which it should be done. In addition, the tuneup procedure depends on the equipment available. If the shop has an oscilloscope or a dynamometer, it is used as part of the tuneup procedure. If these test instruments are not available, the tuneup is performed differently.

SHOP SKILLS

____ 1. If the engine is cold, operate it for at least 20 minutes at 1500 rpm or until it reaches operating temperature. Note any operational problems during this warm-up time.

____ 2. Connect the oscilloscope, if available, and perform an electronic diagnosis. Check for any abnormal ignition-system conditions that appear in the pattern. Make a note of any abnormality and the cylinder or cylinders in which it appears.

____ 3. Remove all spark plugs. Fully open the throttle and choke valves. Disconnect the distributor lead from the coil primary terminal.

____ 4. Check the compression of each cylinder. Record the readings. If one or more cylinders read low, squirt about 1 tablespoon [15 cc] of engine oil through the spark-plug hole. Recheck the compression. Record the new readings. For further diagnosis of engine mechanical problems, perform leakdown and cylinder balance tests.

Note If engine mechanical problems are found, tell the owner the engine cannot be tuned without overhaul or repair.

____ 5. Clean, inspect, file, gap, and test the spark plugs. Discard worn or defective spark plugs. Many mechanics install all new plugs instead of servicing the old plugs. Gap all plugs, old and new. Then install the plugs.

____ 6. Inspect and clean the battery case, terminals, cables, and hold-down brackets. Test the battery. Add water, if necessary. If severe corrosion is present, clean the battery and cables with brushes and a solution of baking soda and water.

____ 7. Test the starting voltage. If the battery is in good condition but cranking speed is low, test the starting system.

____ 8. If the battery is low or the customer complains that the battery keeps running down, check the charging system (alternator and regulator). If the battery is old, it may have worn out. A new battery is required.

____ 9. Check the drive belts and replace any that are in poor condition. If you have to replace one belt of a two-belt drive, replace both belts. Tighten the belts to the correct tension, using a belt-tension gauge.

____ 10. Inspect the distributor rotor, cap, and primary and high-voltage (spark-plug) wires.

____ 11. Clean or replace and adjust distributor contact points by setting the point gap. Lubricate the distributor breaker cam. On distributors with round cam lubricators, turn the cam lubricator 180 degrees or replace it if required.

_____ 12. Check the distributor cap and rotor. Check the centrifugal and vacuum advances. Set the dwell and then adjust ignition timing. Make sure that the idle speed is not too high. This could produce centrifugal advance during timing adjustment.

_____ 13. Use the oscilloscope to recheck the ignition system. Any abnormal conditions that appeared in step 2 should now be eliminated.

_____ 14. Check the manifold heat-control valve. Lubricate with heat-valve lubricant. Free up or replace the valve if necessary.

_____ 15. Check the fuel-pump operation with a fuel-pump tester. Replace the fuel filter. Check the fuel-tank cap, fuel lines, and connections for leakage and damage.

_____ 16. Clean or replace the air-cleaner filter. If the engine is equipped with a thermostatically controlled air cleaner, check the operation of the vacuum motor.

_____ 17. Check the operation of the choke and the fast-idle cam. Check the throttle valve for full opening and the throttle linkage for free movement. Clean all external carburetor linkages.

_____ 18. Inspect all engine vacuum fittings, hoses, and connections. Replace any brittle or cracked hose.

_____ 19. Clean the engine oil-filter cap if a filter-type oil-filler cap is used.

_____ 20. Check the cooling system. Inspect all hoses and connections, the radiator, water pump, and fan clutch if used. Check the strength of the antifreeze and record the reading. Pressure-check the system and radiator cap. Squeeze the hoses to check them. Replace any defective hose (collapsed, soft, cracked, etc.).

_____ 21. Check and replace the PCV valve if necessary. Clean or replace the PCV filter if required. Inspect the PCV hoses and connections. Replace any cracked or brittle hose. Test the system for vacuum.

_____ 22. If the engine is equipped with an air pump, replace the pump inlet air filter if used. Inspect the system hoses and connections. Replace any brittle or cracked hose.

_____ 23. If the vehicle is equipped with an evaporative emission control system, replace the charcoal-canister filter, if used.

_____ 24. Check the transmission-controlled spark system if the vehicle is so equipped.

_____ 25. On engines with exhaust-gas recirculation (EGR), inspect and clean the EGR valve. Inspect and clean the EGR discharge port. Test the system operation by applying vacuum

to the valve with engine at idle. Engine should run rough, then smooth out with the vacuum off.

_____ 26. Tighten the intake-manifold and exhaust-manifold bolts in proper sequence to the proper torque.

_____ 27. Adjust the engine valves if necessary.

_____ 28. Adjust the carburetor idle speed. Use an exhaust-gas analyzer and propane, if required, and adjust the idle-mixture screw. Check the amounts of CO and HC in the exhaust gas. (Many mechanics check the CO and HC both before and after the tuneup to show how much the tuneup reduced these pollutants.)

_____ 29. Road-test the car on a dynamometer or on the road. Check for driveability, power, and idling. Any abnormal condition should be noted on the repair order before returning the car to the customer.

_____ 30. Check the lubrication sticker to determine if an oil and oil-filter change are due. Also note the schedule for chassis lubrication. Recommend an oil change and a chassis lubrication if they are due. Car manufacturers recommend changing the oil filter every other time the oil is changed.

_____ 31. Whenever the car is on the lift, check the exhaust system for leaks which could admit CO into the car. Also check for loose bolts, rust spots, and other under-the-car damage.

JOB 33-4 MULTIPLE-CHOICE TEST

1. An oscilloscope is used to check the
   a. ignition system
   b. cooling system
   c. fuel system
   d. lubricating system   1. _____

2. A hydrometer can be used to test the
   a. coil
   b. battery
   c. points and condenser
   d. compression   2. _____

3. The exhaust-gas analyzer is used to adjust
   a. the idle mixture
   b. the idle speed
   c. the fast-idle cam
   d. the choke valve   3. _____

4. The last step in a tuneup is to
   a. adjust the idle
   b. check the PCV valve
   c. set the timing
   d. road-test the car   4. _____

5. In the tuneup procedure, factors affecting cylinder compression must be checked and corrected
   a. last
   b. first
   c. after setting the timing
   d. after adjusting the idle   5. _____

JOB 34-1

Engine Will Not Crank

Objective: To learn how to find the cause of trouble if an engine will not crank when the ignition switch is turned to START.

References: AM ♦34-4, SG Chap. 34, automotive manufacturers' service manuals.

Equipment: Vehicles and engines that will not crank.
Tools: Hydrometer, battery tester, jumper cables, basic hand tools.

SHOP FACTS

If the engine does not crank when starting is attempted, turn on the headlights (Fig. 34-1) and again try to start the engine. Any one of five things will happen: The lights will (1) stay bright, (2) dim considerably, (3) dim only slightly, (4) go out, (5) burn dimly or not at all when first turned on and before any attempt is made to start the engine. Refer to the applicable procedure below and follow the checks outlined.

SHOP SKILLS

LIGHTS STAY BRIGHT

_____ 1. If the lights stay bright with no cranking action, there is an open circuit between the battery and the starting motor. This could be due to:
   a. An open in the ignition switch or solenoid on the starting motor
   b. A defect in the control circuit or switches
   c. An open in the starting motor itself

_____ 2. Determine where the trouble is by noting whether the solenoid or magnetic switch on the starting motor is op-

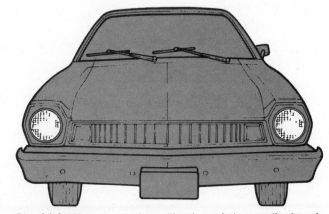

Fig. 34-1 When an engine will not crank, turn on the headlights and try again while you watch their action. **(Ford Motor Company)**

erating. It should click when the ignition switch is turned past ON to START.

_____ 3. If the solenoid or magnetic switch does not click, the circuit to it is not being completed. Connect a jumper wire around each control device until the defective device is located. Follow the procedure in the manufacturer's service manual to locate the problem.

_____ 4. Check the starting motor itself by connecting a jumper cable across the main solenoid or magnetic-switch terminals. Put the jumper on terminal nuts and not on studs to avoid burned threads. The starting motor should now operate and crank the engine.

_____ 5. If the starting motor does not operate and the solenoid or magnetic switch does, then there is an open inside the starting motor itself. Check it as outlined in Job 25-2.

Note One possible cause of an open circuit in the starting motor is an oily or glazed commutator. This condition, if sufficiently bad, will prevent brush contact. Often, correction can be made by sanding the commutator with number 00 sandpaper (on starting motors with a removable cover band). A wood stick can be used to work the sandpaper back and forth on the commutator.

LIGHTS DIM CONSIDERABLY

_____ 1. If the lights dim considerably when starting is attempted (with no cranking action), then either the battery is low or the starting motor or engine is jammed so that it cannot turn over.
   An undersized battery cable may also cause this condition. This would occur only if the original cable had been replaced by an undersized cable.

_____ 2. To determine the cause, first test the battery with the shop tester. If the battery is low, see "Lights Burn Dimly or Not at All" below. If the battery tests in good condition, examine the starting motor more closely.

_____ 3. Remove the cover band, if the starting motor has one. With your fingers try to turn the armature. Do not use a screwdriver since it might damage the commutator. If you cannot turn the armature, remove the starting motor for disassembly.

_____ 4. If the armature does turn, indicating that the starting motor is okay, the jammed condition is probably in the engine itself. The cause could be frozen bearings, broken rods, broken pistons or other broken parts, or pistons stuck because of overheating or lack of lubrication. The engine requires disassembly so that the trouble can be located.

LIGHTS DIM ONLY SLIGHTLY

_____ 1. If the lights dim only slightly when starting is attempted (with no cranking action), note whether or not there is any action at the starting motor.

_____ 2. On overrunning-clutch starting motors operated by solenoid, the solenoid can pull the drive pinion into mesh. Then the armature will not rotate because of excessive resistance or an open circuit inside the starting motor.

_____ 3. With either condition (step 1 or 2 above) the current draw of the starting motor or solenoid could cause a slight dimming of the lights without any cranking action. The starting motor should be checked as outlined in Job 25-2.

LIGHTS GO OUT

_____ 1. If the lights go out when starting is attempted, even though they seemed to be normally bright, there probably is a bad connection between the battery and the starting motor. The most likely location of this connection is at one of the battery terminals.

_____ 2. Test the connections by attempting to move the cable clamps on the terminals. Sometimes, a bad connection can be improved sufficiently by this procedure to permit starting. However, the remedy is to remove the clamps, clean the clamps and the terminals, and reconnect the clamps.

LIGHTS BURN DIMLY OR NOT AT ALL

_____ 1. If the lights burn dimly or not at all when the light switch is turned on (even before starting is attempted), the battery is probably low. However, possibly there is an open in the circuit. The battery and the circuit should be checked.

_____ 2. Whenever a car has a discharged battery, the driver may have run the battery down in trying to start. The cause of

the failure to start may be due to some other defect, as outlined in Job 26-1. If this is the case, the checks detailed in Job 26-1 should be made after the battery is replaced or recharged.

_____ 3. If a discharged battery is found, it must be recharged or replaced. In addition, checks must be made to determine why the battery has run down. Job 26-1 discusses the charging-system checks that should be made when a discharged battery is found.

JOB 34-1   MULTIPLE-CHOICE TEST

1. The headlights stay bright when starting is attempted, and there is no cranking action. Mechanic A says the battery terminals are dirty. Mechanic B says an undersized battery cable has been installed. Who is right?
   a. A only
   b. B only
   c. both A and B
   d. neither A nor B   1. _____

2. When starting is attempted, the lights dim considerably, even after the battery has been charged. Which of the following could be the cause?
   I. There is oil on the commutator.
   II. The starting motor is jammed.
   a. I only
   b. II only
   c. both I and II
   d. neither I nor II   2. _____

3. The lights go out when starting is attempted. The most probable cause is
   a. bad connections at the battery terminals
   b. undersized battery cables
   c. a defective ignition switch
   d. none of the above   3. _____

4. A click can be heard from the solenoid when starting is attempted, but there is no cranking action. The cause of no cranking is:
   I. An open circuit in the starting motor.
   II. Excessive resistance in the starting motor.
   a. I only
   b. II only
   c. either I or II
   d. neither I nor II   4. _____

5. When the headlights do not burn, even before starting is attempted, the cause may be all of the following *except*
   a. a low battery
   b. an open circuit
   c. a burned-out fuse
   d. none of the above   5. _____

JOB 34-2

Engine Cranks But Does Not Start

Objective: To learn how to find the cause of trouble if an engine cranks but does not start when the starting motor is operated.

References: AM ♦34-5, SG Chap. 34, automotive manufacturers' service manuals.

Equipment: Various vehicles and engines that crank but do not start.
Tools: Battery tester, fuel-pump tester, basic hand tools.

SHOP SKILLS

When the engine cranks but does not start as the starting motor is operated, note first whether the engine turns over slowly or at normal cranking speed. Then refer to the applicable procedure below and follow the checks outlined.

ENGINE CRANKS SLOWLY

____ 1. If the engine cranks slowly but does not start, the battery may be discharged, the starting motor or switch may be defective, or there may be mechanical trouble in the engine. This condition might also result if an undersized battery cable has been installed.

____ 2. The most common cause of slow cranking is a run-down battery. Check the battery with a tester. If the battery is in good condition, then it is probable that the starting motor itself is at fault. Check the starting motor as detailed in Job 25-2.

Note The effects of temperature on the engine and the battery should be considered. When the temperature is low, engine oil becomes very thick. In addition, low temperature reduces battery-cranking ability. Also, gasoline does not vaporize as easily at low temperatures. Refer to step 6 in the section below on choke-valve position with a cold engine.

____ 3. If the battery is low, the driver may have discharged it while attempting to start the engine. If so, the basic trouble may actually be due to a problem in the ignition or fuel system, or engine, as detailed in the section below. If this seems likely, recharge or replace the battery. Then make the checks listed in the section below.

____ 4. If the battery and the starting motor are okay, and if low temperature is not reducing cranking speed and preventing starting, the difficulty is probably due to some defect in the engine itself. Lack of lubrication, excessively heavy oil, or tight bearings or pistons could cause slow cranking and failure to start.

ENGINE CRANKS AT NORMAL SPEED

____ 1. If the engine cranks at normal cranking speed but does not start, the cause of trouble probably is in the ignition or fuel system.
    If the engine is hot, failure to start could be due to:
    a. Manifold heat-control valve sticking, so manifold overheats (Fig. 34-2)
    b. Improperly adjusted carburetor linkage, which excessively enriches mixture
    c. Improperly adjusted antipercolator valve (on carburetors so equipped)
    d. Vapor lock
    e. An ignition coil that operates when cold but fails when hot
    f. Automatic-choke valve not opening, so an excessively rich mixture results. (If automatic-choke trouble is suspected, try cranking with the throttle wide open, or check the choke-valve position, as in step 7 below.)

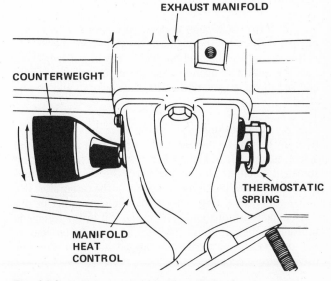

Fig. 34-2 A stuck manifold heat-control valve may cause a hot engine to fail to restart. **(Ford Motor Company)**

____ 2. To check the operation of the ignition system, make a spark test. Disconnect the lead from one spark plug (or from the center terminal of the distributor cap). Hold the end of the wire about ¼ inch [6.35 mm] from the engine block while cranking. If a good spark occurs, the ignition system is probably operating satisfactorily. However, the ignition timing could be off, so normal engine operation would not be possible. This condition should be suspected only if some service work has just been completed. In normal operation, it would be very unusual for the ignition to get so out-of-time by itself as to prevent starting.

♦ **CAUTION** ♦ Be sure there is no spilled gasoline on or around the engine before trying the spark test. When making a spark test on an engine equipped with the electronic high-energy ignition system, insulated or plastic pliers must be used to hold the spark-plug lead. Otherwise, the person holding the lead may be shocked and injured by the high voltage.

Note Badly fouled spark plugs, or spark plugs wet with gasoline from a flooded engine, may prevent starting. If this condition is suspected, remove and inspect one or two spark plugs.

____ 3. If no spark occurs, check the ignition system.

____ 4. If the ignition system seems normal and the engine does not start when cranked at normal cranking speed, the fuel system is probably not functioning normally.

____ 5. To check the fuel system, remove the air cleaner from the carburetor and observe the position of the choke valve. If the engine has an automatic choke, the choke valve should be closed, partly open, or open, according to the engine temperature and the time the ignition has been on.

____ 6. If the choke valve is wide open with a cold engine, the mixture delivered to the engine by the carburetor may be too lean to permit starting. Hold the choke valve closed or partly closed with the linkage to see whether the engine will start when cranked. If the engine now starts, the choke should be serviced.

____ 7. If the choke valve is closed with a warm engine, the mixture delivered to the engine by the carburetor may be too rich to permit starting and the engine may be flooded. Then, hold the valve wide open to see if the engine will start while cranked. If the engine now starts, the choke should be serviced.

____ 8. If the position of the choke valve does not seem to have any bearing on the failure of the engine to start, the fuel system is probably at fault. The fuel system is not delivering sufficient gasoline to the engine. Check the fuel pump to find whether the fault lies in the fuel pump or the carburetor. Use a fuel-pump tester (Fig. 34-3) to determine whether or not the fuel pump is functioning normally. If it is, the trouble is probably in the carburetor. The float level may be too low, or the fuel passages or nozzles are clogged, and the carburetor will require servicing.

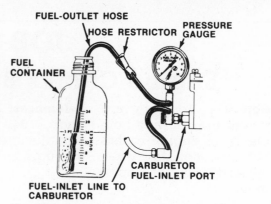

Fig. 34-3 Checking the fuel pump for pressure and capacity. (Ford Motor Company)

____ 9. If the engine does not start, even though the fuel pump and ignition system are functioning normally and the engine is cranked at normal speed, then the fault probably lies in the engine itself. Cylinder compression, valve action, and valve timing should be checked.

JOB 34-2   MULTIPLE-CHOICE TEST

1. When an engine cranks slowly but will not start, the cause could be each of the following *except*
   a. a low battery
   b. mechanical trouble in the engine
   c. a defective starting motor
   d. none of the above   1. ____

2. Mechanic A says the most common cause of slow cranking is a low battery. Mechanic B says that most common cause of slow cranking is a bad fuel pump. Who is right?
   a. A only
   b. B only
   c. both A and B
   d. neither A nor B   2. ____

3. A manifold heat-control valve that is stuck and therefore causes the intake manifold to overheat may cause
   a. a cold engine to fail to start
   b. a hot engine to fail to restart
   c. failure of a hot or cold engine to start
   d. none of the above   3. ____

4. If an engine has good spark on a spark test, failure to start probably is caused by
   a. the fuel system
   b. an out-of-time ignition system
   c. an out-of-time camshaft
   d. the lubricating system   4. ____

5. When an engine has good spark and is getting fuel through the carburetor, failure to start is *probably* caused by
   a. a timing problem
   b. a temperature problem
   c. low compression
   d. coolant leaking into the combustion chamber
                                                            5. ____

JOB 35-1

Adjusting Valves on Pushrod Engines

Objective: To learn to adjust valve clearance on pushrod engines with solid valve lifters.

References: AM ♦35-1 to 35-32, SG Chap. 35, automotive manufacturers' service manuals.
Equipment: Vehicles with pushrod engines, or operable engine on stand.

Tools: Thickness gauges, basic hand tools.
Supplies: Fender cover, valve-cover gasket (as necessary).

♦ **SAFETY** ♦ *Keep hands and clothing away from fan and drive belts when engine is running. While working close to the hot exhaust manifold, be careful not to touch or brush against it.*

SHOP SKILLS

_____ 1. Put the fender cover on the fender.

_____ 2. Start the engine, and run it at fast idle until it reaches normal operating temperature. Then shut off the engine to make the checks and adjustments.

_____ 3. Remove the valve rocker-arm cover. On some engines, the PCV hoses and the air cleaner must be removed.

_____ 4. Make a quick inspection for broken valve springs and valve-stem oil seals. Note the amount of sludge on the cylinder head. Be sure the oil drain passages in the cylinder head are open.

_____ 5. Squirt a liberal amount of light engine oil on all valve stems.

_____ 6. Check the manufacturer's service manual for the proper positioning of the crankshaft and the valves to adjust in each crankshaft position. Adjust the valves, following the procedure in the manufacturer's service manual. If the manufacturer's valve-adjusting procedure is not available, use the following procedure.

_____ 7. Adjust the exhaust valves first (Fig. 35-1). Bump the engine with the starting motor until number 1 piston is at TDC on the compression stroke. Adjust the exhaust valve for number 1 cylinder by inserting the specified thickness gauge between the valve stem and the end of its rocker arm. Make the adjustment according to the type of rocker arm (shaft-supported or ball-pivoted).

_____ 8. On the shaft-supported rocker arm which has an adjusting screw at the pushrod end (Fig. 35-2), back the adjusting screw off enough to allow the gauge to slip in between the valve stem and the end of the rocker arm.

_____ 9. To adjust the screw, turn the screw in until the thickness gauge is gripped firmly between the valve stem and the end of the rocker arm. Then back the screw out until the gauge can be moved in and out with a slight drag. The valve-tappet clearance is now properly adjusted.

Note Some rocker-arm adjusting screws are locked in place with a locknut.

_____ 10. To adjust the ball-pivoted rocker arm, turn the self-locking nut on the stud until the proper clearance between the rocker arm and the valve stem is attained. Figure 35-1 shows the valve clearance being adjusted on this type of rocker arm.

Fig. 35-1 Adjusting valve clearance on an overhead-valve engine with stud-mounted rocker arms. Backing the nut out increases clearance. **(Chevrolet Motor Division of General Motors Corporation)**

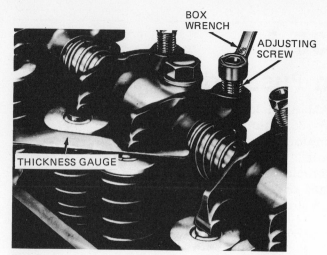

BOX WRENCH

ADJUSTING SCREW

THICKNESS GAUGE

Fig. 35-2 Adjusting valve clearance on an overhead-valve engine which has shaft-mounted rocker arms. **(Ford Motor Company)**

____ 11. Following the engine firing order, bring each piston to TDC on the compression stroke. Adjust the rest of the exhaust valves in the same manner.

____ 12. Then, using the proper thickness gauge, adjust the intake valves, following the same procedure.

____ 13. After all valves are adjusted, install the valve rocker-arm cover. Use a new gasket if the old one is damaged.

____ 14. Install the air cleaner and the PCV hoses, if removed.

JOB 35-1 MULTIPLE-CHOICE TEST

1. To adjust valve clearance on the ball-pivot rocker arm,
   a. turn the adjusting screw
   b. turn the adjusting nut
   c. install or remove shims
   d. grind the end of the valve stem   1. ____

2. When adjusting the screw in the rocker arm, turn it in to
   a. reduce the clearance
   b. increase the clearance
   c. lengthen the valve stem
   d. none of the above   2. ____

3. To adjust valve clearance on the shaft-supported rocker arm,
   a. reposition the rocker arm
   b. grind the end of the valve stem
   c. install or remove shims
   d. turn the adjusting screw   3. ____

4. The adjusting nut used to adjust the ball-pivot rocker arm is
   a. self-locking
   b. locked with a locknut
   c. locked with a lock screw
   d. locked with a cotter pin   4. ____

5. The adjusting screw used on the shaft-supported rocker arm is
   a. locked with a cotter pin
   b. locked with a lock screw
   c. self-locking or locked with a locknut
   d. locked with a rivet   5. ____

JOB 35-2

Adjusting Valve Clearance on Overhead-Camshaft Engines

Objective: To learn to check and adjust valve clearance on overhead-camshaft engines.

References: AM ♦35-17, SG Chap. 35, automotive manufacturers' service manuals.

Equipment: Overhead-camshaft engines.
Tools: Special tappet-adjusting wrench, basic hand tools.

SHOP SKILLS

CHEVROLET VEGA ENGINE

____ 1. With the engine stopped and cold, rotate the camshaft sprocket until the timing mark on the sprocket aligns with the inverted V mark on the timing-belt upper cover. This is number 1 cylinder firing position.

____ 2. In this (number 1 cylinder) firing position, valve clearance can be adjusted for each tappet that is on the base circle of the camshaft lobe. The valves to be adjusted in this position are number 1, intake and exhaust; number 2, intake; number 3, exhaust. Identify each of these valves.

____ 3. Using the specified thickness gauge, measure the clearance between the tappet and the cam lobe of the valve to be adjusted.

____ 4. To obtain the specified clearance, insert the adjusting tool through the hole in the tappet and into the adjusting screw (Fig. 35-3). Turn the screw in, or clockwise, one turn to decrease the clearance 0.003 inch [0.076 mm].

Note The valve-adjusting screw is threaded in all areas except the valve-stem contact surface. It must be turned only in complete revolutions to maintain the proper stem-to-screw relationship.

____ 5. Repeat the adjusting procedure on each valve to be adjusted in this position.

____ 6. Rotate the camshaft timing sprocket 180 degrees to the firing position for number 4. Now repeat the adjustment procedure on each valve not previously adjusted.

CHEVROLET LUV ENGINE

____ 1. The LUV engine has rocker arms which are held in place by springs. The rocker arms have dome-shaped ends

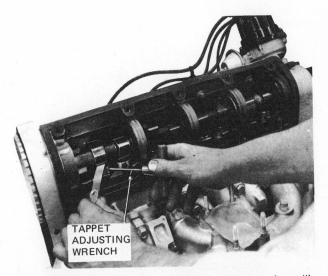

Fig. 35-3 Adjusting the valve clearance on an engine with an overhead camshaft. (**Chevrolet Motor Division of General Motors Corporation**)

which fit over ball studs in the cylinder head. The valve ends of the rocker arms fit into a depression in the valve-spring retainer and rest on the valve stems.

____ 2. To check the valve clearance, measure the clearance between the cam surface of the rocker arm and the base circle of the cam (Fig. 35-4). Use a flat thickness gauge. Adjust with a Phillips-head screwdriver inserted through the hole in the rocker-arm dome.

FORD 2000-CC FOUR-CYLINDER ENGINE

____ 1. This engine has rocker arms which float between a stationary stud on one side and the valve stem on the other. The center of the rocker arm rests on the cam.

____ 2. Use a thickness gauge to check the clearance between the base circle of the cam and the rocker arm (Fig. 35-5).

Fig. 35-4 Adjusting valve clearance on an overhead-camshaft engine which has the rocker arms held in place by springs. (**Chevrolet Motor Division of General Motors Corporation**)

Fig. 35-5 Checking valve clearance on the Ford 2000-cc engine. (**Ford Motor Company**)

_____ 3. Adjustment of the clearance is made by loosening the locknut. Use a 15-mm open-end wrench to turn the adjustment screw in or out. Turning the screw in increases the clearance.

_____ 4. Tighten the locknut securely after the adjustment and recheck the clearance.

JOB 35-2 MULTIPLE-CHOICE TEST

1. Valve adjustment on an overhead-camshaft engine is made with the engine
   a. running and hot
   b. running and cold
   c. stopped and cold
   d. none of the above   1. ____

2. Adjusting the valve clearance on a Chevrolet Vega engine requires the use of a
   a. dial indicator
   b. special adjusting tool
   c. micrometer
   d. box-end wrench   2. ____

3. Each turn of the adjusting screw on a Chevrolet Vega engine changes the clearance
   a. 0.030 inch [0.76 mm]
   b. 0.010 inch [0.25 mm]
   c. 0.001 inch [0.03 mm]
   d. 0.003 inch [0.08 mm]   3. ____

4. The Chevrolet LUV engine has rocker arms which are held in place by
   a. gravity
   b. pins
   c. shafts
   d. springs   4. ____

5. To check the valve clearance on the Ford 2000-cc engine, insert the thickness gauge between the
   a. valve lifter and rocker arm
   b. valve stem and rocker arm
   c. base circle of the cam and the rocker arm
   d. valve stem and camshaft   5. ____

JOB 35-3

Checking Hydraulic-Lifter Valve-Train Clearance

Objective: To learn how to check valve-train clearance in pushrod engines using hydraulic valve lifters.

References: AM ♦35-13 to 35-16, SG Chap. 35, automotive manufacturers' service manuals.

Equipment: Pushrod engines with hydraulic valve lifters.
Tools: Leak-down tool, thickness gauges, stem-height gauge, basic hand tools.

♦ _____ ♦

SHOP FACTS

On some engines with hydraulic valve lifters, no adjustment is provided in the valve train. In normal service, no adjustment is necessary. The hydraulic valve lifter takes care of any small changes in the valve-train length. However, adjustment may be needed if valves and valve seats are ground.

Unusual and severe wear of the pushrod ends, rocker arm, or valve stem may also require adjustment. Then some correction may be required to reestablish the correct valve-train length.

SHOP SKILLS

FORD ENGINES

____ 1. On two types of rocker arms used by Ford, the clearance in the valve train is checked with the valve lifter bled down so that the valve-lifter plunger is bottomed (Fig. 35-6).

____ 2. First, the crankshaft must be turned so that the lifter is on the base circle or low part of the cam (rather than on the lobe). This is done by setting the piston in the number 1 cylinder at TDC at the end of the compression stroke.

____ 3. Then check the stem-to-rocker-arm clearance of both valves in the number 1 cylinder.

____ 4. The crankshaft can then be rotated as necessary to put other lifters on the base circles of their cams so that they can be checked.

____ 5. If the clearance is too small, install a shorter pushrod. If the clearance is excessive, install a longer pushrod. The clearance might become too small if valves and seats have been ground. The clearance might become excessive as a result of wear of the valve-train parts. This includes wear of the pushrod ends, valve stem, and rocker arm.

Fig. 35-6 Checking valve-train clearance on an engine with hydraulic valve lifters and shaft-mounted rocker arms. The hydraulic lifter is bled down from pressure applied with the special tool. **(Ford Motor Company)**

PLYMOUTH AND OLDSMOBILE ENGINES

____ 1. The procedure for setting Plymouth valves is typical of the engines manufactured by Chrysler. It is made only after the valves and valve seats have been ground. Some Oldsmobile engines also require use of a special tool to check valve-stem height after the valves and seats are ground. As with the Chrysler engines, the valve-stem tip must be ground off to reduce the height to within limits. When this happens, the increased height of the valve stem above the cylinder head should be checked (Fig. 35-7).

____ 2. With the valve seated, place the special tool over the valve stem.

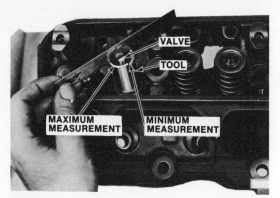

Fig. 35-7 Measuring the valve-stem length with a special tool after installing the valve in the cylinder head. (**Chrysler Corporation**)

____ 3. If the height is excessive, the end of the valve stem must be ground off to reduce the height to within limits. The hydraulic-valve-lifter plunger will then work near its center position rather than near the bottom, as it would with an excessively high valve stem.

CHEVROLET ENGINES

____ 1. The procedure for Chevrolet engines is typical of General Motors engines using the adjustable ball-pivot type of rocker arm (Fig. 35-8).

Fig. 35-8 Adjusting the valve rocker-arm-stud nut to properly position the plunger of the hydraulic valve lifter. (**Chevrolet Motor Division of General Motors Corporation**)

____ 2. With the valve lifter on the base circle of the cam, back off the adjustment nut until the pushrod is loose.

____ 3. Then slowly turn the adjustment nut down. At the same time, rotate the pushrod with your fingers until the pushrod is tight, or until you cannot easily rotate it.

____ 4. Then turn the adjustment nut down the amount specified in the service manual. This places the plunger of the valve lifter in its center position.

____ 5. Repeat this procedure for each valve lifter.

JOB 35-3   MULTIPLE-CHOICE TEST

1. On Ford engines, the clearance check is made with the lifter
   a. on the nose of the cam
   b. out of the engine
   c. plunger extended
   d. on the base circle of the cam   1. ____

2. If the clearance is too small in Ford engines,
   a. install a shorter pushrod
   b. install a new lifter
   c. grind the valves
   d. install a new plunger   2. ____

3. On Plymouth and some Oldsmobile engines, clearance is measured by checking
   a. valve seating
   b. valve-stem clearance
   c. height of stem above head
   d. valve-spring height   3. ____

4. On Plymouth engines, if the valve and seat have been ground, adjustment of clearance can be made by
   a. grinding the valve stem
   b. installing a longer pushrod
   c. installing a new plunger in the lifter
   d. installing a new valve   4. ____

5. On Chevrolet engines with the ball-pivot rocker arm, adjustment of clearance is made by
   a. installing a new pushrod
   b. turning the adjusting screw
   c. turning the adjusting nut
   d. grinding the rocker arm   5. ____

JOB 35-4
Refacing Valves

Objective: To learn how to reface valves.

References: AM ♦35-1 to 35-32, SG Chap. 35, automotive manufacturers' service manuals.

Equipment: Various valves.

Tools: Valve refacer, wire wheel or brush, runout gauge, basic hand tools.

♦ **SAFETY** ♦ *Follow the operating instructions for the valve refacer to avoid getting hurt or damaging the machine. The valve must be tightly chucked so that it does not come loose.*

SHOP FACTS

For some engines, such as the Plymouth Horizon and Dodge Omni engines, the exhaust valves should not be refaced on a machine. Instead, if the valve needs service, the seat should first be ground and then the valve lapped in by hand, using lapping compound. All trace of the lapping compound, which is a cutting abrasive, must be removed after lapping the valve.

In general, the lapping of valves in automotive engines is not recommended. The grinding process using the valve-refacing machine produces a precision finish which can be damaged by lapping.

When new valves are required, they should not be refaced. However, seating should be checked. Never reface or lap coated valves!

SHOP SKILLS

_____ 1. Clean the carbon and gum from the valves and valve stems with a wire wheel or brush and solvent. Polish valve stems, if necessary, with a fine grade of emery cloth, but do not take off more than the dirty coating on the surface. Do not take metal off the stems. Avoid scratching the valve face or valve stem with the wire brush or emery cloth.

_____ 2. If available, use a runout gauge to check the valves for eccentricity.

_____ 3. Examine valves for rough stems and cracked or burned heads. Any such defect requires valve replacement.

_____ 4. If the valves appear to be reusable, except for needing refacing, determine the valve-face angle. Then set the valve refacer to the correct angle.

On some engines, the angle of the valve face must just match the seat angle. For most engines, there should be a slight interference angle of 1 degree. Figure 35-9 shows both types of valve-face angles.

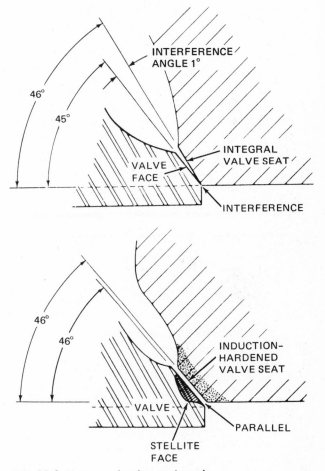

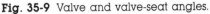

Fig. 35-9 Valve and valve-seat angles.

_____ 5. Chuck the valve in the valve refacer. Position the coolant nozzle, and turn on the motor.

_____ 6. Following the operating instructions for the machine you are using, take a light first cut from the face of the valve. Then note if the valve face has been ground evenly around the entire circumference of the valve. If the cut has removed metal from only one-third or one-half of the face, then possibly the valve is not clamped squarely in the chuck or the stem is bent. If the stem is bent, discard the valve.

Note To accurately reface valves, the grinding wheel on the valve refacer must always be clean and true. It should be trued at specified intervals with the diamond dresser.

_____ 7. Make additional cuts across the valve face as needed. Remove only enough metal to clean and true the face and to remove pits.

Minimum margin thickness is 1/32 inch [0.8 mm]. The valve head will run hotter as the margin thickness is decreased. If the valve is ground until its outer edge is sharp (Fig. 35-10), discard it. A lack of margin causes a valve to overheat and to burn or warp prematurely.

_____ 8. Reface the valve-stem tip end, if necessary. On many new valves, the tip end is slightly crowned. Some valve-refacing machines have an attachment to hold the valve at an angle while grinding the tip. This restores a slight crown to the end of the valve.

Note The ends of some valve stems are hardened and should have no more than 0.020 inch [0.5 mm] ground off. Excessive grinding will expose soft metal, so the stem end will wear and pound out rapidly in a running engine.

_____ 9. When refacing valves, avoid mixing them. Each valve should be returned to the valve guide from which it was removed.

JOB 35-4   MULTIPLE-CHOICE TEST

1. When installing a new valve, you should always
   a. reface it before installation
   b. lap it in by hand, using lapping compound
   c. check the valve seating
   d. none of the above   1. ___

2. "Use a 1 degree interference angle" means that
   a. the seat is ground to 46 degrees and the valve is ground to 45 degrees
   b. the seat is ground to 45 degrees and the valve is ground to 46 degrees
   c. the seat is ground to 1 degree and the valve is ground to 0 degrees
   d. none of the above   2. ___

3. When you are refacing the valve-stem tip end, the maximum amount that should be ground off is
   a. 1/32 inch [0.79 mm]
   b. 0.020 inch [0.5 mm]
   c. zero—no metal should ever be removed from the tip end
   d. none of the above   3. ___

4. A valve that is ground so much that it has a sharp outer edge with no margin will
   a. prevent the engine from starting
   b. allow the engine to "swallow" a valve
   c. cause the engine to overheat
   d. overheat and burn quickly   4. ___

5. An engine has coated exhaust valves. To properly service these valves, you should
   a. lap the valves
   b. reface the valves
   c. replace the valves anytime the seats are ground
   d. only clean the valves   5. ___

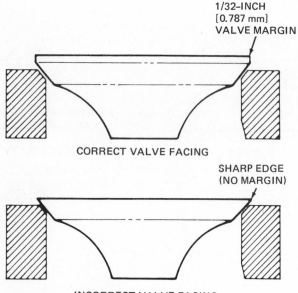

Fig. 35-10 Correct and incorrect valve-face grinding. The valve at the bottom has no margin and would soon burn. (American Motors Corporation)

JOB 35-5

Servicing Valve Seats

Objective: To learn how to service valve seats.
References: AM ♦35-28, SG Chap. 35, automotive manufacturers' service manuals.

Equipment: Cylinder heads with valves removed. Some should have valve-seat inserts.

Tools: Valve-seat grinder, seat gauge, basic hand tools.
Supplies: Prussian blue, lapping compound.

♦ _____ ♦

SHOP FACTS

A valve-seat insert may be badly worn. Or it may have been ground down on previous occasions so there is insufficient metal for another grind. In either case, it must be replaced. The old seat can be removed with a special puller. If a puller is not available, the insert is punch-marked on two opposite sides and a drill motor used to drill holes almost through the insert. Then a chisel and hammer can be used to break the insert into halves so that it can be removed.

Care must be taken that the counterbore is not damaged. If the new insert fits too loosely, the counterbore must be re-bored oversize. Then an oversize insert is installed. The new insert should be chilled in dry ice for 15 minutes to shrink it so that it can be driven into place. Then the valve seat should be ground.

After the valve seat is ground, it may be too wide. It must be narrowed by using upper and lower grinding stones to grind away the upper and lower edges of the seat. The angle and width of a typical valve seat is shown in Fig. 35-11. A steel scale can be used to measure valve-seat width.

Always follow the instructions furnished by the valve-seat-grinder manufacturer. The grinding stone must be dressed frequently with the diamond-tipped dressing tool to maintain an accurate angle.

Another method of refinishing valve seats uses specially designed hardened cutters instead of grinding stones. These seat cutters may be hand- or power-driven. The valve-seat cutter has rigidly mounted carbide steel blades which can remove metal from even the hardened seats. One advantage to the use of cutters is that they do not need frequent redressing, as do the grinding stones.

SHOP SKILLS

____ 1. Remove the valves from the cylinder head.

____ 2. Clean and inspect the valve guides. Then install a pilot in the guide of the first valve seat to be ground (Fig. 35-12).

____ 3. Select a valve-seat grinding stone of the proper grit and angle, and install it on the stone holder.

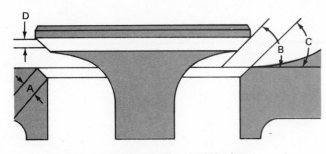

A—SEAT WIDTH (INTAKE: 1/16 TO 3/32 INCH [1.6 TO 2.4 mm] ; EXHAUST: 3/64 TO 1/16 INCH [1.2 TO 1.6 mm])

B—FACE ANGLE (INTAKE: 45°—EXHAUST: 43°)

C—SEAT ANGLE (INTAKE: 45°—EXHAUST: 45°)

D—CONTACT SURFACE

Fig. 35-11 Angles to which the valve seat and upper and lower cuts must be refinished on one engine. The dimensions and angles vary with different engines. (**Chrysler Corporation**)

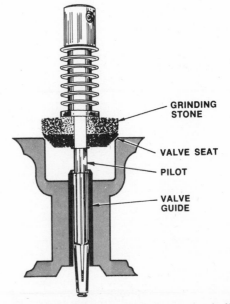

Fig. 35-12 Pilot on which the seat grinding stone rotates. The pilot keeps the stone concentric with the valve seat. (**The Black and Decker Manufacturing Company**)

GRINDING STONE

VALVE SEAT

PILOT

VALVE GUIDE

___ 4. Place a drop of light oil on top of the pilot, and then slip the stone holder over the pilot. The stone should rest on the seat, without dragging or hitting the combustion chamber. To prevent damage to the seat, the stone must be greater in diameter than the seat.

___ 5. Start the grinder, and take a quick light cut. Then inspect the seat. Many seat problems can now be seen. Continue making cuts as necessary. Operate the grinder in accordance with its operating instructions. Avoid overgrinding.

___ 6. Remove the stone holder from the pilot and check the seat width. If the seat is too wide, use upper and lower cutting stones in turn to narrow it to its proper width.

___ 7. A valve-seat gauge can be used to check the seat for concentricity. The gauge is mounted in the valve guide and rotated so that the indicating finger moves around the entire circumference of the valve seat. Movement of the indicating needle on the dial face indicates eccentricity.

Note Excessive eccentricity means the valve seat is out of round or offset and must be reground. In such cases, check the valve guide also.

___ 8. Fit of the valve and the seat may be tested by lightly coating the valve face with Prussian blue, putting the valve in the seat, and turning the valve against the seat about one-quarter revolution. If the Prussian blue transfers evenly to the seat, the seat is concentric with the valve guide.

___ 9. Next, wipe all Prussian blue away, and coat the valve seat with blue. Put the valve in place, and turn it in the seat. If blue is transferred to the valve face all the way round, then the valve is seating properly.

___ 10. The tests may also be made with a soft pencil by marking lines on the valve face or seat about ¼ inch [16 mm] apart and then turning the valve against the seat. If the lines are removed, the seating is good.

JOB 35-5 MULTIPLE-CHOICE TEST

1. A cracked valve seat may be repaired by
   a. grinding the seat
   b. using cutters instead of a grinding stone
   c. installing a valve-seat insert
   d. cold-welding the crack   1. ___

2. After the valve seat has been ground, the seat is often
   a. too narrow
   b. too wide
   c. making contact too far in on the valve face
   d. none of the above   2. ___

3. Before grinding the valve seats, you must first
   a. check the head for warping
   b. reface the valves
   c. clean the valve guides
   d. none of the above   3. ___

4. After you have finished grinding the valve seats and refacing the valves, check for proper seating by using
   a. lapping compound
   b. Magna-Flux
   c. a dial indicator
   d. Prussian blue   4. ___

5. To move the contact pattern in, away from the edge of the valve face, grind the top of a 30 degree seat with
   a. a 15 degree stone
   b. a 30 degree stone
   c. a 45 degree stone
   d. a 60 degree stone   5. ___

JOB 36-1
Removing Piston-Ring Ridge

Objective: To learn how to remove the piston-ring ridge from the top of the cylinder.

References: AM ◆36-1 and 36-2, SG Chap. 36, automotive manufacturers' service manuals.

Equipment: Engines or cylinder blocks with cylinder heads removed.
Tools: Ring-ridge remover, basic hand tools.

SHOP FACTS

Connecting rods and pistons are removed from the engine as assemblies. On most engines, the piston-and-rod assemblies are removed from the top of the engine. Therefore, the first step is to remove the cylinder head; then the cylinders should be examined for wear.

If wear has taken place, there will be a ridge at the top of the cylinder. This ridge, called the *ring ridge*, marks the upper limit of piston-ring travel. If the ring ridge is not removed, the top ring could jam under it as the piston is moved upward. This could break the rings or the piston-ring-groove lands (Fig. 36-1). Any ring ridge, if present, must be removed.

A quick way to check for a ring ridge is to see whether your fingernail catches under it. If your fingernail catches on the ring ridge, so will the piston rings. A more accurate check is to use an inside micrometer. Measure the diameter on the ring ridge and then immediately below it. If the difference is more than 0.004 inch [0.102 mm], remove the ring ridge.

To remove the ring ridge that forms at the top of the cylinder, a ring-ridge remover is used (Fig. 36-2). There are several types of ring-ridge removers. Read and follow the instructions for the remover that you are to use.

SHOP SKILLS

____ 1. With a clean shop towel, wipe any excess oil and loose carbon from the cylinder walls. Turn the crankshaft until the piston in number 1 cylinder is near BDC.

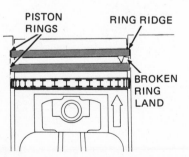

Fig. 36-1 When the ring ridge is not removed, forcing the piston out of the cylinder will often break the piston-ring lands. **(ATW)**

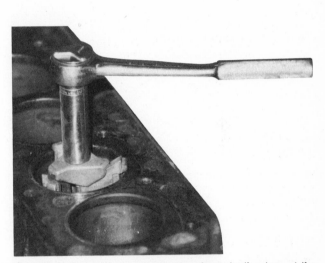

Fig. 36-2 Ring-ridge remover in place in the top of the cylinder. As the tool is turned, cutting blades remove the ring ridge. **(ATW)**

____ 2. Stuff cloths into the cylinder to protect the pistons and rings from metal cuttings. Then cover the other cylinders and openings in the cylinder blocks with cloths.

____ 3. Place the ring-ridge remover in the cylinder (Fig. 36-2). Adjust the cutting blades until they are just under the ring ridge and expanded to press lightly against the cylinder walls.

On the other types of ring-ridge removers, the only adjustment is to set the cutting blades to take the correct depth of cut. Do not oil the ring-ridge remover.

____ 4. Rotate the ring-ridge remover until the ridge has been removed. Some ring-ridge removers must not be turned backwards. With all types of ring-ridge removers, be careful not to undercut the ring ridge or cut deeper into the cylinder wall.

Note Turn the ring-ridge remover by hand, not with an impact wrench! Do not remove too much metal. Never undercut the top of the cylinder deeper than the metal next to the ring ridge. Do not turn the cutting blades out of the top of the cylinder; this would taper the upper edge of the cylinder and might cause compression leakage.

_____ 5. Take the ring-ridge remover out of the cylinder. Then take out the cloths from the cylinders. Try to avoid allowing the metal cuttings to drop down the cylinder.

_____ 6. Wipe the cylinder clean.

_____ 7. Repeat the operation for the other cylinders.

JOB 36-1   MULTIPLE-CHOICE TEST

1. The ridges that must be removed are at the
   a. bottom of cylinders
   b. lower limit of ring travel
   c. top of cylinders
   d. ends of rods   1. _____

2. The ridges mark the
   a. upper limit of ring travel
   b. lower limit of ring travel
   c. limit of piston travel
   d. limit of piston eccentricity   2. _____

3. The ridges are removed with
   a. a grinding tool
   b. a chisel
   c. a cutting tool
   d. emery cloth   3. _____

4. If the ridges were not removed, during engine disassembly they could cause
   a. cylinder breakage
   c. rod damage
   c. piston and ring breakage
   d. bearing breakage   4. _____

5. Before beginning to remove the ring ridge, position the piston at
   a. TDC
   b. BDC
   c. the midpoint of its travel
   d. 1 inch [25.4 mm] below TDC   5. _____

JOB 36-2
Replacing Connecting-Rod Bearings

Objective: To learn how to replace connecting-rod bearings.
References: AM ♦36-14, SG Chap. 36, automotive manufacturers' service manuals.

Equipment: Engine partly disassembled so that the connecting-rod bearings can be replaced.

Tools: Torque wrench, shim stock, Plastigage, inside and outside micrometers, or telescope gauge and outside micrometer, basic hand tools.

SHOP SKILLS

____ 1. With the oil pan drained and removed, remove the bearing cap.

____ 2. Examine the bearings for the causes of wear or failure. Various types of engine bearing failure are shown in Fig. 36-3. Make corrections as necessary to eliminate cause of bearing failure and to avoid future failures from the same cause. Examine the crankpin for roughness. Use a micrometer to check it for taper or out-of-roundness. Service the crankpin by grinding, if necessary (Job 37-2).

____ 3. Bearing clearance can be measured before the old bearings are removed or after new bearings are installed. However, bearing clearance must be checked every time new bearing halves are installed.

____ 4. To check bearing clearance, either Plastigage or shim stock can be used. When shim stock is used, take off the cap, and place a ½-inch-wide [12.7-mm-wide] strip of 0.001-inch-thick [0.025-mm-thick] shim stock in the cap. Lubricate the shim stock with engine oil, and install the cap.

____ 5. Tighten the cap nuts lightly. Feel the ease with which the rod may be moved endwise on the crankshaft. Tighten nuts equally and a slight additional amount. Then recheck endwise movement. Continue to tighten nuts, and recheck endwise movement until nuts have been tightened to specified torque. Then turn the crankshaft one-quarter turn in each direction. A slight drag should be felt, which indicates that the clearance is satisfactory. If it is, remove the cap, take out the shim, and retorque the nuts on the cap.

Note If the rod does not tighten up on the crankshaft, the clearance is greater than the thickness of the shim stock. Clearance may be determined by installing additional thicknesses of shim stock and tightening the rod-cap nuts, as explained above, until the rod does tighten on shaft.

____ 6. Bearing clearance may also be checked by using Plastigage. Place a strip of Plastigage lengthwise in the center

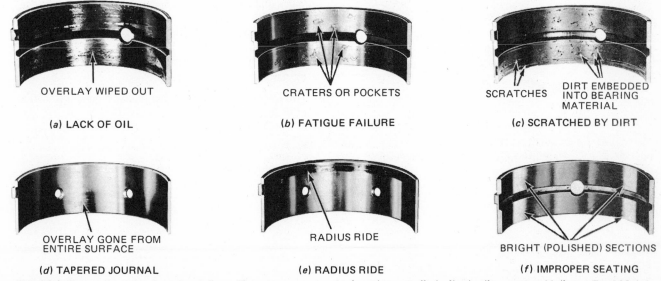

(a) LACK OF OIL — OVERLAY WIPED OUT

(b) FATIGUE FAILURE — CRATERS OR POCKETS

(c) SCRATCHED BY DIRT — SCRATCHES, DIRT EMBEDDED INTO BEARING MATERIAL

(d) TAPERED JOURNAL — OVERLAY GONE FROM ENTIRE SURFACE

(e) RADIUS RIDE — RADIUS RIDE

(f) IMPROPER SEATING — BRIGHT (POLISHED) SECTIONS

Fig. 36-3 Types of engine bearing failure. The appearance of a bearing usually indicates the cause of failure. (**Ford Motor Company**)

of the bearing cap. Install the cap, and tighten nuts to specified torque.

____ 7. Remove the cap. Note amount of flattening of Plastigage by comparing the width to the scale printed on the Plastigage package, as shown in Fig. 36-4. The amount of flattening indicates the amount of clearance. Uneven flattening indicates a tapered or worn crankpin or bearing.

Note When using Plastigage, be sure all oil is removed from the crankpin and bearing. Best position of crankshaft is with the crankpin about 30 degrees before BDC. This measures the point of greatest wear and also keeps Plastigage away from the oilhole in the crankshaft. Do not turn the crankshaft with Plastigage in place.

____ 8. If new bearings are required, select the proper size of bearings that will give the specified clearance. Remove the old bearings. Wipe the cap and rod-bearing seats to make sure they are clean. Then put the new bearings in place. Install the bearings so that the locking tangs fit into the undercuts in the rod and cap.

Note Some bearings are designed to float between the rod, the rod cap, and the crankpin. On these, there is no tang on

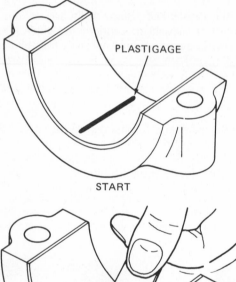

PLASTIGAGE

START

SCALE

FLATTENED

Fig. 36-4 Checking bearing clearance with Plastigage. (Chrysler Corporation)

the shell. When installing new bearings, make sure everything is clean. This includes your hands, the workbench, your tools, and all engine parts.

____ 9. Do not file the edges of the bearings. They will project slightly above the rod and cap surfaces but will crush down to provide a proper fit when the cap nuts are tightened.

____ 10. Complete the installation by lubricating the bearing crankpin surfaces with engine oil. Install the rod cap and tighten cap nuts to the specified torque. With new bearings, check the clearance with shim stock or Plastigage as above (steps 4–8).

____ 11. Another way to check bearing clearance is with inside and outside micrometers. First install the bearings and tighten the cap. Then check the bearing diameter with an inside micrometer or an outside micrometer and telescope gauge. Compare this measurement with the crankpin diameter as measured with an outside micrometer.

JOB 36-2 MULTIPLE-CHOICE TEST

1. To check the clearance of connecting-rod bearings, use Plastigage or
   a. a micrometer
   b. a spring scale
   c. shim stock
   d. a rod gauge   1. ____

2. The more the Plastigage is flattened, the
   a. more the crankpin is worn
   b. less the bearing clearance
   c. thinner the bearing shell
   d. greater the bearing clearance   2. ____

3. If the connecting rod cannot be moved after a piece of shim stock has been placed in the bearing cap and the cap tightened, then the bearing clearance is
   a. just right
   b. excessive
   c. more than the thickness of shim stock
   d. less than the thickness of shim stock   3. ____

4. When Plastigage is used to measure bearing clearance, note
   a. the color of the Plastigage
   b. drag on rod
   c. lengthening of Plastigage
   d. flattening of Plastigage   4. ____

5. Two important factors that help make a good installation of bearing shells are bearing
   a. spread and thickness
   b. width and crush
   c. spread and crush
   d. width and thickness   5. ____

JOB 36-3
Selecting and Installing Piston Rings

Objective: To learn how to select and install piston rings on the pistons.
References: AM ♦36-23 to 36-25, SG Chap. 36, automotive manufacturers'

service manuals.
Equipment: Engines partly disassembled with pistons ready to have new rings installed.

Tools: Thickness gauges, ring-groove cleaning tools, fine-cut file, ring expander, basic hand tools.
Supplies: Piston rings.

SHOP SKILLS

_____ 1. Pistons and connecting-rod assemblies must be removed from engine and pistons cleaned and checked for fit, as detailed in the manufacturer's service manual. Remove the ring ridge from top of the cylinder before removing pistons to avoid damaging the rings and pistons (Job 36-1).

_____ 2. Select the proper-size piston rings to fit the cylinders and pistons. If the cylinder has been rebored or honed oversize so that oversize pistons are to be installed, then you must install comparable oversize rings.

_____ 3. Compress the ring, and slip it squarely into the cylinder. With inverted piston, press the ring down to the bottom of the ring travel in the cylinder. Use a thickness gauge to check the gap between the ends of the ring, as shown in Fig. 36-5. Typical piston-ring end gap is between 0.010 and 0.020 inch [0.25 and 0.51 mm).

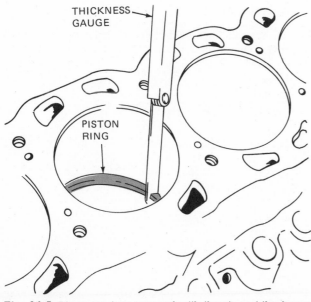

THICKNESS GAUGE

PISTON RING

Fig. 36-5 Ring gap is measured with the ring at the lower limit of its travel in the cylinder. **(Oldsmobile Division of General Motors Corporation)**

_____ 4. If the gap is too small, check that you have received the correct-size ring set for the engine.

_____ 5. On older engines, the recommendation is to file the ends of the ring. Put a fine-cut file in a vise. Hold the ring between thumbs and fingers of both hands. File ends of the ring by moving the ring back and forth on the file. Be careful to avoid bending or breaking the ring. If a ring is bent, it will not function properly and will have to be discarded.
Continue to file and test the ring until the gap is correct.

Note Many manufacturers no longer recommend filing the ring ends. Instead, they recommend the selection of a slightly smaller ring, which will have the larger gap when installed. Filing the ring ends will chip the surface coating of some rings.

_____ 6. Fit each ring separately in the cylinder in which it is to be used.
If the cylinder is worn tapered, the diameter at the lower limit of ring travel will be smaller than at the top. The ring must be fitted to the smaller diameter at the bottom of ring travel.

_____ 7. After all rings have been fitted to a cylinder, take the piston that goes in that cylinder, and check ring fit on the piston.

_____ 8. First, make sure that piston-ring grooves are clean and smooth. Then, slip the outer surface of the ring into the groove, and roll the ring entirely around the groove to make sure that the ring can fit all round in the groove (Fig. 36-6).

Note If binding occurs, a trace of carbon or a burr is probably in the ring groove. This can be dressed off with a fine-cut file. However, if the binding is due to a bent ring, discard the ring.
If the ring groove is worn "bell-mouthed" (wider at surface of piston than at the bottom of the groove), the groove must be squared with a regroover if the piston is to be reused. When the groove is squared with a regrooving tool, a wider ring or a spacer must be used. If so much metal must be removed in squaring the groove that the ring lands are excessively narrowed, discard the piston.

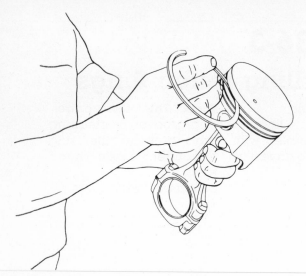

Fig. 36-6 Checking the fit of the piston ring in the ring groove. (Chevrolet Motor Division of General Motors Corporation)

_____ 9. The final step in fitting rings is to check side clearance. Put the rings on the piston. Use a ring-installing tool to expand the rings so that they slip over the piston and into the grooves. Be sure the side of the ring marked TOP is up (on rings so marked). On rings not marked, follow the ring manufacturer's instructions to install rings right side up. Position ring gaps in accordance with engine manufacturer's specifications.

_____ 10. Check the clearance between the sides of the rings and the sides of the ring grooves, as shown in Fig. 36-7.

_____ 11. If the side clearance is excessive, it indicates excessive wear of the piston-ring groove. In such a case, the recommendation of the engine manufacturer often calls for replacement of the piston. However, there are special tools for reconditioning ring grooves. See the Note for step 8.

_____ 12. Make sure that the piston and the rings fitted for a certain cylinder are installed in that particular cylinder.

_____ 13. Repeat the above procedure for all cylinders.

_____ 14. Use the ring expander to install the rings in the proper ring grooves of each piston. Follow the sequence and procedure listed in the instructions that came with the ring set.

_____ 15. After each ring is installed, make a quick check of its fit by sliding the ring around in its ring groove. The ring should slide freely. If it does not, remove the ring and repeat the steps listed above.

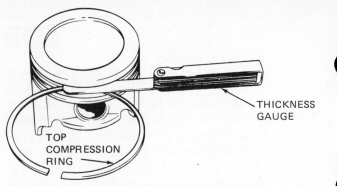

Fig. 36-7 Checking the piston-ring side clearance. (Oldsmobile Division of General Motors Corporation)

JOB 36-3 MULTIPLE-CHOICE TEST

1. If the compression-ring end gap is too large for the cylinder,
   a. use another ring
   b. file the ends of ring
   c. use a ring expander
   d. replace side rails   1. ____

2. To check ring gap,
   a. put ring on piston
   b. put ring in vise
   c. put ring in cylinder
   d. use a micrometer   2. ____

3. To install rings on piston, use
   a. a ring compressor
   b. a ring gapper
   c. a ring expander
   d. two screwdrivers   3. ____

4. The final step in checking ring fit is to measure ring
   a. gap
   b. side clearance
   c. top clearance
   d. base clearance   4. ____

5. Before installing the piston assembly, dip the piston, rings, and pin in
   a. water
   b. gasoline
   c. metallic paint
   d. engine oil   5. ____

JOB 37-1
Checking Main-Bearing Clearances

Objective: To learn how to check main-bearing clearances.

References: AM ♦37-8, SG Chap. 37, automotive manufacturers' service manuals.
Equipment: Various engines.

Tools: Torque wrench, Plastigage, basic hand tools.

SHOP SKILLS

____ 1. Remove the oil pan and the oil pump, if necessary. To check the main-bearing clearances, begin by removing the rear-main-bearing cap (Job 37-3). Wipe the oil from the journal and the bearing half in the cap.

____ 2. Place a strip of Plastigage the full width of the bearing on the journal parallel to the crankshaft, as shown in Fig. 37-1.

Note If the engine is in the vehicle, place the Plastigage in the center of the bearing cap. Also, support the vibration damper and the flywheel to remove any clearance between the crankshaft journal and the upper bearing.

____ 3. Install the bearing cap. Torque the cap bolts to specifications. Do not rotate the crankshaft while the Plastigage is in place.

____ 4. Remove the bearing cap. The flattened Plastigage will stick to either the bearing shell or the crankshaft journal. Do not touch or try to remove the flattened Plastigage until after measuring is completed.

____ 5. Without removing the Plastigage, measure its compressed width at the widest point. Figure 37-2 shows this measurement being made by comparing the width of the flattened Plastigage to the scale printed on the Plastigage envelope.

Note The scale on the Plastigage envelope is printed in thousandths of an inch and in millimeters. The wider the Plastigage, the less the bearing clearance.

Not only does the amount of flattening indicate the clearance, but uneven flattening indicates a tapered or worn crankshaft journal or bearing. An excessively worn or tapered crankshaft journal requires removal of the crankshaft for service, as explained in Job 37-2.

____ 6. Make a thorough visual inspection of the condition of the bearing and its crankshaft journal.

Fig. 37-1 Measuring main-bearing clearance with Plastigage. **(Chevrolet Motor Division of General Motors Corporation)**

Fig. 37-2 Checking flattening of Plastigage to determine main-bearing clearance. **(Chevrolet Motor Division of General Motors Corporation)**

Usually, the lower bearing half (except for number 1 bearing) shows more wear and fatigue than the top half. If the lower half is suitable for reuse, the upper half is probably in good condition. But if the lower half is worn, discolored, or damaged, replace both halves.

Never replace one bearing half without replacing the other half of the same bearing. Always replace all main bearings in a worn engine if one main bearing requires replacement.

_____ 7. Write the number of each main bearing and its clearance on a sheet of paper. Also write down the taper, condition, and discoloration—if any—for each bearing. Then check the manufacturer's specifications for the engine you are servicing.

If the bearing clearance is out of specifications, install the next closest size of undersize bearings. Then recheck the clearance. If the clearance is still out of specifications, the crankshaft must be removed and reground or replaced.

_____ 8. With clean engine oil, coat the journal and bearing. Then install the cap. Torque the cap bolts to specifications.

_____ 9. Repeat the above procedure for each main bearing. After all bearings have been checked, rotate the crankshaft to be sure there is no excessive drag on the crankshaft.

_____ 10. Measure the crankshaft end play by forcing the crankshaft to the extreme front position with a pry bar. Measure the crankshaft end play at the front end of the crankshaft thrust bearing with a thickness gauge. Check the clearance recommended by the engine manufacturer in the service manual.

If the clearance exceeds the specifications, replace the thrust bearing. Then recheck the end play. If the end play is less than the minimum specification, inspect the thrust-bearing faces for scratches, burrs, nicks, or dirt. If none of these problems are found and the thrust-bearing faces are not damaged or dirty, they probably were not aligned properly during installation. To correct the problem, install the thrust bearing and align the faces following the procedure recommended

in the engine manufacturer's service manual. Then recheck the crankshaft end play.

_____ 11. Install a new rear-main-bearing oil seal in the cylinder block and in the rear-main-bearing cap (Job 37-3). Then install the oil pump and oil pan.

JOB 37-1 MULTIPLE-CHOICE TEST

1. To check main-bearing clearance, use Plastigage or
   a. a micrometer
   b. a crankshaft template
   c. shim stock
   d. a spring scale   1. _____

2. The more the Plastigage is flattened, the
   a. more the bearing clearance
   b. thicker the bearing shell
   c. less the bearing clearance
   d. thinner the bearing shell   2. _____

3. When Plastigage is used to measure bearing clearance, note
   a. drag on crankshaft
   b. thinness of Plastigage
   c. lengthening of Plastigage
   d. flattening of Plastigage   3. _____

4. When you are checking main-bearing clearance, the crankshaft must be supported if
   a. the engine is in the vehicle
   b. you are working on a V-type engine
   c. you are working on an in-line engine
   d. the engine is out of the vehicle   4. _____

5. If only one bearing half in an engine is damaged, you should
   a. replace both halves of the damaged bearing
   b. replace all main bearings in the engine
   c. replace only the damaged bearing half
   d. none of the above   5. _____

JOB 37-2
Servicing and Installing a Crankshaft

Objective: To learn how to service and install a crankshaft.
References: AM ♦37-12 and 37-13, SG Chap. 37, automotive manufacturers' service manuals.

Equipment: Engine on stand with cylinder head, oil pan, connecting-rod-and-piston assemblies.

Tools: Torque wrench, pry bar, plastic hammer, V blocks, dial indicator, micrometer, valve-guide brush, basic hand tools.

♦ _____ ♦

SHOP SKILLS

REMOVING THE CRANKSHAFT

_____ 1. Cylinder head, oil pan, and connecting-rod-and-piston assemblies should be removed from the cylinder block. With the engine in a stand, turned so that the crankshaft is at the top, note the locations of the main bearings. Make sure the bearing caps are marked so that they can be restored to their proper positions on reassembly.

_____ 2. Remove the timing gear or sprocket from the crankshaft.

_____ 3. Remove the flywheel and the engine rear cover plate, if used.

_____ 4. Remove the oil pump and any interfering oil lines so that the crankshaft can be taken out. Oil lines may be attached with a coupling nut. Use two wrenches for loosening the nut to avoid damaging the tube.

_____ 5. After all parts that might interfere with crankshaft removal are off the engine, loosen the main-bearing-cap bolts.

Note On some engines, the bolts are sometimes locked in place by lock wires, which must be cut, or by lock-washer tangs, which must be bent out of the way before the bolts can be loosened.

_____ 6. Remove the main-bearing caps. Usually, the bearing caps can then be lifted off easily. However, some caps are set into recesses or on dowels and are stuck tightly in place. A screwdriver or a pry bar can be used to pry the bearing cap loose. In addition, a plastic hammer can be used for lightly tapping the cap, first on one side and then on the other, so that it can be worked off.

_____ 7. Remove the bearing caps. Heavy prying or hammering may bend or break the cap, bend the dowels, or damage the dowel holes. If this happens, the bearing will not fit properly on reassembly, and it may burn out during subsequent operation.

_____ 8. Lift the crankshaft from the cylinder block. Use care in removing the crankshaft. It is heavy, oily, and awkward to handle.

Note Handle the crankshaft with care to avoid bending, breaking, or cracking it and to prevent damage to the bearing surfaces.

SERVICING THE CRANKSHAFT

_____ 1. Use a micrometer to measure the main-bearing and connecting-rod-bearing journals. Take the measurements on each journal in at least four places to find the maximum and minimum measurements.

_____ 2. Write the measurements of the main journals in the spaces of Fig. 37-3. Write the measurements of the connect-

	1	2	3	4	5	6	7
Maximum diameter							
Minimum diameter							
Taper							
Out-of-round							

Fig. 37-3 Measuring crankshaft main-bearing journals.

	1	2	3	4	5	6	7	8
Maximum diameter	____	____	____	____	____	____	____	____
Minimum diameter	____	____	____	____	____	____	____	____
Taper	____	____	____	____	____	____	____	____
Out-of-round	____	____	____	____	____	____	____	____

Fig. 37-4 Measuring connecting-rod journals.

ing-rod journals in Fig. 37-4. Measure and fill in the out-of-roundness and taper for each journal.

____ 3. Set the crankshaft in V blocks. With a dial indicator check the main journals for runout or lack of alignment. Compare all readings with the manufacturer's specifications.

____ 4. If the crankshaft-journal measurements are not within specifications, get a new or reground crankshaft, or have the crankshaft journals reground on a crankshaft grinder. Then undersize bearings may be used in the engine.

____ 5. Clean all oil passages with a valve-guide cleaning brush. Wash the crankshaft with solvent. Then blow out all oil passages with compressed air.

____ 6. Inspect all crankshaft journals for cracks, scratches, and grooves. Check the crankshaft oil-seal surface for nicks, sharp edges, or burrs. Any of these conditions might damage the oil seal during installation or cause premature seal wear shortly after installation.

____ 7. On engines used with a manual transmission, check the fit of the clutch-pilot bushing in the bore of the crankshaft. The clutch-pilot bushing is pressed into the crankshaft and must not be loose.

____ 8. Inspect the inner surface of the pilot bushing for wear or a bell-mouthed condition. Check the inside diameter of the bushing. Replace the bushing if it is worn or damaged or if the internal diameter is not within specifications.

INSTALLING THE CRANKSHAFT

____ 1. To install the crankshaft, first lift it into place. Then put the bearing caps back into place. The rear-main-bearing cap usually has an oil seal to prevent oil leakage into the clutch housing. Make sure the oil seal is new and properly installed before proceeding (Job 37-3).

____ 2. Install the main-bearing-cap bolts. Install and tighten the bolts evenly to specifications with a torque wrench.

Note If tang lock washers are used on the main-bearing caps, install new washers. Be sure the main-bearing-cap bolts are secured by the tangs. If lock wires are used, install new lock wires.

____ 3. Check the main-bearing clearances as outlined in Job 37-1. If necessary, replace the main bearings to adjust the clearance.

JOB 37-2 MULTIPLE-CHOICE TEST

1. Check crankshaft main and connecting-rod journals for diameter, out-of-roundness, and
   a. temperature
   b. taper
   c. sag
   d. oilholes   1. ____

2. To check crankshaft journals, use
   a. a micrometer
   b. calipers
   c. a rule
   d. a thickness gauge   2. ____

3. One way to remove a sticking bearing cap is to use
   a. a sledgehammer
   b. penetrating oil
   c. a rod-bolt puller
   d. a plastic hammer   3. ____

4. If crankshaft main journals require regrinding, then the engine will also require
   a. undersized main bearings
   b. new rod bearings
   c. oversized main bearings
   d. new rod caps   4. ____

5. When reinstalling rod caps, tighten cap bolts with a
   a. hand wrench
   b. short wrench
   c. torque wrench
   d. long wrench   5. ____

JOB 37-3

Replacing Rear-Main-Bearing Oil Seal

Objective: To learn to replace a crankshaft rear-main-bearing oil seal.

References: AM ♦37-11, SG Chap. 37, automotive manufacturers' service manuals.
Equipment: Engine with oil pan and oil pump removed, if required.

Tools: Torque wrench, basic hand tools.
Supplies: Rear-main-bearing oil seal, liquid sealer.

◆ _____ ◆

SHOP SKILLS

REMOVING THE SEAL

_____ 1. With the oil pan and oil pump removed, remove the rear-main-bearing cap, as shown in Fig. 37-5.

_____ 2. Remove the oil seal from the bearing cap (Fig. 37-6). To remove the seal from the cap, use a small screwdriver to pry under the bottom of the seal.

_____ 3. Remove the upper half of the seal. Some split lip-type seals can be removed by tapping one end of the seal with a brass pin punch. When the seal sticks out far enough, remove the seal with pliers. Other lip-type seals and rope seals are removed by using a seal-removal tool or by screwing a small metal screw into one end of the seal. Then pliers are used to pull on the screw to remove the seal. On some engines, the seal comes out more easily if the crankshaft is rotated while pulling.

Note Some manufacturers recommend loosening all main-bearing-cap bolts when replacing the rear-main-bearing oil

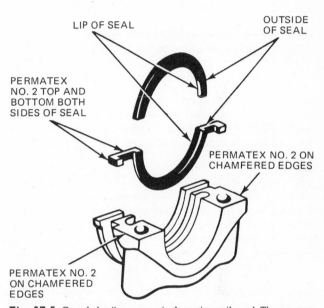

Fig. 37-5 Crankshaft rear-main-bearing oil seal. The upper part fits in a groove in the block. (**American Motors Corporation**)

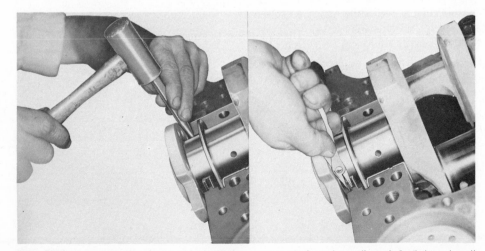

Fig. 37-6 Removing the upper half of the rear-main-bearing oil seal. Left, tapping it partly out with a punch and hammer. Right, pulling it out with pliers. (**Chevrolet Motor Division of General Motors Corporation**)

seal. This procedure lowers the crankshaft slightly, allowing easier removal of the top half of the seal from the cylinder block. Be very careful during removal of the seal to prevent scratching or damaging the crankshaft seal surfaces with any tools you are using.

INSTALLING THE SEAL

____ 1. Clean all sealer and foreign material from the bearing cap and its mating surfaces on the cylinder block. Clean the seal grooves in the cap and cylinder block. Clean any dirt from the crankshaft journal and the bearing surface.

____ 2. Inspect the cylinder block and the bearing-cap mating surfaces for nicks, scratches, burrs, and machining defects. Inspect the crankshaft seal surfaces for damage.

____ 3. To install a split lip-type seal, coat the seal lip and bead with light engine oil. Do not oil the mating ends of the seal.

Note Always replace the upper and lower half of the seal as a unit. Also, one-half of a lip-type seal cannot be combined with one-half of a rope-type seal. Be sure the lip-type seal is installed with the lip facing the front of the engine.

____ 4. An installation tool that works like a shoehorn can be used with the lip-type seal to protect the seal bead when positioning the seal. If the tool is used, put the tip of the tool between the crankshaft and the seat in the cylinder block.

____ 5. Place the lip-type seal between the crankshaft and the tip of the installation tool so that the seal bead contacts the tip of the tool. Roll the seal around the crankshaft using the installation tool like a shoehorn. This will protect the seal bead from being shaved off by the sharp corner of the block. On some engines the seal may be installed more easily by rotating the crankshaft while sliding the seal into the groove in the cylinder block.

Note Some engine manufacturers recommend installing the seal so that approximately ⅜ inch [10 mm] sticks out from one side of the cylinder block and from the opposite side of the bearing cap.

____ 6. When the seal is properly positioned, remove the installation tool. Be careful not to pull out the seal while removing the tool. If all the main-bearing-cap bolts were loosened, tighten the bolts, and torque to specifications.

____ 7. Install the lower seal half in the bearing cap. Use the installation tool as a shoehorn, and feed the seal into the cap using light thumb force.

____ 8. Apply sealer to the cap at the rear of the top mating surfaces.

Be careful to keep the sealer off the seal ends and the seal lip. Also, do not apply sealer to the area forward of the side seal groove, if used.

____ 9. Oil the crankshaft journal and the bearing in the cap. Install the rear-main-bearing cap and bolts. Torque the bolts to specifications.

Note After installing the new rear-main-bearing oil seal, oil pump, and oil pan, start the engine. After the engine runs briefly at idle, check for oil leaks.

____ 10. If side seals are used, coat the seals with diesel fuel, mineral spirits (paint thinner), or engine oil, according to the manufacturer's instructions. Immediately install the side seals in their grooves in the seal retainer. Then install the seal retainer, and tighten the retainer screws to specifications.

Install the side seals as rapidly as possible after oiling. They are made from a material that expands quickly when oiled. Failure to preoil the seals will result in an oil leak.

JOB 37-3 MULTIPLE-CHOICE TEST

1. Two types of rear-main-bearing oils seals are
   a. wire and rope
   b. neoprene and rubber
   c. rope and neoprene
   d. rubber and plastic   1. ____

2. Failure to coat the side seals with oil will result in
   a. a faster job
   b. a slower job
   c. a transmission oil leak
   d. an engine oil leak   2. ____

3. Some manufacturers suggest loosening all main-bearing-cap bolts to
   a. remove the top half of the seal
   b. install the bottom half of the seal
   c. remove the bottom half of the seal
   d. none of the above   3. ____

4. To install a lip-type seal, coat the seal lips with
   a. engine oil
   b. sealer
   c. water
   d. solvent   4. ____

5. The easiest way to remove the upper half of a rope seal is with a
   a. knife
   b. brass pin punch
   c. small metal screw
   d. seal-removal tool   5. ____

JOB 38
Diesel-Engine Service

Objective: To learn about servicing an automotive diesel engine.

References: AM ♦38-1 to 38-17, SG Chap. 38, automotive manufacturers' service manuals.

Equipment: Various automotive diesel engines.
Tools: Basic hand tools.

♦ _____ ♦

SHOP FACTS

The information listed below refers to the servicing of the General Motors V-8 automotive diesel engines. For servicing other automotive diesel engines, follow procedures contained in the manufacturers' service manuals.

Automotive diesel-engine service procedures are similar to those required by the automotive gasoline engine. Because the diesel engine does not have an electric ignition system, no ignition timing adjustment is needed. Also, the diesel engine does not have a carburetor. Therefore, carburetor adjustments are not necessary.

Regular service requires periodic change of the lubricating oil and oil filter, fuel filter, and the air filter. Also, the crankcase ventilation system must be serviced. This includes replacing the breather-cap-and-valve-assembly and the PCV valve every 30,000 miles [48,000 km].

The oil and oil filter on diesel engines must be changed every 3000 miles [4800 km]. This 3000-mile [4800-km] recommendation by General Motors is much shorter than the 7500 miles [12,000 km] or more recommended for spark-ignition engines.

Because of high cylinder-compression pressures and the importance of reducing engine wear, the frequent oil and oil-filter changes are essential. The engine must have clean oil and a working filter to remove the diesel-fuel soot and other contaminants which enter the crankcase and contaminate the engine oil.

Oil change intervals longer than 3000 miles [4800 km] can result in increased engine-wear rates and decreased engine life. Failure to change the oil and oil filter as recommended by the manufacturer may affect the manufacturer's warranty on the new engine. Sometimes the oil and oil-filter change interval should be even shorter than the normal recommendation. For example, after a car is driven in a dust storm, the oil and oil filter should be changed as soon as possible.

Use only the oil recommended by the engine manufacturer. Most automotive diesel engines require oil that is marked with both SF and CD on the can. Other engines require oil that is designated as both SF and CC.

SHOP SKILLS

TIMING THE INJECTION PUMP

____ 1. The marks on the top of the injection-pump adapter and the flange of the injection pump must align (Fig. 38-1). This corrects the timing of the fuel delivery to the nozzles.

____ 2. The adjustment is made with the engine not running. To make the adjustment, loosen the three pump retaining nuts and align the marks.

____ 3. Torque the nuts to specifications. Use a ¾-inch end wrench on the boss at the front of the pump to help when you rotate the pump into alignment.

CHECKING INJECTION-PUMP-HOUSING FUEL PRESSURE

____ 1. Remove the air cleaner and crossover. Cover the manifold openings with screened covers.

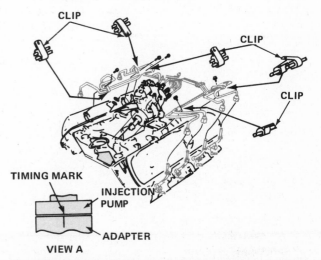

Fig. 38-1 Timing marks and injection-pump lines. (Oldsmobile Division of General Motors Corporation)

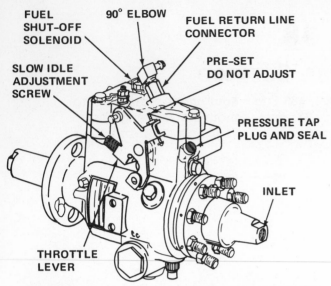

FUEL SHUT-OFF SOLENOID
90° ELBOW
FUEL RETURN LINE CONNECTOR
SLOW IDLE ADJUSTMENT SCREW
PRE-SET DO NOT ADJUST
PRESSURE TAP PLUG AND SEAL
INLET
THROTTLE LEVER

Fig. 38-2 Injection pump, showing locations of the slow-idle adjustment screw and the pressure tap plug. **(Oldsmobile Division of General Motors Corporation)**

_____ 2. From the pump (Fig. 38-2), remove the pressure tap plug. Attach a low-pressure gauge by screwing the adapter into the tap-plug hole.

_____ 3. Install the magnetic-pickup tachometer. Check pressure at 1000 rpm (transmission in PARK). It should be 8 to 12 psi [55 to 83 kPa] with not more than 2 psi [14 kPa] fluctuation. If incorrect, remove the pump for repair.

_____ 4. Reinstall air crossover after removing the screened covers. Install the air cleaner.

SERVICING INJECTION-PUMP FUEL LINES

_____ 1. When fuel lines (Fig. 38-1) are removed, the lines, nozzles, and pump fittings must be capped to keep dirt out. To remove the lines, remove air cleaner, filter and pipes from valve covers, and the air crossover.

_____ 2. Take off the line clamps and disconnect the fuel lines, capping open lines, nozzles, and pipe fittings.

_____ 3. On reassembly, do not bend or twist the lines. Torque the ends to specifications.

JOB 38   MULTIPLE-CHOICE TEST

1. A service not required by an automotive diesel engine is
   a. ignition timing
   b. injection-pump timing
   c. valve timing
   d. camshaft timing   1. _____

2. Filters that must be replaced periodically are the
   a. fuel-injection-pump filter, nozzle filter, crankcase vent filter
   b. fuel-tank filter, fuel-pump filter, fuel filter
   c. oil filter, fuel filter, crankcase vent filter, air filter
   d. air-conditioning filter, block-heater filter, carburetor filter   2. _____

3. Oil for use in General Motors V-8 automotive diesel engines should be designated
   a. SA and SB
   b. CA and CB
   c. SF and CD
   d. SC and CC   3. _____

4. Fuel pressure in the injection-pump housing should be
   a. 2 psi [14kPa]
   b. 8 to 12 psi [55 to 83 kPa]
   c. 35 lb-ft [47.5 N-m]
   d. 25 lb-ft [33.9 N-m]   4. _____

5. Failure to change the oil and oil filter in an automotive diesel engine may cause
   a. excessive fuel consumption
   b. excessive oil consumption
   c. premature transmission failure
   d. premature camshaft failure   5. _____

JOB 39
Clutch Replacement

Objective: To learn how to remove, inspect, service, and install the clutch.
References: AM ♦39-28, SG Chap. 39, automotive manufacturers' service manuals.

Equipment: Various engines on stands, or vehicles with transmissions removed in readiness for clutch removal.

Tools: Clutch-pilot tool, engine-support fixture, safety stands, goggles or safety glasses, basic hand tools.

SHOP FACTS

Variations in construction and design make it necessary to use different procedures and tools when removing and installing clutches on different cars. As a first step in clutch removal, the transmission must be removed.

SHOP SKILLS

CLUTCH REMOVAL

_____ 1. When the transmission is being removed, pull it straight back from the clutch housing until the clutch shaft is clear of the friction-disk hub. Then the transmission can be lowered from the car. This procedure prevents bending and damage to the friction disk. To protect the friction disk during transmission removal, install two guide pins in place of two of the transmission attaching bolts. This maintains transmission alignment as it is moved back and prevents its weight from springing the hub in the friction disk.

CAREFUL The pressure-plate cover must be reattached to the flywheel in the same position as originally. If not, dynamic balance may be lost, and vibration and damage will occur. To ensure correct alignment on installation, both the flywheel and the pressure-plate cover are stamped with an X or some similar marking. These markings should align when the clutch pressure-plate assembly is reinstalled on the flywheel. Before removing the pressure plate from the flywheel, if you cannot locate the markings, carefully mark the pressure-plate cover and the flywheel with a hammer and punch (Fig. 39-1). Then you can reinstall the pressure plate in its original position by aligning the marks.

_____ 2. Some clutches use a cross shaft inside the clutch housing as part of the linkage to operate the release bearing. The release fork and shaft must be pulled partly out of the clutch housing to provide room for the pressure plate to clear the cross shaft. This can be done after the clutch release-fork bracket is disconnected at the clutch housing and the release-

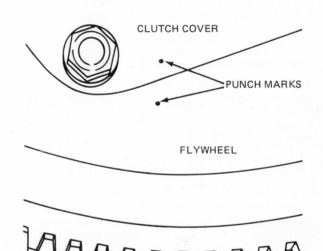

Fig. 39-1 Marking the clutch cover and flywheel. **(Chrysler Corporation)**

fork-flange cap screws are taken out. On other cross-shaft clutches, it is necessary only to detach the cross shaft so that the fork can be swung up out of the way. On the diaphragm-spring clutch or the clutch using a ball stud on which the fork pivots, snap the fork off its pivot with a screwdriver after removing the clutch linkage from the fork.

_____ 3. Loosen the pressure-plate-cover attaching screws one turn at a time so that the cover will be evenly loosened and distortion will not occur (Fig. 39-2). Loosen the screws evenly until the spring pressure is relieved. Then take the screws out. A flywheel turner is used to rotate the flywheel to get at the upper screws. When the spring force is relieved and the screws are out, the pressure plate and disk can be lowered from the car.

CAREFUL On some coil-spring clutches, the combined force of the clutch springs may be nearly 3000 pounds [13,344 N] or higher. Always follow the proper procedure when loosening or tightening the screws on the pressure-plate cover.

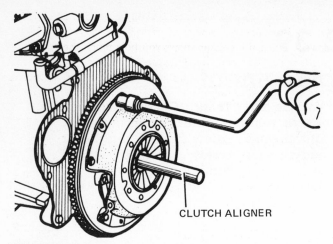

CLUTCH ALIGNER

Fig. 39-2 Use a clutch aligner to properly position the friction disk while removing or installing the pressure-plate assembly. (Chrysler Corporation)

CLUTCH INSPECTION AND REPAIR

____ 1. Any parts in the pressure plate that are worn or damaged can be replaced by a clutch rebuilder. For example, if the pressure-plate springs lose tension because of overheating, or if the release-lever bearings wear excessively, then the pressure-plate-and-cover assembly can be disassembled so that these parts can be replaced. However, most manufacturers recommend replacing a worn or defective clutch with a complete new one. Shop manuals no longer provide disassembly-assembly instructions for the technician. Today the components of the clutch are replaced as required.

____ 2. Some coil-spring clutches have adjustable release levers. The adjustment requires a clutch-gauge plate and a clutch-lever height gauge. First, place the clutch-gauge plate on the flywheel. Then place the cover assembly on top with the release levers over the machined lands on the gauge. Next, attach the cover assembly to the flywheel. Tighten the screws one turn at a time in rotation to avoid distorting the cover. Depress the release levers several times to seat them. Then measure their height with the height gauge. The height gauge has four settings that can be used for measuring above and below the hub.

____ 3. On the indirect spring-pressure-type clutch, remove the release clip, loosen the locknut, and turn the adjusting screw until the lever is at the specified height. Tighten the locknut and recheck. If okay, install the release clip.

____ 4. On the direct spring-pressure-type clutch, turn the adjusting nuts until the lever is at the correct height. Work the lever several times. Recheck. If okay, stake the nut with a dull punch.

INSPECTING AND SERVICING CLUTCH PARTS

Clutch parts can be checked as follows after the clutch is removed from the vehicle.

♦ **CAUTION** ♦ Never use compressed air to blow the dust out of the clutch housing. This dust may contain asbestos. Asbestos, when breathed into your lungs, can cause

lung cancer. Instead, wipe out the housing with a damp cloth. Dispose of the cloth so no one else will use it. Wash your hands after handling the friction disk and other clutch components.

____ 1. Check for oil leakage through the engine rear-main-bearing oil seal and transmission drive-pinion seal. If leakage is evident, replace the seal.

____ 2. Check the friction face of the flywheel for uniform appearance and for cracks, grooves, and uneven wear. If there is uneven wear, check the flywheel runout with a dial indicator. A warped or damaged flywheel should be replaced.

____ 3. Check the pilot bushing in the end of the crankshaft. Replace the bushing if it is worn. To remove it, use a bushing puller, or fill the crankshaft cavity and bushing bore with heavy grease. Then insert a clutch-aligning tool or spare transmission drive pinion into the pilot bushing. Tap the end of the tool or drive pinion with a lead hammer. Pressure from the grease will force the bushing out. Install a new bushing with the aligning tool.

____ 4. Check the pilot-bearing surface on the end of the clutch shaft for wear. Replace the clutch shaft if the pilot-bearing surface is rough or worn.

____ 5. Handle the disk with care. Do not touch the facings. Any oil or grease will cause clutch slippage and rapid facing wear. Replace the disk if the facings show evidence of oil or grease, are worn to within 0.015 inch [0.38 mm] of the rivet heads, or are loose. The disk should also be replaced if there is other damage, such as worn splines, loose rivets, or evidence of heat.

____ 6. Wipe the pressure-plate face with solvent. Check the face for flatness with a straightedge. Then check the face for burns, cracks, grooves, and ridges.

Note If the friction disk is replaced, most manufacturers recommend replacing the pressure-plate assembly also.

____ 7. Check the condition of the release levers. The inner ends should have a uniform wear pattern from contact with the throwout bearing.

____ 8. Test the cover for flatness on a surface plate.

____ 9. If any of the pressure-plate parts are not up to specifications, replace the pressure-plate assembly. A new friction disk should be installed at the same time.

____ 10. Examine the throwout bearing. The bearing should turn freely when held in the hand under a light thrust load. There should be no noise. The bearing should turn smoothly without roughness. Note the condition of the face where the release levers touch. Replace the bearing if it is not in good condition. Figure 39-3 shows the lubrication points of throwout bearings. Light graphite grease is recommended.

CAREFUL Never clean the bearing in solvent or carburetor cleaner. The bearing is prelubricated and sealed. Liquid cleaners remove the lubricant and ruin the bearing.

____ 11. Check the fork for wear on throwout-bearing attachments or other damage. On reassembly, be sure that the dust seal or cover is in good condition to prevent dirt from entering.

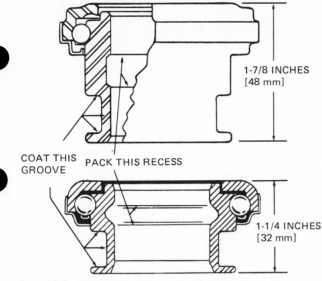

Fig. 39-3 Release-bearing lubrication points. (**Chevrolet Motor Division of General Motors Corporation**)

CAREFUL Steam cleaning can cause clutch trouble. Steam may enter and condense on the facings of the friction disk, pressure plate, and flywheel. The disk facings will absorb moisture. If the car is allowed to stand with the facings wet, they may stick to either the flywheel or the pressure plate. Then the clutch would not disengage. To prevent this, start the engine immediately after steam cleaning. Slip the clutch slightly to heat and dry the facings. Do not overdo it or you could burn out the clutch.

____ 12. Check the alignment of the clutch housing (see the part below).

CHECKING CLUTCH-HOUSING ALIGNMENT

____ 1. Whenever a clutch has been serviced, the clutch housing should be checked for alignment. This procedure includes checking the housing-bore runout and housing-face squareness.

____ 2. To check bore runout (Fig. 39-4), substitute a 3-inch [76.2-mm] bolt for one of the crankshaft bolts. Mount a dial indicator in the bore (Fig. 39-4). Rotate the engine slowly clockwise to check runout. If the runout is excessive, it can be corrected by installing offset dowels.

Fig. 39-4 Measuring clutch-housing-bore runout with a dial indicator. (**Chrysler Corporation**)

____ 3. Dowels are available with varying amounts of offset. To install the dowels, remove the clutch housing and the old dowels. The dial indicator shows you how much the bore is out of alignment and in which direction. This determines which pair of dowels to select (the pair with the correct amount of offset). The slots in the dowels should align in the direction of maximum bore runout to correct the alignment.

____ 4. To check housing-face squareness, reposition the dial indicator as shown in Fig. 39-5. Rotate the engine clockwise slowly to note how much the housing face is out of line. To correct alignment, place shim stock of the necessary thickness in the proper positions between the clutch housing and engine block.

CLUTCH INSTALLATION

____ 1. In general, installation of the clutch is the reverse of removal. Before the clutch is installed, the condition and lubrication of the pilot bearing in the end of the crankshaft should be checked and replacement made, if necessary. In addition, the condition of the throwout bearing and other clutch parts should be checked. Any defective parts should be replaced.

Note The clutch-housing alignment should be checked whenever the clutch is removed for service. A misaligned housing can cause improper clutch release, friction-disk failure, front-transmission-bearing failure, uneven wear of the pilot bushing in the crankshaft, clutch noise, clutch vibration, and jumping out of gear.

____ 2. Turn the flywheel until the X or other alignment mark is at the bottom. Then use the clutch aligner to maintain alignment of the friction disk with the pilot bearing in the crankshaft, or you can use a spare clutch shaft or transmission drive pinion. Hold the friction disk and clutch cover in place. Turn the cover until the X or other mark on it aligns with the similar mark on the flywheel. Install the attaching bolts, turning them down one turn at a time to take up the spring tension gradually and evenly. Use the flywheel turner to rotate the flywheel for access to the upper bolts.

____ 3. As a final step in the procedure, after the transmission has been reinstalled and the clutch linkages reattached, check the clutch-pedal free travel. Make any adjustments that are necessary.

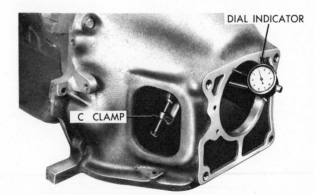

Fig. 39-5 Measuring clutch-housing face for squareness with a dial indicator. (**Chrysler Corporation**)

1. Before the clutch is removed from the car, it is first necessary to remove the
   a. engine
   b. differential
   c. rear wheels
   d. transmission   1. ___

2. The clutch cover is attached to the
   a. flywheel
   b. hub splines
   c. throwout bearing
   d. friction disk   2. ___

3. The clutch pressure plate is mounted in the
   a. flywheel
   b. friction disk
   c. clutch cover
   d. crankshaft   3. ___

4. The amount of travel that the clutch pedal has before the throwout bearing comes up against the release levers is called the clutch-pedal
   a. free travel
   b. fixed travel
   c. declutching movement
   d. overcenter travel   4. ___

5. The purpose of the pilot tool or clutch arbor is to align the
   a. pressure plate
   b. cover
   c. friction disk
   d. throwout bearing   5. ___

JOB 40

Types and Constructions of Manual Transmissions and Transaxles

Objective: To learn about the types and constructions of manually shifted transmissions and of manual transaxles.

References: AM ♦40-1 to 40-25, SG Chap. 40, automotive manufacturers' service manuals.

Equipment: Various manual transmissions, transmission parts, and assembled and disassembled transaxles.

Tools: Basic hand tools.

SHOP SKILLS

MANUAL-TRANSMISSION OPERATION

_____ 1. Examine various transmissions and transmission parts. In the textbook or in the manufacturer's service manual, locate illustrations of each type of transmission. By studying the parts and the illustrations, you will learn the names of the parts and the construction of each type of transmission.

_____ 2. Select a transmission, and make a list of all major parts. Then make another list of all bearings, gaskets, and seals.

_____ 3. Describe the actions in a four-speed transmission when it is in neutral. Explain which major parts are moving and which are stationary. Now describe the actions and movements of parts as the transmission is shifted from neutral to first; from first to second; from second to third; from third to fourth; and from fourth to reverse.

_____ 4. Name the gears transmitting power through a three-speed transmission in first gear; in second gear; in third gear; and in reverse.

_____ 5. Discuss the difference between a four-speed transmission with direct drive in fourth gear and a four-speed transmission with overdrive in fourth gear.

_____ 6. Explain how a manual transmission, a transaxle, and a transfer case differ from each other.

_____ 7. Not all gearboxes (such as manual transmissions, transaxles, and transfer cases) require the same type of lubricant. List three different types of lubricant used in gearboxes and the most common lubricant for each type of gearbox.

TRANSAXLE OPERATION

_____ 1. Figure 40-1 is a sectional view of a four-speed manual transaxle. Identify each gear, the two synchronizers, the four bearings, and the other parts in the transmission section. The synchronizers work the same way as in other manual transmissions.

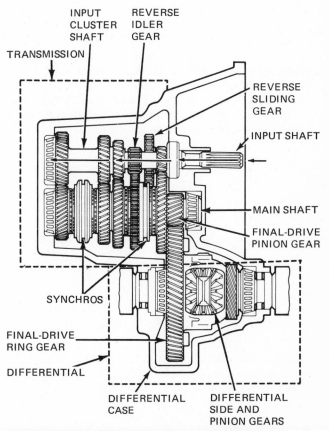

Fig. 40-1 The manual transaxle combines the manual transmission, final-drive gearing, and differential into a single unit. **(Ford Motor Company)**

_____ 2. In Fig. 40-1, the transmission is shown in neutral. Note the power flow through the input cluster shaft. However, no gear is locked to the main shaft, because both synchros are in neutral. With no gear locked to the main shaft, it is stationary and there is no power flow to the differential.

_____ 3. The synchro to the right (in Fig. 40-1) is the 1-2 synchro. To obtain first gear, the synchro hub is moved forward (to the right in Fig. 40-1), locking first gear to the main shaft. The 3-4 synchro remains centered in its neutral position. Now describe the power flow from the input shaft, through the transaxle, to the drive shafts.

_____ 4. Second gear is obtained by moving the 1-2 synchro hub from first gear to second gear. This means the synchro hub moves to the left (in Fig. 40-1) to lock second gear to the main shaft. The 3-4 synchro hub remains in neutral. Now describe the power flow from the input shaft, through the transaxle, to the drive shafts.

_____ 5. To get third gear, the 1-2 synchro is returned to its neutral position. Now the 3-4 synchro is moved forward (to the right in Fig. 40-1). This locks third gear to the main shaft. Describe the power flow from the input cluster shaft through the transaxle to the drive shafts.

_____ 6. Fourth gear is obtained by moving the 3-4 synchro hub (to the left in Fig. 40-1) to engage fourth gear and lock it to the main shaft. The 1-2 synchro remains in neutral. Now describe the power flow from the input cluster shaft through the transaxle to the drive shafts.

_____ 7. As long as the engine is running and the clutch is engaged, the cluster shaft turns, turning the reverse idler gear. To obtain reverse, both synchros are in neutral. The reverse sliding gear is moved (to the left in Fig. 40-1) so that it is driven by the reverse idler gear and, in turn, drives the reverse gear on the main shaft. This reverses the rotation of the main shaft. Now describe the power flow from the input shaft, through the transaxle, to the drive shafts.

JOB 40   MULTIPLE-CHOICE TEST

1. The largest gear on the countershaft is meshed with the
   a. main-shaft reverse gear
   b. clutch gear
   c. main-shaft second gear
   d. main-shaft high gear   1. ____

2. A transaxle is a single unit usually found on small cars with a front-mounted engine that combines
   a. the engine and transmission
   b. the transmission and drive axle
   c. the clutch and final-drive gearing
   d. none of the above   2. ____

3. When a car is equipped with a dual-speed transaxle, the car has
   a. four forward speeds
   b. six forward speeds
   c. eight forward speeds
   d. ten forward speeds   3. ____

4. When a car has *overdrive*, this means that in the highest gear the crankshaft turns.
   a. faster than the transmission output shaft
   b. at the same speed as the transmission output shaft
   c. more slowly than the transmission output shaft
   d. in the direction opposite the transmission output shaft
                                                   4. ____

5. The purpose of the differential in the transaxle is to allow
   a. the drive wheels to rotate at different speeds during cornering
   b. the front and rear axles to rotate at different speeds during cornering
   c. engagement of the front axle if the rear wheels begin to spin
   d. engagement of the opposite wheel on the axle if one wheel begins to spin
                                                   5. ____

Name _____ Date _____

JOB 41-1
Manual-Transmission Trouble Diagnosis

Objective: To learn to diagnose trouble in the manual transmission.

References: AM ♦41-2, SG Chap. 41, automotive manufacturers' service manuals.

Equipment: Vehicles with various troubles in manual transmissions.

Tools: Basic hand tools.

SHOP FACTS

The type of trouble a transmission has is often a clue to the cause of that trouble. Before attempting any repairs, try to determine the cause. Driver complaints, their possible causes, and the checks or corrections to be made are listed and discussed in later sections. Internal transmission troubles are fixed by disassembling the transmission. Or the old transmission can be replaced with a new, rebuilt, or used transmission.

To accurately diagnose a complaint about a manual transmission, you must follow a procedure. Road-test the car with the owner to verify that the complaint exists. Road testing with the owner gives you the opportunity to identify the condition that the owner wants corrected. There are two general types of manual-transmission troubles. They are (1) noise and (2) improper operation.

During the road test, determine any related symptoms that may be occurring. Get all the facts and service history possible from the owner. Then, as you drive, determine when, where, and how the symptoms occur.

Immediately begin to analyze the symptoms. Now you are performing the diagnosis step by answering the question "What is wrong?" As soon as you know, tell the owner what to expect. Then, with the owner's permission, perform the required adjustments or repairs. When the job is completed, road-test the car again. This time make sure that the trouble you found on the first road test no longer exists.

When proper operation has been restored, you know that the trouble has been corrected. This second road test serves as a quality-control check. As far as possible, it assures both you and the car owner that the job has been done right the first time. This helps prevent shop comebacks based on the installation of defective parts or faulty repair work.

Most internal transmission problems can be accurately diagnosed before disassembling the transmission. For example, there are three general types of noise from a manual transmission (Fig. 41-1). The noise provides you with information about what is taking place inside the transmission. A periodic clunking noise indicates broken teeth. A growl or whine indicates a defective bearing or worn contact faces on the gear teeth. Gear clash during shifting or when shifting is attempted indicates a defective synchronizer.

Note Certain clutch problems produce symptoms similar to transmission problems. Follow the trouble-diagnosis proce-

NOISE	CAUSE
PERIODIC CLUNK	= BROKEN TEETH
GROWL OR WHINE	= DEFECTIVE BEARING OR WORN TEETH
GEAR CLASH	= DEFECTIVE SYNCHRONIZER

Fig. 41-1 Three types of transmission noise and their causes.

dures for the transmission you are servicing to determine the actual cause of the problem before attempting any repair. It may be that what you thought was transmission trouble is actually a trouble located in some other part of the car.

SHOP SKILLS

HARD SHIFTING INTO GEAR

____ 1. Hard shifting into gear may be caused by improper linkage adjustment between the gearshift lever and the transmission. Improper adjustment can greatly increase the force necessary for gear shifting. The same trouble may result when the linkage is badly in need of lubrication and is rusted or jammed at any of the pivot points.

____ 2. Another cause of this trouble is failure of the clutch to disengage completely. If the clutch linkage is out of adjustment or if other conditions prevent full clutch disengagement, it will be difficult to shift gears into or out of mesh. Gear clashing will probably result since the engine will still be delivering at least some power through the clutch to the transmission.

____ 3. Inside the transmission, hard gear shifting may be caused by a bent shifter fork, sliding gear or synchronizer tight on the shaft splines, battered gear teeth, or a damaged synchronizing unit. A bent shifter fork, which can make it necessary to exert greater than necessary force to shift gears, should be replaced.

____ 4. The splines in the gears or on the shaft may become gummed up or battered from excessive wear so the gear will not move easily along the shaft splines. If this happens, the shaft and gears should be cleaned or, if worn, replaced. If the gear teeth are battered, they will not slip into mesh easily. Nothing can be done to repair gears with battered teeth. New gears will be required. The synchronizing unit may be tight on the shaft, or it may have loose parts or worn or scored cones. Any of these conditions will increase the difficulty of meshing. To correct troubles in the transmission, you must remove and disassemble it.

_____ 5. Another condition that can cause hard shifting is binding of the shifter tube in the steering column. The steering column must be partly disassembled so that the binding can be relieved.

TRANSMISSION STICKS IN GEAR

_____ 1. Several conditions that cause hard shifting into gear can also cause the transmission to stick in gear. For example, improper linkage adjustment between the gearshift lever and the transmission or lack of lubrication in the linkage can make it hard to shift out of mesh. The linkage should be adjusted and lubricated.

_____ 2. Another cause could be failure of the clutch to disengage completely. Improper clutch-linkage adjustment, and other conditions that prevent full disengagement of the clutch, could make it hard to shift out of mesh.

_____ 3. If the detent balls (or the lockout mechanism in the transmission) stick and do not unlock readily when shifting is attempted, it will be hard to shift out of gear. They should be freed and lubricated.

_____ 4. If the synchronizers do not slide freely on the shaft splines, it will be hard to come out of mesh. The shaft and synchronizers should be cleaned or, if worn, replaced. Lack of lubricant in the transmission can cause gears to stick in mesh (Fig. 41-2). Adding lubricant may correct the problem. If not, transmission removal and overhaul is required.

TRANSMISSION SLIPS OUT OF GEAR

_____ 1. Improperly adjusted linkage between the gearshift lever and the transmission can produce force on the linkage

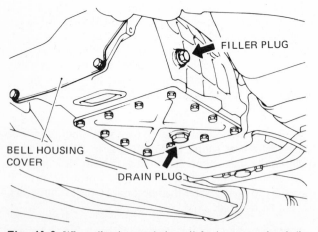

Fig. 41-2 When the transmission sticks in gear, check the lubricant level. It should reach the bottom of the filler-plug hole. **(Chrysler Corporation)**

in such a way that gears would work out of mesh. Check and adjust the linkage, if necessary. An excessively stiff boot on the shift lever may pull the shift lever back to neutral from any gear position. To check the boot, squeeze it. If it is too stiff, replace it.

_____ 2. Worn gears or gear teeth may also increase the chances of gears coming out of mesh. If the detent balls (or lockout mechanism in the transmission) lack sufficient spring force, there will be little to hold the gears in mesh and they may slip out. Worn bearings or synchronizers loose on the shaft tend to cause excessive end play, or free motion, that allows the gears to de-mesh.

_____ 3. When the transmission slips out of high gear, it could be due to misalignment between the transmission and the engine. This condition can soon damage the clutch and transmission parts. Misalignment often causes clutch-pedal pulsations. Check the clutch-housing alignment. If the clutch housing is out of line, the transmission will also be out of line.

NO POWER THROUGH TRANSMISSION

_____ 1. If the transmission gears are in mesh, the clutch is engaged, and no power passes through the transmission, the clutch may be slipping. If the clutch is not slipping, the trouble is in the transmission. The indication is that something serious has taken place which will require transmission overhaul.

_____ 2. Conditions inside the transmission that would prevent power from passing through include gear teeth stripped from gears, a shifter fork or other linkage part broken, a gear or shaft broken (Fig. 41-3), and a drive key or spline sheared off. The transmission must be taken out and disassembled so that the damaged or broken parts can be replaced.

TRANSMISSION NOISE

_____ 1. Several types of noise may be encountered in transmissions. Whining or growling, either steady or intermittent, may be due to worn, chipped, rough, or cracked gears. As the gears continue to wear, the noise may take on a grinding characteristic, particularly in the gear position that throws the greatest load on the worn gears.

_____ 2. Bearing trouble often produces a hissing noise that will develop into a bumping or thudding sound as bearings wear badly.

_____ 3. Metallic rattles could be due to worn or loose shifting parts in the linkage or to gears loose on the shaft splines. Sometimes, if the clutch friction-disk-cushion springs or the engine torsional-vibration dampener are defective, the torsional vibration of the engine will carry back into the transmission. This noise is apparent only at certain engine speeds.

_____ 4. In analyzing noise in the transmission, first note whether the noise is obtained in neutral with the car stationary or in certain gear positions. If the noise is evident with the transmission in neutral with the car stationary, disengage

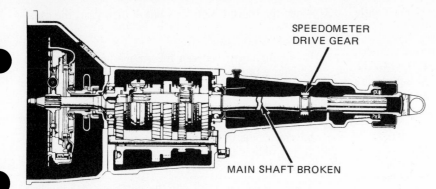

SPEEDOMETER DRIVE GEAR

MAIN SHAFT BROKEN

Fig. 41-3 A broken main shaft prevents power flow through the transmission. (Toyota Motor Sales Company, Ltd.)

the clutch. If this does not stop the noise, the trouble probably is not in the transmission (provided the clutch actually disengages and does not have troubles). In this case, the noise is probably in the engine or clutch. But if the noise stops when the clutch is disengaged, then the trouble is probably in the transmission.

____ 5. A squeal when the clutch is disengaged usually means that the clutch throwout bearing needs lubrication or is defective. Also, a worn or dry pilot bushing in the crankshaft can become noisy. Noise can occur because the crankshaft continues to turn with the clutch disengaged but the clutch shaft itself (which pilots in the crankshaft bushing) stops turning.

____ 6. Noise in neutral with the clutch engaged could come from transmission misalignment with the engine, worn or dry bearings, worn gears, a worn or bent countershaft, or excessive end play of the countershaft. Notice that these are the parts which are in motion when the clutch is engaged and the transmission is in neutral.

____ 7. Noise obtained in gear could result from any of the conditions noted in step 6 above. Also, it could be due to a defective friction disk in the clutch or a defective engine torsional-vibration dampener. In addition, the rear main bearing of the transmission could be worn or dry, gears could be loose on the main shaft, or gear teeth could be worn.

____ 8. Another cause of noise could be worn speedometer gears (Fig. 41-3). Careful listening to notice the particular gear position in which the most noise is obtained is often helpful in pinpointing the worn parts that are producing the noise. Worn parts should be replaced after transmission removal and disassembly.

GEARS CLASH IN SHIFTING

____ 1. Gear clashing that accompanies shifting may be due to failure of the synchronizing mechanism to operate properly (Fig. 41-4). This condition might be caused by a broken synchronizer spring, incorrect synchronizer end play, or defective synchronizer cone surfaces. It could also be due to gears sticking on the main shaft or failure of the clutch to release fully.

____ 2. Gear clash can be obtained in low or reverse on many cars if a sudden shift is made to either of these gears while gears are still in motion. In some transmissions, these

two gear positions do not have synchromesh devices. To prevent gear clash when shifting into either of these positions, the driver must pause long enough to allow the gears to stop turning. If the clutch is not disengaging fully, the gears will still be driven and may clash when the shift is made.

____ 3. A worn or dry pilot bushing can keep the clutch shaft spinning even when the clutch is disengaged. This condition can cause gear clash when shifting. So can incorrect lubricant in the transmission.

NOISY IN REVERSE

This is probably due to a damaged or worn reverse idler gear or bushing, reverse gear on the main shaft, countergear, or a damaged shift mechanism. The transmission should be removed for disassembly and inspection of the parts so that damaged or worn parts can be replaced.

OIL LEAKS

____ 1. If the lubricant in the transmission case is not the correct type or if different brands of lubricant are put into the transmission, the lubricant may foam excessively. As it foams, it will completely fill the case and begin to leak out. The same thing may happen if the oil level is too high.

____ 2. If gaskets are broken or missing or if oil seals or oil slingers are damaged or missing, oil will work past the shafts at the two ends of the transmission. Also, if the drain plug is

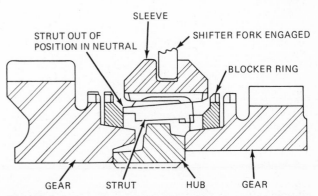

SLEEVE

STRUT OUT OF POSITION IN NEUTRAL

SHIFTER FORK ENGAGED

BLOCKER RING

GEAR   STRUT   HUB   GEAR

Fig. 41-4 A defective synchronizer causes gear clash during shifts.

loose or if the transmission bearing retainer is not tightly bolted to the case, oil will be lost.

____ 3. A cracked transmission or extension case will also leak oil. The right amount of the recommended oil should be used in the transmission to prevent excessive oil leakage due to foaming. The transmission must be disassembled so that defective gaskets, oil seals, and slingers can be replaced.

JOB 41-1 MULTIPLE-CHOICE TEST

1. Two general types of manual-transmission troubles are
   a. bearings and shift levers
   b. lubricant and gaskets
   c. noise and improper operation
   d. none of the above   1. ____

2. A periodic clunking noise in a transmission indicates a
   a. defective bearing
   b. defective synchronizer
   c. defective gasket
   d. gear with broken teeth   2. ____

3. When the transmission slips out of high gear, the cause may be
   a. lack of lubricant
   b. misalignment between the engine and transmission
   c. failure of the clutch to disengage completely
   d. a broken main shaft   3. ____

4. A noise that continues after the clutch is disengaged
   a. probably is in the transmission
   b. probably is in the clutch
   c. probably is the speedometer gears
   d. is none of the above   4. ____

5. A noise heard in neutral with the clutch engaged may be a
   a. defective input-shaft bearing
   b. defective throwout bearing
   c. defective output-shaft bearing
   d. defective universal joint   5. ____

JOB 41-2
Cleaning and Inspecting Manual-Transmission Parts

Objective: To learn to clean and inspect the parts in a manual transmission.

References: AM ♦41-1 to 41-6, SG Chap. 41, automotive manufacturers' service manuals.

Equipment: Disassembled transmission to be cleaned and inspected for reassembly.
Tools: Fine-cut mill file, basic hand tools.

♦ _____ ♦

SHOP SKILLS

CLEANING TRANSMISSION PARTS

____ 1. Wash all transmission parts, except for bearings and seals, in solvent. Brush or scrape all dirt from the parts. Do not damage the parts with the scraper. Dry the parts with compressed air.

♦ **CAUTION** ♦ To protect your eyes, wear goggles when using solvent. If you get solvent in your eyes, wash them out with water at once.

____ 2. To clean the bearings, rotate them slowly in clean solvent to remove all lubricant. Then hold the bearing assembly stationary so that it will not rotate and dry it with compressed air.

CAREFUL Do not spin the bearing with compressed air. Spinning a dry bearing this way, when it is not lubricated, can damage it.

____ 3. As soon as the bearing is dry, immediately lubricate it with transmission lubricant. Then wrap each bearing in clean, lint-free cloth or paper for later inspection.

____ 4. Some transmissions have a magnet at the bottom of the case. If present, clean the magnet with solvent and remove any metal particles and dirt.

PARTS INSPECTION

____ 1. Inspect the transmission case for cracks or worn or damaged bearing bores and threads. Check the front and back of the case for nicks or burrs that could cause misalignment of the case with the flywheel housing or extension housing. Remove all burrs with a fine file.

____ 2. Check the condition of the shift levers, forks, shift rails, and the lever and shafts. Replace the roller bearings if they are broken, worn, or rough.

____ 3. Replace the countergear assembly, or any other gears, if they have teeth that are worn, broken, chipped, or otherwise damaged. Replace the countershaft if it is worn, bent, or scored.

____ 4. The bushing in the reverse gear and the bushing in the reverse idler gear are not serviced separately. If a bushing is worn, the gear-and-bushing assembly must be replaced as a unit.

BEARING INSPECTION

____ 1. Bad bearings usually produce a rough growl or grating noise rather than a whine, which is typical of gear noise. Noise is often the clue that points to bad bearings. To inspect a bearing, first clean it as explained in the first part of this job sheet. If the bearing has become magnetized, metal particles will be attracted to it. Cleaning the bearing by normal methods will not remove them. The bearing must be demagnetized first.

____ 2. Bearings fail from various causes, including lapping, spalling, and locking (Fig. 41-5).

LAPPING Lapping is caused by fine particles of abrasive material such as scale, sand, or emery. These particles circulate with the oil and cause wear of the roller or ball and race surfaces. Bearings which are worn enough to be loose but appear smooth without pitting or spalling have been running with dirty oil. This gradually wears away the surfaces.

SPALLING Spalling is caused by overloading or faulty assembly. Bearings that fail by spalling have either flaked or pitted rollers or races. Spalling can be caused by faulty assembly such as cocking of bearings, misalignment, or excessively tight adjustments.

LOCKING Locking is caused by large particles of dirt or other material wedging between rollers and races. This usually causes one of the races to spin. If a race spins in the housing, it will wear the housing in which it is assembled, so the housing must be replaced.

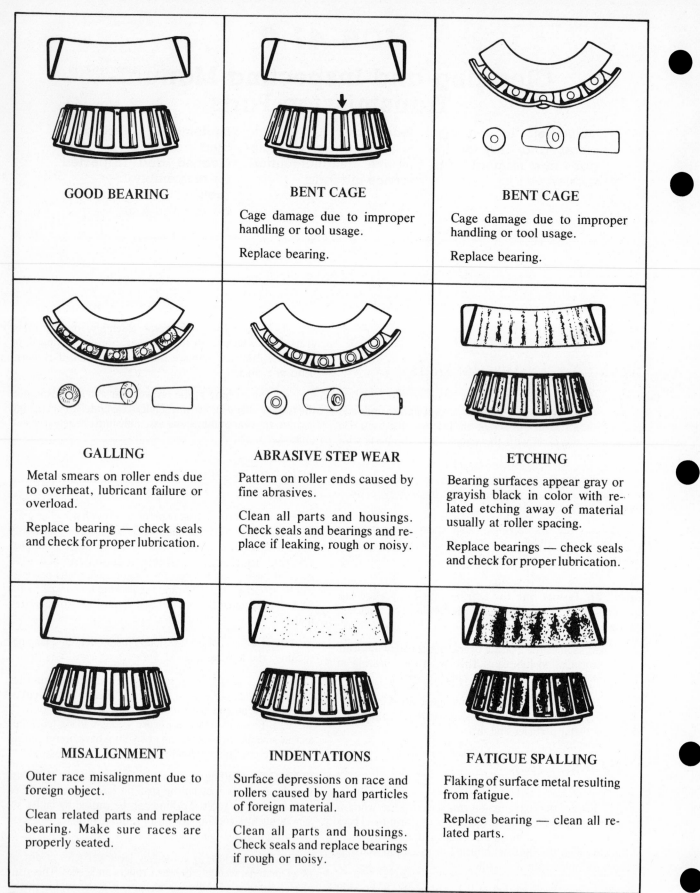

GOOD BEARING

BENT CAGE

Cage damage due to improper handling or tool usage.

Replace bearing.

BENT CAGE

Cage damage due to improper handling or tool usage.

Replace bearing.

GALLING

Metal smears on roller ends due to overheat, lubricant failure or overload.

Replace bearing — check seals and check for proper lubrication.

ABRASIVE STEP WEAR

Pattern on roller ends caused by fine abrasives.

Clean all parts and housings. Check seals and bearings and replace if leaking, rough or noisy.

ETCHING

Bearing surfaces appear gray or grayish black in color with related etching away of material usually at roller spacing.

Replace bearings — check seals and check for proper lubrication.

MISALIGNMENT

Outer race misalignment due to foreign object.

Clean related parts and replace bearing. Make sure races are properly seated.

INDENTATIONS

Surface depressions on race and rollers caused by hard particles of foreign material.

Clean all parts and housings. Check seals and replace bearings if rough or noisy.

FATIGUE SPALLING

Flaking of surface metal resulting from fatigue.

Replace bearing — clean all related parts.

Fig. 41-5 Roller-bearing problems and their causes. **(Ford Motor Company)**

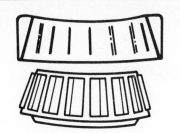

BRINELLING

Surface indentations in raceway caused by rollers either under impact loading or vibration while the bearing is not rotating.

Replace bearing if rough or noisy.

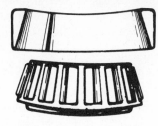

ABRASIVE ROLLER WEAR

Pattern on races and rollers caused by fine abrasives.

Clean all parts and housings. Check seals and bearings and re-place if leaking, rough or noisy.

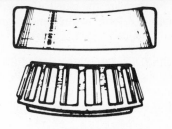

CAGE WEAR

Wear around outside diameter of cage and roller pockets caused by abrasive material and inefficient lubrication. Check seals and replace bearings.

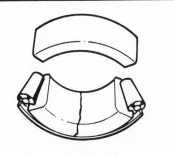

CRACKED INNER RACE

Race cracked due to improper fit, cocking, or poor bearing seats.

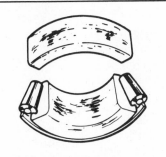

FRETTAGE

Corrosion set up by small relative movement of parts with no lubrication.

Replace bearing. Clean related parts. Check seals and check for proper lubrication.

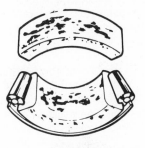

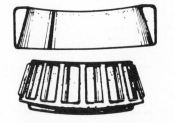

SMEARS

Smearing of metal due to slippage. Slippage can be caused by poor fit, lubrication, overheating, overloads or handling damage.

Replace bearings. Clean related parts and check for proper fit and lubrication.

Replace shaft if damaged.

HEAT DISCOLORATION

Heat discoloration can range from faint yellow to dark blue resulting from overload or incorrect lubricant.

Excessive heat can cause softening of races or rollers.

To check for loss of temper on races or rollers a simple file test may be made. A file drawn over a tempered part will grab and cut metal. A file drawn over a hard part will glide readily with no metal cutting.

Replace bearings if overheating damage is indicated. Check seals and other parts.

STAIN DISCOLORATION

Discoloration can range from light brown to black caused by incorrect lubricant or moisture.

Re-use bearings if stains can be removed by light polishing or if no evidence of overheating is observed.

Check seals and related parts for damage.

Fig. 41-5 (continued)

___ 3. Here are the four basic checks to be made on ball bearings to determine whether they are in good enough condition to be used again.

INNER-RING RACEWAY Hold the outer ring stationary and rotate the inner ring three times. Examine the raceway of the inner ring for pits or spalling. Note the types of damage and those that require replacement of the bearing.

OUTER-RING RACEWAY Hold the inner ring stationary and rotate the outer ring three times. Examine the outer-ring raceway for damage. Note the types of damage and those that require bearing replacement.

EXTERNAL SURFACES Replace the bearing if there are radial cracks on the front or rear faces of the outer or inner rings. Replace the bearing if there are cracks on the outside diameter or outer ring. Check carefully around the snap-ring groove. Also replace the bearing if the ball cage is cracked or deformed.

SPIN TEST Lubricate the bearing raceways lightly with clean oil. Turn the bearing back and forth slowly to coat the raceways and balls. Hold the bearing by the inner ring in a vertical position. Some vertical movement between the inner and outer rings is okay.

___ 4. Spin the outer ring several times by hand. *Do not use an air hose!* If you notice roughness or vibration or if the outer ring stops abruptly, reclean the bearing, relubricate it, and spin it again. Roughness is usually caused by particles of dirt in the bearing. If the bearing is still rough after cleaning and lubricating it three times, discard it.

___ 5. Hold the bearing by the inner ring in a horizontal position with the snap-ring groove up. Spin the outer bearing several times by hand, as described above. If the bearing is still rough after cleaning and relubricating it three times, discard it.

JOB 41-2 MULTIPLE-CHOICE TEST

1. All transmission parts should be washed in solvent except
   a. seals
   b. gears
   c. shafts
   d. thrust washers   1. ___

2. After they are washed in solvent, transmission bearings should be dried by
   a. air drying
   b. wiping with cloth
   c. shaking
   d. compressed air   2. ___

3. Spin-drying ball bearings causes damage to the
   a. race and balls
   b. air nozzle
   c. clutch shaft
   d. case bore   3. ___

4. Small nicks and burrs on the front and rear faces of a transmission case can be removed with a
   a. hammer and chisel
   b. piece of sandpaper
   c. fine-cut mill file
   d. scraper   4. ___

5. The main shaft must be replaced
   a. if any splines are damaged
   b. every overhaul
   c. if a new rear bearing is needed
   d. every 50,000 miles [80,467 km]   5. ___

JOB 42

Manual-Transaxle Trouble Diagnosis

Objective: To learn to diagnose trouble in the manual transaxle.

References: AM ◆42-1 to 42-12, SG Chap. 42-1, automotive manufacturers' service manuals.

Equipment: Vehicles with trouble in the manual transaxle.
Tools: Basic hand tools.

SHOP FACTS

Before attempting any repair of the clutch, transaxle, or operating linkages, identify the problem and its possible cause. Many clutch and transaxle problems show up as shifting difficulties. These include excessive shift effort, gear clash, grinding, and inability to shift into some gears.

In addition, there may be noise problems. These vary with vehicle size, type and size of engine, and amount of body insulation used. The fact that the entire drive train is located at the front of the car almost under the feet of the driver makes any drive-train noise more audible to the driver. But noises that you might believe are coming from the drive train could be coming from tires, road surfaces, wheel bearings, engine, and exhaust system. For this reason, a thorough and careful check should be made to locate the cause of the noise before removing and disassembling the transaxle.

SHOP SKILLS

NOISES

Transaxle gears are not absolutely quiet and will produce some noise. If the noise is annoying, try the following steps to see if it is excessive. If the noise is excessive, then determine what could be causing it.

_____ 1. Drive on a smooth, level asphalt road which will reduce tire and road noise to a minimum.

_____ 2. Drive the vehicle long enough to warm up all lubricant.

_____ 3. Note the speed at which noise occurs and in which gear range.

_____ 4. Stop the vehicle and see whether noise is still present with transaxle in neutral. Then listen with the transaxle in gear with the clutch pedal depressed.

_____ 5. Determine in which of the following driving conditions the noise is most noticeable:

a. Driving—light acceleration or heavy pull
b. Float—constant vehicle speed with light throttle on a level road
c. Coast—partly or fully closed throttle with transaxle in gear
d. All of the above

_____ 6. After road-testing the vehicle, consider the following:

a. If the noise is the same in drive or coast, it could be due to excessive drive-axle angle. The front suspension may be binding or the springs weak. This could cause the drive-axle universal joints to be driving through an excessive angle.

b. A knock at low speed could be caused by worn drive-axle universal joints or by worn counterbores in the side-gear hubs.

c. A clunk on acceleration or deceleration could be caused by loose engine or transaxle mounts.

d. Bad bearings usually produce a rough growl or grating noise rather than the whine that is typical of gear noise. If bearing noise is suspected, it will be necessary to remove the transaxle and disassemble it so that the bearings can be inspected (Job 41-2).

e. Side bearings are preloaded, so noise will not go away or diminish when the differential is run with the wheels off the ground. Noise in this area can easily be confused with wheel-bearing noise.

f. A rough wheel bearing produces a vibration or growl which continues with the vehicle coasting and transmission in neutral. Wheel bearings are not preloaded, so noise should diminish if the differential is run with the wheels off the ground. A brinelled bearing causes a knock or click about every two wheel revolutions. The bearing race is brinelled (Job 41-1) when it has an indentation caused by a roller or ball. To check for brinelling, spin the wheel by hand while listening at the hub for brinelling or rough bearing noise. Wheel bearings are not serviceable as a separate item. They must be replaced as an integral part of the hub and spindle.

SLIPS OUT OF GEAR

Check for worn or out-of-adjustment linkage, transaxle loose on the engine housing, shift-lever binding, bent or damaged shift cables, stiff shift-lever seal, or troubles inside the transaxle.

HARD SHIFTING INTO GEAR

Check for the linkage being out of adjustment or needing lubrication, the clutch not disengaging, the clutch linkage being out of adjustment, or troubles inside the transaxle.

TRANSAXLE STICKS IN GEAR

Check for the gearshift linkage being out of adjustment, disconnected, or needing lubrication. If the problem is not located, check for clutch not disengaging or troubles inside the transaxle.

GEARS CLASH IN SHIFTING

_____ 1. When gears clash during a shift, check for improper adjustment of the gearshift linkage.

_____ 2. If the trouble is not located, check for the clutch not disengaging and improper adjustment of the clutch linkage. If the trouble is not located, it probably is inside the transaxle.

LUBRICANT LEAKING OUT

If the transaxle is overfilled with lubricant, some will leak out. If this is not the cause, then one or more of the seals is faulty.

BROKEN TRANSAXLE MOUNTS

_____ 1. Raise the car on a lift. Push up and pull down on the transaxle case while watching the mounts. If the rubber separates from the metal plate of the mount or if the case moves up but not down (mount is bottomed out), replace the mount (Fig. 42-1).

_____ 2. If there is relative movement between a metal plate of the mount and its attaching point, tighten the screws or nuts that attach the mount to the case or cross member.

LOW LUBRICANT LEVEL

To check the level of the lubricant in the transaxle, remove the plug. The lubricant level should be within ½ inch [13 mm] of the lower edge of the filler opening. If lubricant is

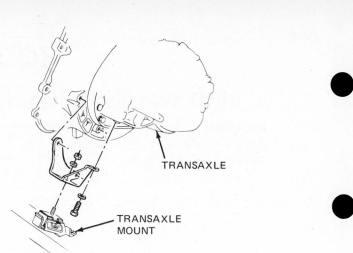

Fig. 42-1 Manual-transaxle mount. **(Pontiac Motor Division of General Motors Corporation)**

needed, add Dexron II, or equivalent, to bring the lubricant up to the proper level. Install the plug and torque it to specifications.

JOB 42   MULTIPLE-CHOICE TEST

1. Many transaxle problems show up as
   a. lubricant leaks
   b. broken transaxle mounts
   c. clutch failure
   d. shifting difficulties   1. _____

2. A broken engine mount may cause
   a. noise while idling
   b. a rough growl or grating noise
   c. a clunk on acceleration or deceleration
   d. a whine   2. _____

3. Inspecting the bearings in the transaxle
   a. requires you to disassemble the transaxle
   b. requires you to remove the transaxle inspection cover
   c. requires you to road-test the car
   d. cannot be done   3. _____

4. The bearing noise from a differential remains the same on a road test and while running raised on a lift. The *most probable* cause is
   a. a rough wheel bearing
   b. a defective differential side bearing
   c. a brinelled bearing
   d. none of the above   4. _____

5. When the car is raised off the ground, the differential noise is less. Mechanic A says the cause is a defective side bearing. Mechanic B says the cause is a defective wheel bearing. Who is right?
   a. Mechanic A
   b. Mechanic B
   c. both A and B
   d. neither A nor B   5. _____

JOB 43

Construction and Operation of Transfer Cases

Objective: To learn about the types and constructions of transfer cases.

References: AM ♦43-1 to 43-7, SG Chap. 43, automotive manufacturers' service manuals.

Equipment: Various assembled and disassembled transfer cases.

Tools: Basic hand tools.

SHOP FACTS

TRANSFER CASES

The transfer case is used in vehicles with four-wheel drive (Fig. 43-1). Its purpose is to provide a means of sending engine power to both the front and rear wheels.

Various types of transfer cases are installed in automotive vehicles. Some operate entirely with gears. Some are full-time units that use a chain to drive the front drive shaft (Fig. 43-1), instead of gears. This reduces the weight of the transfer case, improving fuel economy. Other full-time transfer cases, such as the one used in the American Motors Eagle cars, have no low range.

While there is a slight fuel-mileage penalty when full-time four-wheel drive is used, it does have some advantages. On vehicles equipped with certain types of four-wheel drive, when a wheel spins, power continues to flow to the spinning wheel. As a result, so little power reaches the other axle that the vehicle may not move. In the latest types of full-time four-wheel drive, the transfer case transfers the power from the axle with the spinning wheels through a clutch to the other axle. This improves traction and keeps the vehicle moving.

In the full-time transfer case, power is available to all four wheels at any time. In most vehicles, the full-time transfer case can be manually shifted into low range for gear reduction and torque increase at the wheels. The transfer-case shift is made by the driver when additional torque is needed, as for climbing steep hills.

The part-time transfer case can be shifted into gear reduction, just like the full-time unit. In addition, the part-time unit can be shifted to send power to only the rear wheels or to both the front and rear wheels.

The transfer-case shift lever usually is located on the floor of the passenger compartment. Shift patterns may vary according to the design of the transfer case.

SHOP SKILLS

TRANSFER-CASE OPERATION

_____ 1. On a vehicle with four-wheel drive, determine whether the four-wheel drive is part-time or full-time. With part-time four-wheel drive, hubs that can be manually locked and unlocked are used on the front wheels. Full-time four-wheel drive does not require the use of this type of hub. Inspect the front hubs on the vehicle you are examining and determine the type of hubs used.

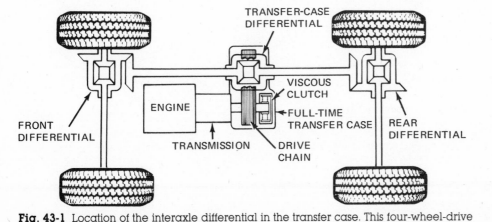

Fig. 43-1 Location of the interaxle differential in the transfer case. This four-wheel-drive vehicle has three separate differentials. **(American Motors Corporation)**

____ 2. Examine the transfer-case controls inside the vehicle. Note the shift pattern and any labels that provide information about when and how the transfer-case range may be changed. Then determine how to shift the transfer case from low range to high range and from two-wheel drive to four-wheel drive.

JOB 43   MULTIPLE-CHOICE TEST

1. When a vehicle has four-wheel drive, it provides power to the front and rear axle through a
   a. transaxle
   b. transmission
   c. differential
   d. transfer case   1. ____

2. The transfer case is used in
   a. vehicles with four-wheel drive
   b. any vehicle
   c. vehicles with front-wheel drive
   d. vehicles with rear-wheel drive   2. ____

3. The purpose of the transfer case is to provide a means of sending engine power to
   a. the rear wheels
   b. both the front and the rear wheels
   c. the front wheels
   d. none of the above   3. ____

4. In the full-time transfer case, power is available to
   a. the front wheels some of the time
   b. the front wheels all of the time
   c. all four wheels at any time
   d. none of the above   4. ____

5. The transfer-case shift lever usually is located
   a. under the hood near the air filter
   b. on the floor of the passenger compartment
   c. near the ignition
   d. under the driver's seat   5. ____

JOB 44-1
Hydraulic Controls for Planetary Gears

Objective: To learn how planetary gears in automotive automatic transmissions are controlled.

References: AM ◆44-7 to 44-11, SG Chap. 44, automotive manufacturers' service manuals.

Equipment: Various automatic transmissions partly disassembled and cut away.
Tools: Basic hand tools.

SHOP FACTS

In automatic transmissions, drums, bands, and clutches are used to control planetary gears and cause a change of gear ratio through the transmission. These control devices are hydraulically operated. When the ring gear of a planetary gearset is held stationary, a speed increase or reduction occurs. If the sun gear is driving when the internal, or ring, gear is held stationary, the planet-pinion carrier will turn slower than the sun gear and in the same direction. One way to hold the ring gear is by clamping a brake band around the outside surface of the ring gear, which now acts as a brake drum.

A band is shown in Fig. 44-1. It is made of steel and has a lining of asbestos or other friction material bonded to it. In a typical arrangement used in automatic transmissions, the band fits loosely around the drum (Fig. 44-1). The band is tightened, or *applied*, by hydraulic pressure under certain conditions to bring the ring gear to a stop. This produces a speed change through the planetary gearset.

The device that hydraulically applies the band is called a *servo* (Fig. 44-1). It converts hydraulic pressure into mechanical movement. The typical servo consists of a piston that moves in a cylinder when hydraulic pressure acts on the piston. The transmission servo shown in Fig. 44-1 illustrates the operation of the servo as it applies and releases the band. This, in turn, allows or stops rotation of the drum. There are usually one or two servos in an automatic transmission.

In a servo, hydraulic pressure can be admitted to either end (or both ends) of the cylinder. This pressure causes the piston to move. Then mechanical linkage from the piston causes movement of some mechanism. Therefore, hydraulic pressure is used to produce a mechanical action. In Fig. 44-1, when hydraulic pressure is applied to the piston, it moves to the right. This action causes the piston rod to apply the band. Drum rotation is stopped by increasing the hydraulic pressure.

The *apply pressure* for applying the band comes from the control valves in the hydraulic control system. Transmission fluid flows from the hydraulic system through a hole in the piston stem and fills the chamber on the apply side of the piston. This pressure forces the piston to move. As the piston moves, it tightens the band around the drum, stopping it.

When car speed and throttle opening signal the need for an upshift, hydraulic pressure is applied to the release side of the piston (which has a larger area than the apply side). This release-side pressure plus the spring force pushes the piston back. Now the band loosens on the drum. The drum and the member of the planetary gearset it is connected to are free to revolve. This prepares the transmission for an upshift.

MULTIPLE-DISK CLUTCHES

Hydraulically operated clutches provide another means for locking or releasing a rotating member of the planetary-gear system. The hydraulic clutches used in automatic transmissions are the multiple-disk, or multiple-plate, type (Fig. 44-2). The plates are alternately attached to an outer housing, or drum, and to an inner hub. When the clutch is disengaged, the two members can rotate independently of each other. But when the clutch is engaged, the plates are forced together. Then the friction between them locks the two members so they rotate together. With the clutch engaged, there is direct drive through the planetary gearset.

Engagement of the clutch is produced by oil pressure, which forces an annular piston to push the plates together. The annular piston is a ring that fits snugly into the *clutch-drum assembly,* also called the *piston-retainer assembly.* The piston is sealed by a sliding seal to the drum's inner surface. A spring or a series of springs that rest against the piston return

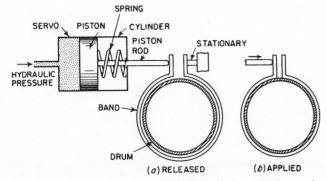

SPRING
SERVO PISTON CYLINDER
PISTON ROD
STATIONARY
HYDRAULIC PRESSURE
BAND
DRUM
(*a*) RELEASED
(*b*) APPLIED

Fig. 44-1 The servo consists of a piston that moves in a cylinder in relation to changes in hydraulic pressure. The piston movement applies or releases the band.

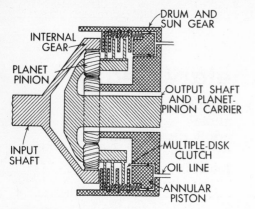

Fig. 44-2 A multiple-disk clutch used in automatic transmissions.

seat normally hold the piston slightly away from the plates. To engage the clutch, oil pressure must overcome the spring force and move the piston. This causes it to force the plates together.

In various transmissions, when the band is applied, it may hold the sun gear, ring gear, or the planet-pinion carrier stationary. Different transmissions may lock different members of the planetary gearset together when the clutch is engaged. However, the principle is the same in all transmissions. There is direct drive, reduction, reverse, or overdrive through the planetary gearset when the clutch is engaged. There is gear reduction or overdrive when the band is applied. A clutch can also be used, like a band, to hold one member stationary.

SHOP SKILLS

_____ 1. Disassemble a complete planetary gearset that includes a band around the drum (Fig. 44-2). Note how the band is controlled by a servo. In transmissions without overdrive, when a band is applied, the planetary gearset is in gear reduction.

_____ 2. Examine the parts of a multiple-disk clutch. Basically, the clutch consists of a series of plates (Fig. 44-2). Half the plates are splined to an outer ring, called the *clutch drum*. The other half are splined to the clutch hub, which in turn is splined to one of the members of the planetary gearset. Locate the hole through which the oil enters the clutch.

When the oil pressure forces the two sets of clutch plates together, the planetary gearset is locked up and in direct drive.

_____ 3. Examine the servo that operates the band. Determine whether the band is normally applied and whether it is released by spring force or by oil pressure.

_____ 4. Look at an accumulator. Study its construction to see how it is connected into the system. Notice that it is a small reservoir that must be filled with oil. As the accumulator fills, a rough shift that could be caused by sudden application of a band or engagement of a clutch is prevented.

JOB 44-1   MULTIPLE-CHOICE TEST

1. Planetary gears are controlled by
   a. drums and bands
   b. clutches
   c. neither a nor b
   d. both a and b   1. ____

2. The hydraulic device that applies the band is called the
   a. clutch
   b. accumulator
   c. pump
   d. servo   2. ____

3. The purpose of the accumulator is to
   a. cushion the shock of clutch and servo actions
   b. catch and contain any oil leakage
   c. apply and release the band
   d. engage and disengage the clutch   3. ____

4. When the clutch is engaged, locking two members together, the planetary gearset is in
   a. reverse
   b. neutral
   c. direct drive
   d. overdrive   4. ____

5. In the clutch, the piston is held slightly away from the plates by
   a. oil pressure
   b. spring force
   c. servo action
   d. centrifugal force   5. ____

JOB 44-2
Planetary-Gear-System Operation

Objective: To learn the operation of the planetary gearset and how the various conditions are produced.

References: AM ♦44-9, SG Chap. 44, automotive manufacturers' service manuals.

Equipment: Planetary gearsets, various automatic transmissions partly disassembled and cut away.
Tools: Basic hand tools.

SHOP FACTS

Planetary gears are an essential component of automotive automatic transmissions. In its simplest form, a planetary gearset (Fig. 44-3) is made up of three gears. In the center is the sun gear. All gears revolve around the sun gear. Meshing with the sun gear is the planet-pinion gear. For balance, and to distribute the load, three or four planet-pinion gears usually are used in the planetary gearset. The gearset shown in Fig. 44-3 has four planet-pinion gears. The planet-pinion gears are meshed with the ring gear.

The planet-pinion gears, or planet pinions, are mounted on short shafts that are part of a plate called the *planet-pinion carrier* or *cage*. The carrier is mounted on a shaft that can rotate and carry the planet pinions around with it in a circle. When this happens, the teeth of the planet-pinion gears, meshed with both the sun gear and the ring gear, cause movement of these gears.

Each part of the planetary gearset is called a *member*. The three members are the sun gear, the planet-pinion carrier with the planet pinions, and the ring gear. When any one member of a planetary gearset is held stationary and another is turned, the third member will produce either a speed increase, a speed reduction, or a direction reversal.

A planetary gearset can provide any of five conditions. These are:

_____ 1. A speed increase with a torque decrease (overdrive)

_____ 2. A speed decrease with a torque increase (reduction)

_____ 3. Direct drive (lockup)
_____ 4. Neutral
_____ 5. Reverse

All these variations (except neutral) are made possible by applying the input rotation to different planetary members while holding one of the other two members stationary.

The planetary-gear-system operating conditions are shown in Fig. 44-4. Consider condition 1. The letter T in this column indicates the driving member, which is the pinion carrier. H indicates that the sun gear is held stationary. D indicates that the ring gear is being driven. I designates an increase of speed between the pinion carrier and the ring gear.

The three conditions used most frequently in automatic transmissions are listed in columns 3, 4, and 6.

	CONDITION					
	1	2	3	4	5	6
Internal gear	D	H	T	H	T	D
Carrier	T	T	D	D	H	H
Sun gear	H	D	H	T	D	T
Speed	I	I	L	L	IR	LR

D—driven
H—held
I—increase speed
L—reduction in speed
R—reverse
T—turning or driving

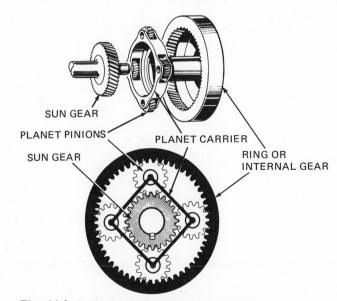

Fig. 44-3 A simple single planetary gearset.

Fig. 44-4 Various conditions that are possible in the planetary-gear system when one member is held and another is turned.

Note Different manufacturers give different names to the parts of the planetary gearset. For example, the internal gear is also called the *ring gear* or *annulus gear.* The planet-pinion carrier is also called the *planet-pinion cage,* and sometimes the *spider.* The planet pinions are also called *planet gears.* Planetary-gear systems are often called *planetary gearsets.* These names are used throughout this book and in various manufacturers' service manuals.

SHOP SKILLS

____ 1. Understanding automatic transmissions requires a knowledge of how the planetary gearset works. On a planetary gearset, identify the ring gear, sun gear, and planet pinions.

____ 2. Note how the planet pinions can turn on short shafts that are attached to the planet carrier. Hold the sun gear stationary and turn the planet carrier. Count the number of times a planet-pinion gear rotates on its shaft while making one complete revolution around the sun gear. Then watch the ring gear while turning the planet carrier with the sun gear stationary. You will see that the ring gear increases in speed.

____ 3. Hold the ring gear stationary and turn the planet-pinion carrier. Notice how the sun gear is forced to rotate faster than the planet carrier.

____ 4. With the sun gear held stationary, turn the ring gear. The planet carrier will now turn slower than the ring gear to provide speed reduction.

____ 5. Hold the ring gear stationary and turn the sun gear. Now the planet carrier rotates in the same direction as the sun gear, but at a slower speed.

____ 6. Hold the planet carrier stationary and turn the ring gear. Now the sun gear turns in the direction opposite to that of ring-gear rotation. This provides a "high-speed" reverse, which is not used for reverse gear in automatic transmissions.

____ 7. Hold the planet carrier stationary and turn the sun gear. Now the ring gear turns in the reverse direction and more slowly than the sun gear. This condition is used to provide reverse gear in an automatic transmission.

____ 8. Lock any two members of the planetary gearset together. This causes the input and output shafts to turn at the same speed. The gearset is in direct drive.

____ 9. Release all the planetary members and let them turn freely. Now no power can be transmitted through the gearset. It is in neutral.

JOB 44-2 MULTIPLE-CHOICE TEST

1. In a planetary gearset, when the sun gear is held stationary and the ring gear is turned, the planet-pinion carrier
   a. increases in speed
   b. turns faster in the reverse direction
   c. decreases in speed
   d. turns more slowly in the reverse direction 1. ____

2. To get speed reduction in reverse from a planetary gearset, the planet-pinion carrier is held stationary and the
   a. ring gear is turned
   b. ring gear is held stationary
   c. sun gear is turned
   d. sun gear is held stationary   2. ____

3. The three members of the planetary gearset are the planet-pinion carrier with the planet pinions and
   a. the sun gear and ring gear
   b. the ring gear and internal gear
   c. the pinion carrier and pinion cage
   d. none of the above   3. ____

4. Which of the following conditions cannot be provided by a planetary gearset?
   a. a speed increase with a torque decrease
   b. a speed decrease with a torque decrease
   c. a speed decrease with a torque increase
   d. none of the above   4. ____

5. When the planetary gearset is in overdrive, the output member is
   a. turning more slowly than the input member
   b. turning at the same speed as the input member
   c. held stationary
   d. turning faster than the input member   5. ____

JOB 44-3

Automatic-Transmission Fundamentals

Objective: To learn the construction and operation of various devices that control the automatic transmission.

References: AM ♦44-1 and 44-2, SG Chap. 44, automotive manufacturers' service manuals.

Equipment: Cars with automatic transmission, various disassembled automatic transmissions.
Tools: None.

SHOP FACTS

Shifting from one gear to another must be controlled so that it takes place only under the desired operating conditions. Figure 44-5 is a simplified diagram of a hydraulic control system for a single planetary gearset in an automatic transmission. The band is controlled by a servo. In hydraulic systems, a servo is a device that converts hydraulic pressure into mechanical movement, as the oil acts on a piston inside the servo.

The major purpose of the hydraulic control system is to apply and release a band or to engage and disengage a clutch. By this action, the hydraulic system controls the shifting of the planetary gearset from speed reduction to direct drive. The shift must take place at the right time. This depends on car speed and throttle opening, or engine load. These two factors produce varying oil pressures that work against the two ends of the *shift valve*.

The shift valve is a spool-type valve inside a bore or hole in the valve body. Pressure at one end of the shift valve (Fig. 44-5) comes from the governor and is known as *governor pressure*. Pressure at the other end of the shift valve changes as engine intake-manifold vacuum changes, and is known as *throttle pressure*. Throttle pressure and governor pressure are the two signals, or forces, that determine when the transmission will shift.

GOVERNOR ACTION

The automatic-transmission governor is a device that controls or governs gear shifting in relation to car speed. In the hydraulic system, the governor controls pressure on one end of the shift valve. Governor pressure changes with car speed, because the governor is driven by the transmission output shaft. As output-shaft speed and car speed go up, governor pressure increases proportionally.

Governor pressure is actually a modified line pressure. An oil pump in the transmission produces the line pressure, which then passes into the governor, as shown in Fig. 44-5. As car speed increases, the governor spins faster. This allows more pressure to pass through, resulting in greater pressure against the right end of the shift valve. The higher the car speed, the higher the pressure released by the governor.

THROTTLE PRESSURE

Working on the left end of the shift valve is the throttle pressure that changes as intake-manifold vacuum changes. Line pressure enters the modulator valve at the upper right in Fig. 44-5. The modulator valve contains a spool valve attached to a

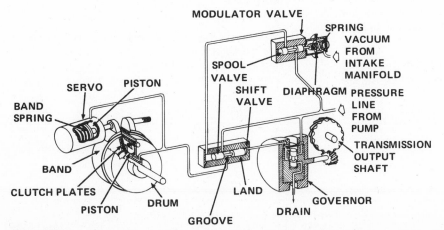

Fig. 44-5 One type of hydraulic control system that has been used to operate the band and clutch.

spring-loaded diaphragm. Vacuum increases in the engine intake manifold when the throttle valve is partly closed or when engine load decreases. This vacuum pulls the diaphragm in (to the right in Fig. 44-5), which then causes the modulator valve to also move to the right. Movement of the modulator valve reduces line pressure to the left end of the shift valve.

As the modulator valve moves, a band on the valve closes off the line-pressure passage from the pump. When this happens, it reduces the pressure on the left end of the shift valve. Then the shift valve is pushed to the left by governor pressure. As a result, line pressure can now pass through the shift valve to the band servo and clutch for the planetary gearset. The line pressure releases the band and engages the clutch. This puts the planetary gearset into direct drive, as the shift from speed reduction to direct drive is made.

SHIFT ACTION

When the planetary gearset changes from a lower speed ratio to a higher speed ratio, such as from speed reduction to direct drive, this is called an *upshift*. When the speed ratio through the planetary gearset is changed from a higher speed ratio to a lower speed ratio, a *downshift* has taken place. In an automatic transmission, the hydraulic control system must control both the upshifts and the downshifts.

SHOP SKILLS

____ 1. Road-test the car, with your instructor's permission, on a street or road with little traffic. If this is not possible, road-test the car on a dynamometer or in the shop with the drive wheels off the floor and the car supported on safety stands.

____ 2. Start the engine, noting that the selector lever must be in park or neutral. With the engine running, think about the power flow from the engine through the transmission. As the crankshaft turns, it spins the converter housing and the pump which is driven by it. Oil flows through the stator to the turbine, but the car does not move because all the planetary gearsets are freewheeling.

____ 3. Pull the selector lever into the drive range. Linkage attached to the selector lever causes movement of the manual valve in the valve body. Now oil is directed to the combination of bands and clutches necessary for the transmission to be in first gear.

____ 4. Gradually accelerate, allowing car speed to slowly increase. As the car reaches the speed necessary for the upshift from first to second, listen carefully to detect the change in engine speed. Try to feel the shift take place and note the

speed. The driver can often feel the shift in the steering wheel. When the car is on stands, you can watch the speedometer and see the sudden jump of the speedometer needle or speed display.

____ 5. Continue to gradually increase engine speed until the shift from second to third takes place. Note the speed at which it happens. Now the planetary gearsets in the transmission are locked. The power flow is from the crankshaft through the torque converter and through the transmission to the output shaft.

____ 6. Allow the car speed to decrease, and feel the downshifts from third to second and from second to first. At closed throttle, the governor is controlling the shift points.

____ 7. Now make the same checks of the shift points with greater throttle opening and note the speeds at which the upshifts occur. With heavier throttle, the modulator valve (when used) acts to delay the upshifts until a higher car speed is reached.

JOB 44-3   MULTIPLE-CHOICE TEST

1. The two factors that control the shift point are
   a. car speed and throttle opening
   b. input-shaft speed and oil pressure
   c. intake-manifold vacuum and throttle opening
   d. none of the above   1. ____

2. The valve that controls when the shift occurs is the
   a. throttle-modulator valve
   b. shift valve
   c. manual valve
   d. selector lever   2. ____

3. Pressure at one end of the shift valve comes from the governor and is called
   a. throttle pressure
   b. intake-manifold vacuum
   c. governor pressure
   d. line pressure   3. ____

4. A pressure on the shift valve which changes as intake-manifold vacuum changes is the
   a. governor pressure
   b. throttle pressure
   c. line pressure
   d. apply pressure   4. ____

5. The valve in the transmission that moves as the selector lever is moved is the
   a. shift valve
   b. spool valve
   c. modulator valve
   d. manual valve   5. ____

JOB 45-1

Changing Automatic-Transmission Fluid and Filter

Objective: To learn how to change the fluid and filter in automatic transmissions.

References: AM ♦45-1 to 45-12, SG Chap. 45, automotive manufacturers' service manuals.

Equipment: Various vehicles equipped with automatic transmission.
Tools: Torque wrench, basic hand tools.

SHOP FACTS

The level of the automatic-transmission fluid (also called ATF or oil) should be checked every time the engine oil is changed. In addition, many car manufacturers recommend changing the transmission fluid and filter at periodic intervals. The length of the intervals depends on how the car is used.

For example, Chevrolet recommends changing the fluid and filter every 100,000 miles [161,000 km] for normal service. For severe service, such as taxi, trailer hauling, police, and stop-and-go city or delivery service, Chevrolet recommends changing the fluid and filter every 15,000 miles [24,000 km].

Linkages and bands may require relatively frequent adjustment if the vehicle is in severe service.

SHOP SKILLS

____ 1. Raise the vehicle on a lift or safety stands. If a lift is used, set the lift lock or safety pin. Place an oil drain pan under the transmission.

____ 2. Remove the oil drain plug from the transmission oil pan. On some transmissions, the oil is drained by removing an oil filler tube from the pan. On other transmissions, no oil drain plug is provided. To drain the oil, remove the transmission-oil-pan attaching bolts (Fig. 45-1).

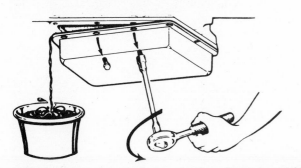

Fig. 45-1 Place a container under the oil pan to catch the oil that drains out as the pan is removed. **(American Motors Corporation)**

____ 3. Remove the pan by unscrewing the bolts that hold the pan in place. If the pan is without a drain plug, start on one end of the pan. Remove a bolt from one side, and then the other, until the pan tilts down (Fig. 45-1). This allows the oil trapped within the pan flange to drain into the oil drain pan.

____ 4. Figure 45-2 shows the bottom view of an automatic transmission with the oil pan removed. Remove the screws that hold the transmission oil filter in place, then pull the filter from the transmission.

____ 5. Examine the fluid that remains in the pan. The condition of the fluid can tell you a lot about the condition of an automatic transmission.

Fluid that is clean and normal in color indicates that no serious damage has occurred to the transmission. Fluid that is burned and discolored indicates that a clutch or band has burned in the transmission. To correct this condition, overhaul the transmission and clean all parts. Then flush the torque converter and the cooler lines.

Fluid that contains solid material also indicates that an

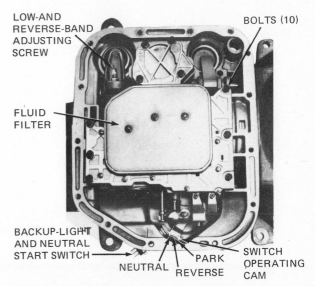

Fig. 45-2 Bottom view of an automatic transmission with the oil pan removed. **(Chrysler Corporation)**

overhaul is necessary. Repair the transmission and clean all parts. Then flush the torque converter and the cooler lines.

Varnish on the dipstick, pan, and transmission case indicates overheating. It also means that an overhaul may be necessary. Check the oil cooler to see whether it is leaking coolant from the radiator into the transmission fluid. If no coolant leak is found, check the engine for overheating. Solid material and varnish in the pan indicate the need for a transmission overhaul. Then flush the torque converter and cooler lines.

_____ 6. Remove the gasket or O-ring seal from the filter neck on the transmission case. Install the new gasket or O-ring seal.

_____ 7. Wash the transmission oil pan with solvent. Clean all gasket surfaces on the pan and on the transmission.

_____ 8. Install the new filter and tighten the filter hold-down bolts, if used.

_____ 9. Place the pan gasket on the oil pan and install the pan on the transmission. Tighten the transmission bolts to the recommended torque. Install the oil filler tube, if disconnected.

_____ 10. Drain the torque converter if it has a drain plug.

_____ 11. Remove the oil drain pan from under the vehicle. Lower the lift.

_____ 12. Refill the transmission to the ADD mark with the recommended transmission fluid following the manufacturer's refill procedure.

Note Be sure the vehicle is sitting level. The transmission must be filled with the fluid recommended by the vehicle manufacturer and to the level specified.

_____ 13. After refilling the transmission, check for oil leaks from the transmission oil pan before returning the vehicle to the customer.

JOB 45-1 MULTIPLE-CHOICE TEST

1. To change the oil filter in an automatic transmission, first
   a. drain the transmission oil pan
   b. drain the torque converter
   c. drain the engine oil
   d. drain the coolant   1. _____

2. When changing the transmission filter, always install a new
   a. drain plug
   b. filler tube
   c. dipstick
   d. transmission-pan gasket   2. _____

3. Before refilling the transmission, be sure that the vehicle is sitting
   a. with the rear down
   b. with the front up
   c. with the front down
   d. level   3. _____

4. Changing a transmission oil filter requires
   a. a strap wrench
   b. a grease gun
   c. no special tools
   d. compressed air   4. _____

5. On some automatic transmissions, the filter neck is sealed to the transmission case by
   a. an O-ring seal
   b. a slip fit
   c. an interference fit
   d. a liquid sealer   5. _____

JOB 45-2

Automatic-Transmission Trouble Diagnosis

Objective: To learn how to diagnose troubles in automatic transmissions.

References: AM ♦45-6, SG Chap. 45, automotive manufacturers' service manuals.

Equipment: Various vehicles equipped with automatic transmission.

Tools: Automatic-transmission tester (includes tachometer, vacuum gauge, and pressure gauge), hand vacuum pump, basic hand tools.

SHOP FACTS

Each automatic transmission has its own specific trouble-diagnosis guide issued by the manufacturer. These guides list in step-by-step order the best diagnostic procedure for each transmission. If it is available, locate the trouble-diagnosis section in the service manual covering the transmission you are diagnosing. Figure 45-3 shows a diagnosis checklist provided to Ford technicians. This job sheet follows the sequence shown on the Ford check sheet.

SHOP SKILLS

TESTING THE AUTOMATIC TRANSMISSION

____ 1. Automatic-transmission troubles are caused by fluid leaks, improper band and linkage adjustments, hydraulic and mechanical trouble inside the transmission, and poor engine performance. Before trying to isolate any of these problems, make a quick check under and around the car for any large transmission-fluid leaks.

____ 2. Pull the dipstick and check the level and condition of the transmission fluid. Be sure the transmission is at normal temperature and that the car is sitting level before you make this test. Let a few drops of fluid from the dipstick drip onto a paper towel (Fig. 45-4). Write down under Remarks in Fig. 45-3B any abnormal conditions that you find. The condition of the fluid can tell you a lot about the condition of an automatic transmission.

Fluid that is clean and normal in color indicates that no serious damage has occurred inside the transmission. Fluid that is burned and discolored indicates that a clutch or band has burned in the transmission. To correct this condition, overhaul the transmission and clean all parts. Then flush the torque converter and the cooler lines.

Fluid that contains solid material (Fig. 45-4) indicates that an overhaul is necessary. Repair the transmission and clean all parts. Then flush the torque converter and the cooler lines.

Varnish on the dipstick indicates overheating. It means that an overhaul may be necessary. Check the oil cooler to see whether it is leaking coolant from the radiator into the transmission fluid. If no coolant leak is found, check the engine for overheating. When both solid material and varnish are found on the dipstick, they indicate the need for a transmission overhaul. Then flush the torque converter and the cooler lines.

____ 3. Check the engine idle speed with a tachometer. Reset the idle speed, if necessary. When the idle speed is too fast, the driver may complain of harsh engagement as the shift lever is moved from park or neutral to reverse or drive. A slow idle speed may cause slow engagement of the automatic transmission. A rough or loping engine can cause erratic engagement and shift problems. Write down any abnormal conditions that you find under Remarks in Fig. 45-3C.

____ 4. Be sure the engine is not causing the customer complaint. An engine that lacks power, acceleration, or high-speed performance probably needs a tuneup. A poorly running engine can cause many of the problems blamed on automatic transmissions. Complaints of hard and erratic shifts often are caused by improper engine performance. Use an oscilloscope or engine analyzer to make sure the engine is operating properly.

____ 5. With the parking brake set and the engine idling, remove the vacuum hose from the modulator. The engine should begin to idle rough. If it does not, find and correct the vacuum problem. You may find the vacuum hose already disconnected. This will cause complaints of hard shifts and no upshift. When the vacuum hose is reinstalled, proper transmission operation is restored.

____ 6. Figure 45-3D lists a check of the exhaust-gas recirculation (EGR) system. Because a malfunction in the EGR system can affect intake-manifold vacuum, this in turn can affect the shift points. After the engine is at normal operating temperature, make an operational check of the EGR valve. The purpose of the operational check is to answer the question: Does the EGR valve work?

DIAGNOSIS CHECK SHEET

R.O. _____ Trans. _____

Engine _____

Code on Diagnosis Wheel	Check/Test	Remarks

☐ B — TRANSMISSION FLUID
1. Level _____ _____
2. Condition _____ _____

☐ C — ENGINE
Idle _____ _____
Power _____ _____

☐ D — EGR SYSTEM

☐ E — LINKAGE
Downshift _____ _____
Manual _____ _____

☐ F — SHIFT TESTS

Throttle Opening	Range	Shift	Shift Points (MPH)	
			Record Actual	Record Spec.
Minimum (Above 12" Vacuum)	D	1-2		
	D	2-3		
	D	3-1		
	1	2-1		
To Detent (Torque Demand)	D	1-2		
	D	2-3		
		3-2		
Thru Detent (Wide Open Throttle)	D	1-2		
	D	2-3		
	D	3-2		
	D	2-1 or 3-1		

☐ G — PRESSURE TEST

Engine RPM	Manifold Vacuum In-Hg	Throttle	Range	PSI	
				Record Actual	Record Spec.
Idle	Above 12	Closed	P N D 2 1 R		
As Required	10	As Required	D, 2, 1		
As Required	Below 3	Wide Open	D 2 1 R		

Results _____

☐ H — STALL TEST

Range	Specified Engine RPM	Record Actual Engine RPM
D		
2		
1		
R		

Results _____

☐ I — GOVERNOR TEST
Cutback Speed (C3, C4, C6)
10" Vacuum _____ MPH _____
0-2" Vacuum _____ MPH _____
Pressure at MPH (FMX)
10 _____ PSI _____
20 _____ PSI _____
30 _____ PSI _____

☐ J — LEAK TEST

CHECK THESE	OK	OIL/FLUID *(COLOR)
CONVERTER AREA		
OIL PAN GASKET		
FILLER TUBE/SEAL		
COOLER/CONNECTIONS		
LEVER SHAFT SEALS		
PRESSURE PORT PLUGS		
EXTENSION/CASE GASKET		
EXTENSION SEAL/BUSHING		
SPEEDOMETER ADAPTER		
SERVO COVERS		
AIR VENT		

*Color Codes	Auto. Trans.	Red
	Power Steering	Yellow-Green
	Engine Oil	Golden Brown

☐ K — VACUUM HOSE ROUTING
☐ L — BAND AND SERVO
1. Intermediate Band Adj.
2. Reverse Band Adj.
3. Polished, Glazed Band, Drum
☐ M — DRIVE SHAFT, U JOINTS, ENGINE MOUNTS
☐ N — TRANSMISSION END PLAY
☐ O — CLUTCH PACK FREE PLAY
☐ P — VALVE BODY DIRTY, STICKING
☐ Q — INTERNAL LINKAGE
☐ R — VALVE BODY BOLT TORQUE
☐ S — AIR PRESSURE TEST
☐ T — MECHANICAL PARTS
☐ U — VERIFY PROBLEM
☐ V — VALVE BODY MOUNTING FACES
☐ W — SPEEDO DRIVEN GEAR
☐ X — VACUUM TO DIAPHRAGM
☐ Y — CHECK DIAPHRAGM FOR LEAKAGE

REFER TO DIAGNOSIS WHEEL OR TO CAR DIAGNOSIS MANUAL FOR ACTION TO TAKE ON ANY "NOT OK" CONDITION.

Fig. 45-3 Diagnosis check sheet for Ford automatic transmissions. **(Ford Motor Company)**

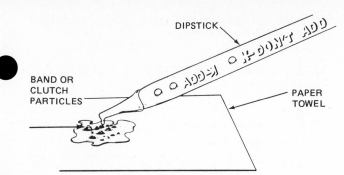

Fig. 45-4 Checking the condition of the fluid in an automatic transmission or transaxle. (Ford Motor Company)

____ 7. To find out if the EGR valve works, apply the parking brake and run the engine at idle. Then, while you watch the stem of the EGR valve, increase the engine speed to about 1500 rpm. The valve stem should move outward. If it doesn't move when the engine is accelerated, the valve is stuck, or no vacuum is reaching the valve. Check for vacuum in the hose attached to the EGR valve. If you can feel vacuum, then clean or replace the EGR valve. If there is no vacuum, correct the problem with the vacuum hose or clean the restriction in the passage from the intake manifold.

____ 8. To make the automatic transmission shift properly, the shift-lever manual linkage must be correctly adjusted. To get full engine power and proper shifting, the throttle linkage (also called downshift linkage) also must be correctly adjusted. For information on how to check and correct the manual linkage and the throttle linkage, refer to the manufacturer's service manual for the car you are servicing.

____ 9. To make shift tests of an automatic transmission, first locate the specifications for the shift points. Write each of these specifications in the space provided in Fig. 45-3. At the same time, write in the specifications for the pressure tests in G and for the stall test in H. You will need these later.

____ 10. Road-test the car on a dynamometer or by making a test drive to check for any shift or slipping problems. On the road test, check for shift "feel" and shift speed. Drive the car as necessary to note the shift points required in Fig. 45-3F. Write in, on the chart, the actual speeds at which each shift occurs. Compare each actual shift point with the specified shift point.

Note If you operate the car on a dynamometer, watch the speedometer on the dynamometer for the shift points. It usually is larger, steadier, and more accurate than the speedometer in the car. However, shift feel is very difficult to sense on the dynamometer.

____ 11. The first section in Fig. 45-3F is a check of the shift valves and governor circuits. The second section, "To Detent," checks the throttle boost and shift delay systems (used in Ford transmissions). Detent occurs slightly before the foot pedal reaches the floor. The third section tests the shift speeds at wide-open throttle. These speeds must be higher than those obtained during "To Detent" tests.

____ 12. If you must test the shift speeds of an automatic transmission in the shop, raise the car on a lift until the drive wheels are clear of the floor. Or raise the drive wheels with a jack and place safety stands under the car.

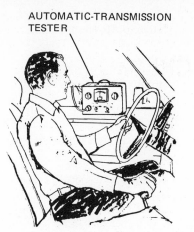

Fig. 45-5 An automatic-transmission tester. It combines in one unit a tachometer, vacuum gauge, and oil-pressure gauge. (Ford Motor Company)

____ 13. To control the vacuum to the modulator when checking shift points in the shop, connect a hand vacuum pump to the modulator. Operate the pump to apply 18 inches [450 mm] of vacuum to the modulator. Then make the tests as outlined above. Write in the actual shift points on the chart. To make the "To Detent" and "Through Detent" tests, release the vacuum until the vacuum-pump gauge shows from 0 to 2 inches [0 to 50 mm].

____ 14. To make the pressure tests in Fig. 45-3G, install an automatic-transmission tester. This tester, shown in Fig. 45-5, contains a vacuum gauge, a pressure gauge, and a tachometer. If an automatic-transmission tester is not available, the individual gauges and tachometer may be used. The vacuum gauge is installed with a T fitting into the manifold-vacuum line to the modulator, as shown in Fig. 45-6. The pressure gauge should read from 0 to 400 psi [2758 kPa]. It is connected to the control-pressure fitting on the transmission case. The tachometer is connected to the distributor terminal of the coil and to ground.

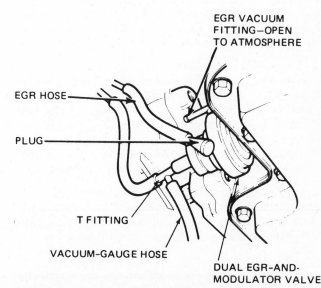

Fig. 45-6 To pressure-test an automatic transmission with a dual EGR-and-modulator valve, disconnect the EGR hose and plug it. (Ford Motor Company)

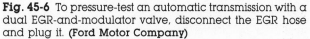

Note When connecting the gauge, be careful in routing the hose. It must not touch or run too close to any part of the hot exhaust system.

_____ 15. With the engine idling, and the tester on the window so you can see the needles from the driver's seat (Fig. 45-5), make the pressure tests. The parking brake should be applied. With your foot firmly on the service brake, shift the selector lever into each transmission range. Write the pressure recorded on the pressure gauge in each range in the top section in Fig. 45-3G.

_____ 16. On transmissions equipped with a dual EGR-and-modulator valve, the EGR hose must be disconnected and plugged (Fig. 45-6). Then increase engine speed as required until the manifold vacuum is 10 inches [250 mm]. Note the pressure reading. Write it in the space in the center of Fig. 45-3G.

_____ 17. To get the pressures during full throttle with very little manifold vacuum, a stall test must be made in each range. The stall test is needed because specifications for control pressure require that the output shaft not be turning. This means that the governor is not turning. Therefore it cannot affect shift speeds or pressures. When a stall test is made, the throttle is briefly held wide open with both brakes firmly set. To avoid damage to the transmission caused by excess heat generated inside the transmission during the stall test, observe the following:

    a. Never run the engine for longer than 5 seconds per test with the transmission stalled.
    b. If the transmission begins to slip or the tachometer begins to read much higher than it should, immediately release the throttle. Continuing the stall test further can seriously damage the transmission.
    c. After each 5-second stall test, shift into neutral. Allow the transmission to cool by running the engine at fast idle for 15 seconds before checking the pressure in the next range.

Note Some manufacturers recommend against making stall tests of their automatic transmissions. Be sure that the stall test is allowed by the manufacturer. If it is not allowed, an alternative method described in steps 18 to 20 below can be used.

_____ 18. An alternative method of reducing the vacuum to the modulator can be used if a stall test is not allowed. This method avoids making the stall test and reduces the time needed to make the pressure tests. Install a T fitting into the vacuum line to the modulator. Run a hose from the T up to the pressure tester. On the end of the hose attach a bleed valve, or cover the end of the valve with your thumb.

_____ 19. Close the hose and make the closed-throttle tests. Then partially open the bleed valve until the vacuum gauge shows the 10 inches [250 mm] required for the part-throttle test. Note the pressure and record it.

_____ 20. To get maximum pressure in each range, completely open the bleed valve (or remove your thumb) until the vacuum gauge reads 3 inches [75 mm] of vacuum or less. Write down the reading in each range. This method fools the modulator by making it "think" that the engine is under heavy load, as indicated by the very low manifold vacuum

applied to it. With no modulator action, maximum pressures are developed in the transmission.

DIAGNOSIS OF AUTOMATIC-TRANSMISSION TROUBLES

_____ 1. To perform a diagnosis means to answer the question: What is wrong? Now, we will use the test results in Fig. 45-3 to determine what, if anything, is wrong with the automatic transmission that you tested.

_____ 2. Look at the pressures that you recorded in Fig. 45-3G during the pressure tests. Compare each actual pressure to the specifications that you found in the service manual. In comparing the pressures, you must decide if the pressures you recorded were the same as, lower than, or higher than specifications. Figure 45-7 is a pressure-test diagnosis chart. It specifically applies to Ford transmissions. Generally, the chart applies to many of the automatic transmissions in use today.

_____ 3. Look in the chart for each pressure problem that you found. For example, a transmission that has low pressure in drive, second, and first but normal pressure in other ranges indicates a problem with the forward clutch. It is applied in all forward gears. For more details on the diagnosis of the transmission you are testing, refer to the manufacturer's service manual. In the Results section in Fig. 45-3G write in your diagnosis of the transmission you tested.

_____ 4. A stall test checks for clutch or band slipping and for torque-converter operation. The stall-test measurement is made by reading engine speed in rpm on a tachometer. Compare each actual engine speed that you recorded in Fig. 45-3H to the specifications that you found in the shop manual. In comparing the actual speed to the specified speed, you must decide if the actual speed was the same as, lower than, or higher than specifications.

_____ 5. Figure 45-8 is a chart showing how to diagnose band, clutch, and torque-converter troubles based on stall-test results. Look in the chart for each engine-speed problem that you found in Fig. 45-3H. For example, in Fig. 45-8, notice that when stall speed is high in drive, second, and first, this indicates that the forward clutch is slipping. This confirms the diagnosis we made in the example in step 3, where the pressure test was low in all forward-gear positions.

_____ 6. Notice in Fig. 45-8 that the stall speed may test low. This could be caused by an improperly running engine. However, we will assume that this was checked and corrected earlier in step 5 of the part above. The *only* other cause of a low stall speed is a defective stator clutch inside the torque converter. If the stator clutch is slipping, the stall speed will be low. This is because of poor torque multiplication through the torque converter. But after the car is running at cruising speed, the slipping stator clutch is not noticeable.

_____ 7. Should the stator clutch seize, or lock up on the shaft, the car will have normal acceleration. However, as the car approaches cruising speed, you will have to open the throttle too far to sustain the cruising speed. This is because the seized stator clutch does not allow the stator to freewheel out of the way of the recirculating oil. Instead, the seized stator impedes the oil flow at cruising speed.

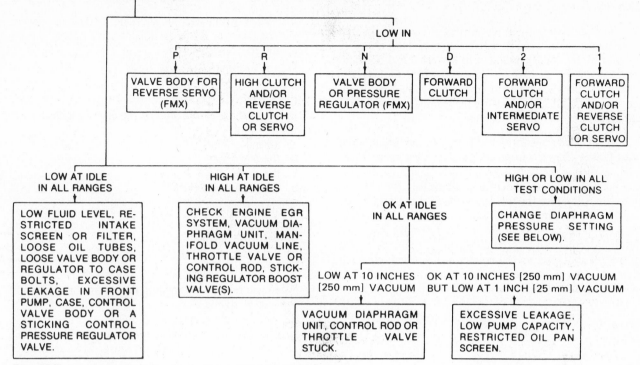

Fig. 45-7 A pressure-test diagnosis chart. **(Ford Motor Company)**

Stall Test Results	Selector Position	Stall Speeds High (Slip)	Stall Speeds Low
	D only	Transmission one-way clutch	
	D, 2, & 1	Forward clutch	
	D, 2, 1, & R	Control pressure test	Converter stator one-way clutch or engine performance
	R only	High and/or reverse clutch or reverse band	

Fig. 45-8 A stall-speed diagnosis chart. **(Ford Motor Company)**

GEAR AND RANGE	FORWARD CLUTCH	HIGH-REVERSE CLUTCH	INTERMEDIATE (FRONT) BAND	LOW-REVERSE (REAR) BAND OR CLUTCH	ONE-WAY CLUTCH
1 (MANUAL LOW)	ON			ON	
2 (MANUAL SECOND)	ON		ON		
D LOW GEAR	ON				ON
D SECOND GEAR	ON		ON		
D HIGH GEAR	ON	ON			
REVERSE		ON		ON	

Fig. 45-9 Band-and-clutch application chart. **(Ford Motor Company)**

_____ 8. Figure 45-9 is a band-and-clutch application chart. It tells what combinations of bands and clutches are applied, or on, in each gear. To correct a slipping clutch, the transmission must be overhauled. However, bands can be adjusted. On Ford transmissions, the intermediate band has an adjustment on the outside of the transmission. Except for the Ford C4 transmission, the low-reverse band for Ford transmissions is adjusted inside the transmission. When a band adjustment fails to correct slipping, further tests should be made of the servo that operates the band.

____ 9. High stall speed in reverse (Fig. 45-8) indicates that if the transmission has a reverse band (some have a reverse clutch instead), the slipping may be corrected by a band adjustment. Figure 45-10 shows how and where to make the band adjustment on the C4 transmission. To find the band-adjustment specifications, refer to the manufacturer's service manual for the car you are servicing.

____ 10. The intermediate band is applied (ON in Fig. 45-9) when the shift lever is in second (this is called *manual second*), and when the shift lever is in drive and the transmission is in second gear. When the intermediate band is slipping, you will notice the problem while road-testing the car. In drive, the transmission will skip second gear and shift directly from first to third. On some cars, the transmission will shift into second, but an erratic shift and slipping will be felt on the 1-2 shift. Failure of the intermediate band often will show up in the pressure tests as low pressure in second. This condition is listed under "Low in 2" in Fig. 45-8.

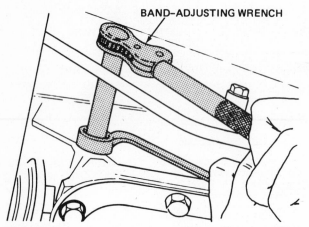

BAND–ADJUSTING WRENCH

Fig. 45-10 Adjusting the low-reverse band. **(Ford Motor Company)**

JOB 45-2 MULTIPLE-CHOICE TEST

1. Instead of a stall test, an alternate method of applying various vacuums to the modulator can be done by using
   a. the shop air supply
   b. a tire pump
   c. a hand vacuum pump
   d. intake-manifold vacuum   1. ____

2. Burned and discolored fluid on the dipstick indicates failure of
   a. a band or clutch
   b. the governor
   c. the servo
   d. the torque converter   2. ____

3. A high idle speed may cause the driver to complain of
   a. slow engagement
   b. harsh engagement
   c. fluid leaks under the car
   d. no upshift   3. ____

4. When you remove the vacuum hose from the modulator, the engine should
   a. begin to idle rough
   b. continue to idle with the same speed and smoothness
   c. have transmission fluid run out of the disconnected hose
   d. fail to deliver power to the transmission when in gear   4. ____

5. An automatic-transmission tester contains an oil-pressure gauge, a vacuum gauge, and a
   a. dwell meter
   b. timing light
   c. compression tester
   d. tachometer   5. ____

JOB 46
Universal-Joint Service

Objective: To learn to service a universal joint.

References: AM ♦46-9, SG Chap. 46, automotive manufacturers' service manuals.

Equipment: Various cars with a front engine and rear-wheel drive.

Tools: Shop press and basic hand tools.

SHOP FACTS

Various disassembly procedures are required on different types of universal joints. Refer to the proper service manual for details of disassembly, repair, and reassembly of universal joints. The following procedure covers servicing the cross-and-two-yoke type of universal joint when used in a single-piece drive shaft.

SHOP SKILLS

REMOVING THE DRIVE SHAFT

____ 1. Raise the vehicle on a lift. To maintain drive-line balance during reassembly, mark the rear drive-shaft yoke and the flange on the differential (Fig. 46-1). Next, mark the front of the drive shaft and then scribe a line on the front drive-shaft yoke and on the transmission yoke.

____ 2. Disconnect the rear differential joint by removing the needle-bearing-cup U-bolts. Tape the bearing cups to the cross to prevent dropping the cups and losing any needle bearings.

____ 3. Slide the drive shaft from the transmission by pulling the drive shaft to the rear of the vehicle under the axle housing. Install a plug in the transmission extension housing to prevent transmission oil leakage.

Many universal joints do not require periodic inspection or

lubrication. However, when these universal joints are disassembled, always repack the needle bearings and fill the lubricant reservoirs in the cross with proper lubricant.

DISASSEMBLING THE UNIVERSAL JOINT

____ 1. Remove the bearing-cup lock rings from the yoke with needle-nose pliers. Use a soft-drift punch to tap the outside of the cup to loosen the snap ring.

____ 2. Support the yoke on a piece of pipe on the bed of a shop press. The inside diameter of the pipe should be larger than the diameter of the cup.

If the drive shaft is too long to handle easily in a shop press, a bench vise may be used for removal and installation of the universal joint.

____ 3. Using a suitable metal rod, press the bearing cup in until the opposite bearing cup is pressed as far out of the yoke as possible. Then grasp the cup in the vise and work the cup out of the yoke.

____ 4. Press the end of the cross against the remaining cup, and remove the cup as in step 3. The universal joint may also be removed and installed with a special U-joint press (Fig. 46-2).

____ 5. Clean and inspect the dust seal, rings, needle-bearing cups, needle bearings, cross (or spider), and yokes. A disassembled universal joint is shown in Fig. 46-3. Lubricate the cross and needle bearings with the proper lubricant. Make sure that the lubricant reservoir at each end of the cross is completely filled with lubricant. In filling these reservoirs, pack lubricant into the hole so as to completely fill the reservoir. Use of a squeeze bottle filled with lubricant will prevent air pockets and ensure adequate filling.

ASSEMBLING A UNIVERSAL JOINT

In assembly, do not use a new cross with old bearings or an old cross with new bearings. Inspect all parts of the universal joint carefully. If either the cross or bearings are worn, replace both with a new cross and bearing kit.

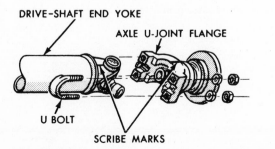

DRIVE-SHAFT END YOKE

AXLE U-JOINT FLANGE

U BOLT

SCRIBE MARKS

Fig. 46-1 Scribe marks on the drive-shaft-to-universal-joint connection. **(Ford Motor Company)**

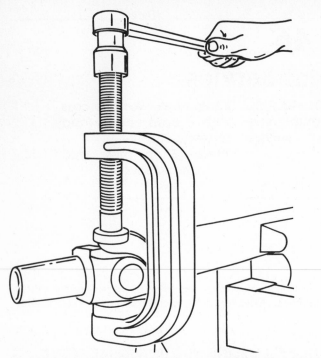

Fig. 46-2 A special U-joint press for removing and installing universal joints. (Owatonna Tool Company)

_____ 1. If you are not installing a universal-joint service kit, place the dust seals on the cross with the seal cavity toward the end of each arm of the cross. Be careful during installation to prevent seal distortion and to assure proper seating of the seal on the cross.

_____ 2. Attach the transmission yoke on the front of the drive shaft in the position marked in the first part of this jobsheet. Failure to properly position the drive shaft to the yoke could result in drive-line vibration.

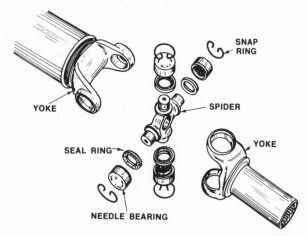

Fig. 46-3 A disassembled cross-and-two-yoke universal joint.

_____ 3. Position the cross into the yoke. Partially install one bearing cup into the yoke. Start the cross into the bearing cup. Then partially install the other cup. Align the cross into the cups, and press the cups into the yoke using the shop press or bench vise.

_____ 4. Install the lock rings behind the needle-bearing cups. Be sure the universal joints are free from binds before proceeding with the installation of the drive shaft.

INSTALLING THE DRIVE SHAFT

_____ 1. Inspect the yoke seal in the transmission extension housing. Replace the seal, if necessary.

_____ 2. Insert the transmission yoke into the transmission extension housing. Make sure that the output-shaft splines mate smoothly with the splines in the yoke.

_____ 3. Align the drive shaft with the flange on the differential using the marks made in the first part of this jobsheet (Fig. 46-1). Remove the tape used to retain the bearing cups to the cross. Install the needle-bearing-cup U-bolts and torque to specifications.

JOB 46 MULTIPLE-CHOICE TEST

1. Marking the drive shaft and yokes before disassembly is necessary to prevent
   a. difficult assembly
   b. noise
   c. lack of lubrication
   d. vibration   1. _____

2. When the splined yoke is removed from the transmission,
   a. a puller is required
   b. engine oil leaks out
   c. the extension-housing seal must be replaced
   d. transmission oil may leak out   2. _____

3. Bearing-cup lock rings are removed with
   a. a hammer
   b. a punch
   c. needle-nose pliers
   d. a screwdriver   3. _____

4. The holes in the arms of the cross are
   a. lubricant reservoirs
   b. machining marks
   c. balance holes
   d. bearing guides   4. _____

5. When an inspection shows that the bearings in a universal joint are worn, always install
   a. new bearings
   b. new bearings and a new cross
   c. a new cross
   d. new dust seals   5. _____

JOB 47-1
Differential Trouble Diagnosis

Objective: To learn to diagnose trouble in the differential of a rear-drive vehicle.

References: AM ♦47-11, SG Chap. 47, automotive manufacturers' service manuals.

Equipment: Various vehicles with differential trouble.

Tools: Basic hand tools.

♦ ——————————————————————————————————— ♦

SHOP FACTS

Noise is usually the first indication of differential trouble. However, the location of the differential at the rear of the vehicle makes it difficult to pinpoint the source of noise. Several other components could produce a similar sound. Figure 47-1 is a rear-axle noise diagnosis chart listing noise problems and their possible causes.

A road test is often essential to diagnosing noise in the differential.

SHOP SKILLS

_____ 1. Tire noise is sometimes mistaken for differential noise. However, tire noise differs greatly with the type of pavement over which the car is driven. Differential noise is little affected by the type of pavement. Note in Fig. 47-1 how many different types of noise problems can be caused by tires. To determine if tires are causing the noise, drive the car over various types of pavement. Listen carefully for any change in the noise when the road surface changes.

PROBLEM	CAUSE	PROBLEM	CAUSE
1. Noise is the same in drive or coast	1. a Road noise b Tire noise c Front wheel bearing noise	7. Noise most pronounced on turns	7. Differential side gear and pinion
2. Noise changes on a different type of road	2. a Road noise b Tire noise	8. A continuous low pitch whirring or scraping noise starting at relatively low speed	8. Pinion bearing
3. Noise tone lowers as car speed is lowered	3. Tire noise	9. Drive noise, coast noise or float noise	9. Ring and pinion gear
4. Similar noise is produced with car standing and driving	4. a Engine noise b Transmission noise	10. Clunk on acceleration or deceleration	10. Worn differential cross shaft in case
5. Vibration	5. a Rough rear wheel bearing b Unbalanced or damaged propeller shaft c Tire unbalance d Worn universal joint in propeller shaft e Mis-indexed propeller shaft at companion flange f Companion flange runout too great	11. Grunt on stops	11. No grease in propeller shaft slip yoke
		12. Groan in Forward or Reverse	12. Wrong lube in differential
		13. Chatter on turns	13. a Wrong lube in differential b Clutch plates worn
6. A knock or click approximately every two revolutions of rear wheel	6. A brinelled rear wheel bearing	14. Clunk or knock on rough road operation	14. Excessive end play of axle shafts to differential cross shaft

Fig. 47-1 Rear-axle noise trouble-diagnosis chart. **(Chevrolet Motor Division of General Motors Corporation)**

_____ 2. Some clue to the source of the noise may be gained during a road test. Drive the car on a straight road and note if the noise is a hum, growl, or knock that occurs during acceleration or coasting. Then make right and left turns while listening carefully to determine if the noise becomes louder or occurs only during a turn.

Humming is often caused by improper drive-pinion or ring-gear adjustment, which in turn produces the humming noise and rapid gear wear. With wear, the noise takes on a growling sound. Knocking is caused by badly worn bearings or damaged gears.

If the noise is most noticeable when the car is accelerated, there probably is heavy heel contact on the ring-gear teeth. This type of noise could also be caused by a defective pinion bearing. If the noise is most noticeable when the car is driving the engine (coasting), there probably is heavy toe contact on the ring-gear teeth. To avoid rapid gear wear, the ring-gear tooth-contact pattern must be adjusted (Job 47-2).

If the noise is heard only when the car rounds a curve, the cause is probably some trouble in the differential case itself. Such conditions as pinion gears tight on the shaft, side gears tight in the case, damaged gears or thrust washers, and excessive gear backlash could produce noise during a turn. Worn or loose axle-shaft bearings could also cause noise as the car rounds a curve.

_____ 3. To check for backlash in the differential, shut off the engine, raise one rear wheel from the floor, and place a safety stand under the car to support it. Hold the companion flange stationary. With your hand, turn the wheel forward and back. Measure the amount of free rotary motion as you move the wheel. This can be an indication of excessive backlash in the differential. To correct excessive backlash, the differential must be disassembled for adjustment (Job 47-2).

JOB 47-1 MULTIPLE-CHOICE TEST

1. If the noise is the same with the car standing still and moving, the cause could be
   a. engine noise
   b. defective ring gear
   c. defective pinion gear
   d. tire noise   1. _____

2. Most often, the condition that draws attention to trouble in the differential is
   a. rough operation
   b. power loss
   c. noise
   d. lubricant leaks   2. _____

3. A humming noise in the differential is often caused by improper tooth contact between
   a. the pinion and side gears
   b. the axle and side gear
   c. the drive pinion and ring gear
   d. none of the above   3. _____

4. If the noise is louder when the car is being accelerated, there probably
   a. are worn bearings
   b. is heavy heel contact on gear teeth
   c. are loose gears
   d. are tight bearings   4. _____

5. If noise is present in the differential only when the car rounds a curve, the trouble probably is caused by some condition in the
   a. axle bearings
   b. drive-gear bearing
   c. ring-gear assembly
   d. differential-case assembly   5. _____

Name _____ Date _____

JOB 47-2

Differential Overhaul

Objective: To learn how to disassemble, assemble, and adjust differentials.
References: AM ♦47-12, SG Chap. 47, automotive manufacturers' service manuals.

Equipment: Automobiles with differentials to be overhauled.
Tools: Carrier stand, bearing-adjusting tools, dial indicator, bearing pullers and installers, basic hand tools.

Supplies: Prussian blue to test tooth contact, Permatex or similar sealer.

SHOP FACTS

Different procedures are required to remove, disassemble, assemble, adjust, and reinstall differentials in vehicles with rear drive. In reassembly, always coat all splines and gears with lubricant to provide initial lubrication.

SHOP SKILLS

REMOVAL AND DISASSEMBLY OF THE DIFFERENTIAL

_____ 1. Raise the vehicle on a lift. Remove the two rear wheels and axle shafts. Disconnect the drive shaft. Mark the position of the drive shaft and differential flange as described in Job 46.

_____ 2. Place a drain pan under the differential and drain the lubricant from the differential. Then remove the carrier assembly.

_____ 3. Before disassembling a differential, place it in a carrier stand. Then check the gear wear, backlash, ring-gear runout, and tooth-contact pattern (Fig. 47-2).

_____ 4. Note the differences between the patterns for different gear adjustments. Some incorrect patterns can be corrected by turning adjustment nuts or installing or removing shims.

If the differential is the integral carrier type, in which the carrier is not removable, the patterns must be checked before removing the case assembly from the housing.

_____ 5. Use punch marks and scribe lines to mark the proper relationship of the bearing adjustment nuts and carrier. By doing this before disassembly, all parts can be later reassembled in the proper relationship.

_____ 6. Remove the adjustment-nut locks, bearing caps, and nuts.

CORRECT TOOTH CONTACT

FACE CONTACT

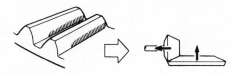
FLANK CONTACT

TOE CONTACT

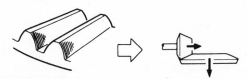
HEEL CONTACT

Fig. 47-2 Adjustment of gear-tooth contact patterns. **(Chrysler Corporation)**

_____ 7. Lift differential-case assembly from the carrier. Use a puller to remove the differential bearings. Take the pinion gear from the case, using a soft-face hammer or the shop press to loosen it. Drive out the lockpin from the differential pinion shaft with a punch. Separate the two-piece differential case. Drive out the pinion shaft with a brass drift punch and remove the gears and thrust washers.

_____ 8. If necessary, the drive pinion and bearing retainer can be disassembled by removing the U-joint flange and pinion seal. Then the bearings must be pressed out. Use a protective sleeve on the drive-pinion pilot-bearing surface and a fiber block on the end of the shaft to protect finished surfaces.

_____ 9. Inspect all parts carefully, discarding worn or damaged bearings, gears, shafts, or other parts. If the ring-gear runout is excessive, the cause could be a warped gear, warped case, or worn differential bearings. To determine the cause, assemble the two halves of the differential case without the drive gear, press the two differential side bearings, and set the case in the carrier. Install the bearing caps and adjusting nuts and adjust the bearings as explained in the references. If the runout of the differential-case flange is excessive, the case is defective or the bearings are worn. If the runout is not excessive, the drive gear is defective.

ASSEMBLY, ADJUSTMENT, AND INSTALLATION

_____ 1. To reassemble, install the drive pinion and bearing retainer in the carrier. Then install a new oil seal and the U-joint flange. Lubricate all parts as you install them.

_____ 2. Assemble the differential case. Be sure to line up the pinion-shaft lockpin holes when driving the pinion shaft into place.

_____ 3. Install the ring gear on the case. It will help, during reassembly, to install two long bolts through the case flange. Thread them several turns into the ring gear. The bolts will aid in aligning the ring gear on the case.

_____ 4. Adjust the backlash and drive-pinion location to get the proper tooth pattern, as outlined in the references.

_____ 5. To install the carrier assembly, clean the mating surfaces of the axle housing and carrier.

_____ 6. Position the carrier in the axle housing, using a new gasket or RTV sealer as required. Install the carrier, and attach the drive shaft.

_____ 7. Install the axle shafts, brake drums, and rear wheels.

_____ 8. Fill the differential to the correct level with the proper lubricant.

_____ 9. Road-test the vehicle to be sure the problem has been corrected before returning the car to the customer.

JOB 47-2 MULTIPLE-CHOICE TEST

1. To remove differential from the car, first
   a. check gear-tooth-contact pattern
   b. drain fuel tank
   c. remove differential bearings
   d. remove axle shafts   1. _____

2. Some incorrect gear-tooth-contact patterns can be corrected by installing or removing shims or by
   a. replacing gears
   b. coating gears with Prussian blue
   c. turning adjustment nuts
   d. grinding gears   2. _____

3. Before disassembling a differential, check tooth-contact pattern, ring-gear runout, and
   a. backlash
   b. clutch-gear wear
   c. forelash
   d. main-shaft wear   3. _____

4. If ring-gear runout is excessive, it could be a result of a warped gear or case, or of
   a. defective drive-shaft bearings
   b. worn bearings
   c. incorrect bearing adjustment
   d. leaking seals   4. _____

5. Two long guide bolts can be used to aid in installing the
   a. ring gear
   b. pinion gear
   c. case
   d. carrier   5. _____

JOB 48

Springs and Suspension Systems

Objective: To learn the construction and operation of different types of rear-suspension and front-suspension systems.

References: AM ♦48-1 to 48-16, SG Chap. 48, automotive manufacturers' service manuals.

Equipment: Various vehicles.

Tools: Shop lift.

SHOP SKILLS

REAR-SUSPENSION SYSTEMS

_____ 1. Examine various cars and note the types of rear-suspension systems used and the different arrangements of the springs and suspension-system parts.

_____ 2. Note the different ways the coil springs may be positioned on coil-spring suspension systems (Figs. 48-1 and 48-2). Locate the control arms that must be used to position the rear-axle housing.

_____ 3. On leaf-spring suspension systems, note how the spring is suspended from the axle housing and how it is attached at back and front to the car frame or body (Fig. 48-3). Look for a stabilizer bar that is sometimes used to prevent the body from rubbing the tires.

_____ 4. Locate the shock absorbers. Note how one end moves with the springing of the wheel and how the other end is attached to the body or frame.

_____ 5. If you are able to study heavy-duty equipment such as trucks and buses, note the types of springs they use and how the springs are attached to the vehicle frame.

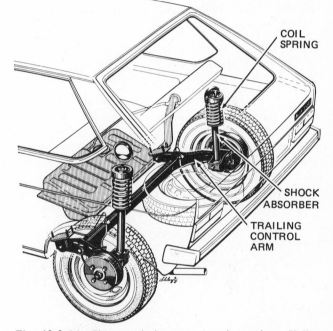

Fig. 48-2 MacPherson-strut rear-suspension system. (Volkswagen of America, Inc.)

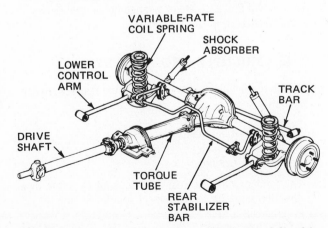

Fig. 48-1 Rear-suspension system using torque-tube drive and coil springs. (Chevrolet Motor Division of General Motors Corporation)

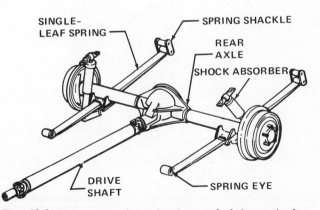

Fig. 48-3 Rear suspension using tapered-plate, or single-leaf, springs. (Chevrolet Motor Division of General Motors Corporation)

CAR MAKE AND YEAR	TYPE OF REAR SUSPENSION—COIL OR LEAF	LOCATION OF SHOCK ABSORBER	IF LEAF, MULTI- OR SINGLE-LEAF	IF COIL, LOCATION OF SPRING
1 83 VW	Coil	In strut		On strut
2				
3				
4				
5				

Fig. 48-4 Fill in the types and components in rear-suspension systems.

_____ 6. As you study different vehicles, fill out the table shown in Fig. 48-4. Write down the information called for at the tops of the columns.

FRONT-SUSPENSION SYSTEMS

_____ 1. Examine various vehicles and note the different types of front-suspension and steering systems used. Note that coil springs can rest on either the lower or upper control arm (Fig. 48-5).

_____ 2. Note that some lower control arms have two points of attachment to the car frame and that other lower control arms have only one point of attachment (Fig. 48-6). Study the position of the strut, or brake-reaction rod, used with the lower control arm having a single point of attachment. This rod prevents forward or backward movement of the outer end of the lower control arm but allows it to move up and down.

_____ 3. Study torsion-bar suspension systems (Figs. 48-7 and 48-8). Note how the torsion bar is attached to the body or frame and to the lower control arm. Find and identify the method of adjusting the torsion bar to correct the car height.

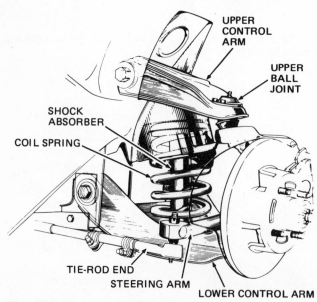

Fig. 48-5 Front-suspension system for one wheel, using a coil spring located between two control arms. (**Chevrolet Motor Division of General Motors Corporation**)

_____ 4. Locate the ball joints. Note how the steering knuckle is mounted in them. This arrangement permits the steering knuckle to pivot in the ball joints so that the front wheels can be swung from side to side for steering.

_____ 5. Study how the brake and the wheel are mounted on the spindle and steering knuckle. Note the location of the flexible brake tubing that carries the hydraulic fluid to the brake mechanism.

_____ 6. Locate the shock absorbers. Note their positions inside the coil springs on some cars and elsewhere on others.

_____ 7. As you study different cars, fill out the table in Fig. 48-9. Write in the blanks the information called for at the tops of the columns.

_____ 8. Locate the stabilizer bar. Note its attachment to the lower control arms.

_____ 9. If you can locate an early-model car or a heavy-duty vehicle, study the location of the kingpin. Note how it supports the knuckle. Contrast this arrangement with the ball-joint system.

_____ 10. If you can locate a Ford truck with twin I-beam suspension, note the attachment points of the I-beams to the frame and at the front wheels. Identify the radius arms that prevent backward and forward swinging of the I-beams and the wheels.

_____ 11. Other front-suspension systems you should study include solid front axles, four-wheel drive, and heavy-duty trucks. You will find a variety of arrangements used. Some of these are illustrated in the references.

JOB 48   MULTIPLE-CHOICE TEST

1. Which of the following is _not_ true of the rear-suspension system?
    a. supports the vehicle
    b. improves ride quality
    c. steers the vehicle
    d. prolongs tire life   1. _____

2. The tendency for the rear-axle housing to rotate in a direction opposite to rear-wheel rotation is due to
    a. rear-end torque
    b. Hotchkiss drive
    c. torque-tube drive
    d. brake action   2. _____

196

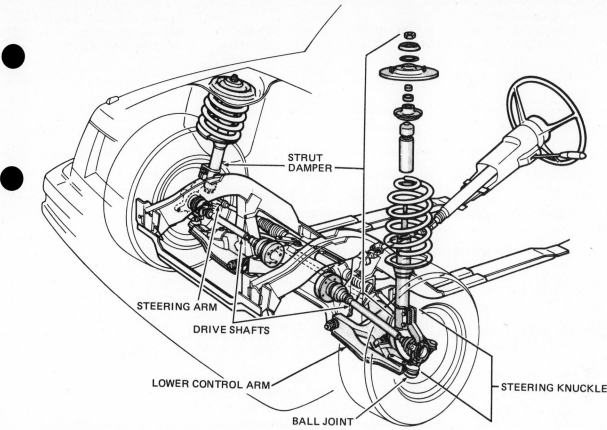

Fig. 48-6 MacPherson-strut front-suspension system. **(Chrysler Corporation)**

3. In the rear-suspension system using coil springs, the parts that prevent forward or backward movement of the axle housing are called.
   a. radius rods
   b. axle arms
   c. stabilizers
   d. control arms or links

   3. ____

4. In the typical leaf-spring installation, the spring is hung from the axle housing by
   a. a hanger
   b. two U-bolts
   c. a shackle
   d. a through bolt

   4. ____

5. A rear suspension that uses a single leaf spring to suspend one wheel at each end of the spring is called
   a. torque-tube drive
   b. Hotchkiss drive
   c. twin I-beam suspension
   d. transverse-leaf-spring rear suspension

   5. ____

6. The lower control arm that has a single point of attachment to the car frame has four suspension parts attached to it in addition to the frame: the steering knuckle, the shock absorber, the stabilizer bar, and the
   a. brake-reaction rod
   b. upper control arm
   c. wheel
   d. brake drum

   6. ____

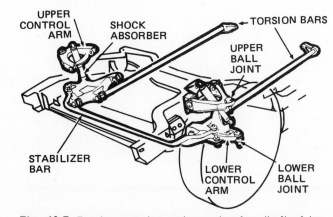

Fig. 48-7 Front-suspension system using longitudinal torsion bars. **(Moog Automotive, Inc.)**

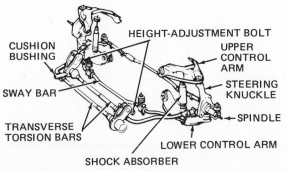

Fig. 48-8 Front-suspension system using transverse torsion bars. **(Chrysler Corporation)**

CAR MAKE AND YEAR	TYPE OF FRONT SUSPENSION—COIL OR TORSION BAR	IF COIL, GIVE LOCATION	LOCATION OF SHOCK ABSORBER	LOWER CONTROL ARM—SINGLE- OR DOUBLE-ATTACHMENT JOINT
1 83 VW	Coil	On strut	In strut	Single
2				
3				
4				
5				
6				

Fig. 48-9 Fill in the types and components in front-suspension systems.

7. The two ends of the stabilizer bar are attached to the
   a. car frame
   b. lower control arms
   c. upper control arms
   d. steering arms   7. ____

8. In the coil-spring front suspension in which the spring is between the two control arms, the shock absorber is located
   a. above the upper control arm
   b. below the lower control arm
   c. between the control arms
   d. none of the above   8. ____

9. In the torsion-bar front-suspension system, one end of the torsion bar is attached to the
   a. upper control arm
   b. lower control arm
   c. stabilizer bar
   d. steering arm   9. ____

10. The ball joints are located between the steering knuckle and the
    a. steering linkage
    b. steering arms
    c. stabilizer bar
    d. control arms   10. ____

JOB 49

Steering Systems

Objective: To learn about the construction and operation of automotive steering systems.

References: AM ♦49-1 to 49-25, SG Chap. 49, automotive manufacturers' service manuals.

Equipment: Various vehicles with different types of steering systems.
Tools: None.

SHOP FACTS

Various methods are used to support the front-wheel spindles so that the wheels can be swung to the left or right for steering. This movement is produced by gearing and linkage between the steering wheel and the steering knuckle. The complete arrangement is called the *steering system.*

The automotive steering system is composed of two elements: (1) a steering gear at the lower end of the steering column and (2) the linkage between the steering gear and the steering knuckle at each wheel.

There are several different types of steering gears. In the type shown in Fig. 49-1, when the steering wheel and shaft turn, the pitman-arm shaft also turns. As a result, the pitman arm, which is mounted on the end of the shaft, swings to one side or the other, according to which direction the steering shaft has turned.

In the rack-and-pinion steering gear (Fig. 49-2), the lower end of the steering shaft has a pinion (a small gear). This pinion is meshed with a rack which is like a straight section of gear teeth. As the pinion turns, it causes the rack to move

to one side or the other. This motion is carried to the steering arms by the tie rods.

Many steering systems have a power assist. It causes additional force to be applied to the steering system when the steering wheel is turned. This provides most of the force required to steer. Figure 49-1 shows an integral type of power-steering gear. Figure 49-2 shows a rack-and-pinion power-steering gear.

SHOP SKILLS

MANUAL- AND POWER-STEERING GEARS

____ 1. Open the hood of the car and locate the steering gear (Fig. 49-1). Look for any hydraulic lines attached to it. They indicate that this is a power-steering unit. Identify the pitman arm, which is attached to the shaft from the steering gear. If the car is equipped with power steering, locate the belt-driven power-steering pump, which is mounted at the front of the engine.

____ 2. Raise the car on a lift.

____ 3. Under the car, look at the different types of linkage used to carry the motion of the pitman arm on the steering gear to the steering arms at the front wheels.

____ 4. From the pitman arm, trace the linkage to the tie rod and steering arm for each wheel. Note any lubrication fittings that may be installed at each moving ball joint or ball socket.

____ 5. Note any hydraulic lines that may be connected to a large cylinder on the steering linkage. If present, this indicates that the car is equipped with a linkage-type power-steering unit.

____ 6. Turn the front wheels to the right and watch the action of the steering linkage. Then turn the front wheels all the way to the left. Watch the movement of each part of the steering linkage as a turn is made. Identify each part that moves.

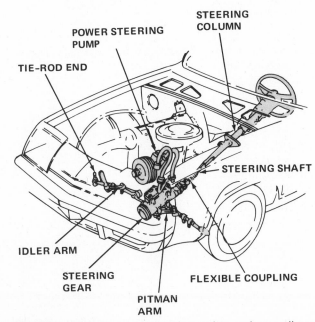

Fig. 49-1 Integral power-steering system, using a pitman-arm steering gear.

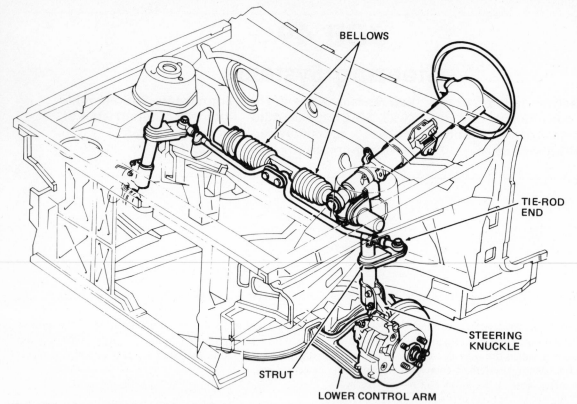

Fig. 49-2 Rack-and-pinion power-steering system. (Chevrolet Motor Division of General Motors Corporation)

Labels in figure: BELLOWS, TIE-ROD END, STEERING KNUCKLE, LOWER CONTROL ARM, STRUT

RACK-AND-PINION STEERING GEARS

_____ 1. Open the hood on a car with rack-and-pinion steering (Fig. 49-2). Determine whether the car has manual or power steering.

_____ 2. Raise the car on a lift or safety stands. Then have an assistant turn the steering wheel. Note how the tie-rod ends move as the steering wheel turns.

_____ 3. Follow the motion from the tie-rod ends to the steering knuckle. Note how the entire strut and steering knuckle turn as an assembly. The bearing in the upper retainer of the strut allows it to pivot.

JOB 49   MULTIPLE-CHOICE TEST

1. The steering linkage connects between the steering arms at the front wheels and the
   a. steering gear
   b. wheel backing plates
   c. pitman arm
   d. wheel bearings   1. ____

2. The adjuster sleeves used to adjust the toe of the front wheels are located on the
   a. pitman arm
   b. idler arm
   c. tie rods
   d. intermediate rod   2. ____

3. Linkage components are insulated from each other by
   a. tubes
   b. washers
   c. bushings
   d. collars   3. ____

4. In steering systems, the pitman arm is assembled on the
   a. steering arm
   b. steering gear
   c. car frame
   d. tie rods   4. ____

5. Steering-knuckle arms are permitted to swing from right to left by
   a. tie rods
   b. steering gear
   c. backing plates
   d. ball joints   5. ____

JOB 50-1

Checking Wheel Bearings

Objective: To learn how to check front-wheel bearings on rear-drive vehicles and rear-wheel bearings on front-drive vehicles.

References: AM ♦50-1 to 50-24, SG Chap. 50, automotive manufacturers' service manuals.

Equipment: Various vehicles with wheel bearings to be checked.
Tools: Dial indicator, steel scale, basic hand tools.

SHOP FACTS

Loose wheel bearings can cause poor steering control, car wander, uneven front-brake action, and rapid tire wear. Lifting locations vary for measuring wheel-bearing looseness.

On vehicles with a coil spring or torsion bar on the lower control arm, lift under the frame. On vehicles with a coil spring on the upper control arm, lift under the lower control arm. On front-wheel-drive vehicles, refer to the manufacturer's service manual.

SHOP SKILLS

CHECKING FRONT- AND REAR-WHEEL BEARINGS ON GM FRONT-DRIVE VEHICLES

____ 1. Use a lift or jack and safety stands to raise the wheels off the ground.

____ 2. Remove the wheel-and-tire assembly. On disk brakes, reinstall two wheel nuts to secure the disk to the hub.

____ 3. Attach a dial indicator as shown in Fig. 50-1.

____ 4. Grasp the top and bottom of the disk (on disk brakes) or hub flange (on drum brakes). Push in and pull out, while watching the dial indicator.

____ 5. If the looseness exceeds 0.005 inch [0.13 mm], the wheel bearing should be adjusted.

CHECKING FRONT-WHEEL BEARINGS ON REAR-DRIVE VEHICLES OR REAR-WHEEL BEARINGS ON FRONT-DRIVE VEHICLES

____ 1. Raise the wheels off the ground with a lift or jack and safety stands. Lift points differ according to the type of front suspension. If the spring is between the upper and lower control arms, place a safety stand under the frame cross member (Fig. 50-2). If the spring is above the upper control

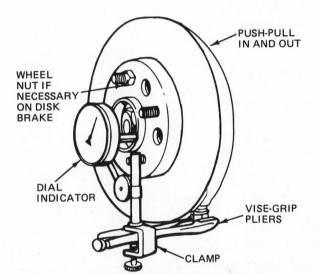

Fig. 50-1 Using a dial indicator to measure play in the wheel bearings. **(Motor Vehicle Manufacturers Association)**

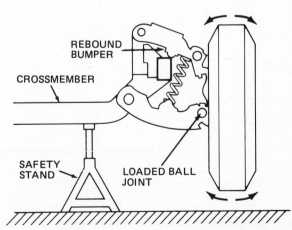

Fig. 50-2 When the coil spring is on the lower control arm, support the frame cross member as shown to check wheel-bearing play.

arm, place a safety stand under the lower control arm close to the ball joint (Fig. 50-3). Use this same support point if a torsion bar is attached to the upper control arm. With either type of spring, the weight of the wheel takes up any play in the ball joints.

____ 2. Grasp the tire at the top and bottom, and rock it in and out. Any movement indicates looseness in the wheel bearing or in the ball joints (Job 50-2).

____ 3. Look at the brake drum or disk and the backing plate or shield as you rock the wheel. If you see movement between the drum or disk and the plate or shield, there is looseness in the wheel bearing. If the wheel can be rocked more than ⅛ inch [3 mm], measured at the outer circumference of the tire with a steel scale, the wheel bearing must be adjusted.

____ 4. To check that the looseness is in the wheel bearing, use a brake depressor or have an assistant depress the service brake pedal while you try rocking the wheel. If applying the brakes eliminates the free play, a loose wheel bearing is permitting the rocking motion.

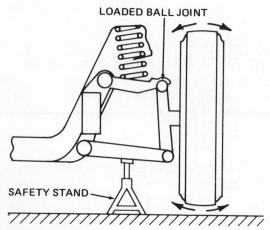

Fig. 50-3 When the coil spring is on the upper control arm, support the lower control arm as shown to check wheel-bearing play.

JOB 50-1 MULTIPLE-CHOICE TEST

1. To check wheel bearings for looseness on cars with a coil spring on the lower control arm, lift under the
   a. lower control arm
   b. frame cross member
   c. lower ball joint
   d. tire   1. ____

2. To check the wheel bearings on a car with a torsion bar on the lower control arm, lift under the
   a. lower control arm
   b. frame cross member
   c. lower ball joint
   d. tire   2. ____

3. On vehicles with a coil spring on the upper control arm, check the wheel bearings by lifting under the
   a. lower control arm
   b. frame cross member
   c. lower ball joint
   d. tire   3. ____

4. The wheel bearings on GM front-drive vehicles should be adjusted if a dial indicator shows the looseness to exceed
   a. 0.0005 inch [0.013 mm]
   b. 0.005 inch [0.13 mm]
   c. 0.050 inch [1.3 mm]
   d. none of the above   4. ____

5. Front-wheel bearings on rear-drive vehicles should be adjusted if the wheel can be rocked more than
   a. 0.005 inch [0.13 mm]
   b. ⅛ inch [3 mm]
   c. ¼ inch [6 mm]
   d. ½ inch [13 mm]   5. ____

Name _____ Date _____

JOB 50-2

Checking Ball Joints

Objective: To learn to inspect front-suspension-system ball joints.

References: AM ♦50-1 to 50-24, SG Chap. 50, automotive manufacturers' service manuals.

Equipment: Various vehicles with ball joints to be checked.
Tools: Dial indicator, pry bar, steel scale, basic hand tools.

♦ _____ ♦

SHOP SKILLS

INSPECTING BALL JOINTS WITHOUT WEAR INDICATORS

_____ 1. To inspect ball joints without wear indicators, raise the front end of the vehicle. Support it at the proper points, which depend on the type of suspension as shown in Figs. 50-4 and 50-5. This removes the weight of the vehicle from the balls joints.

_____ 2. Attach a dial indicator to the control arm so that any movement between the ball joint and its socket can be accurately measured (Fig. 50-6).

_____ 3. To check vertical movement, position a pry bar under the front tire. Lift the tire-and-wheel assembly up and down, as you observe the movement of the needle on the dial indicator.

_____ 4. To check horizontal movement, grasp the top and bottom of the tire with your hands. Move the tire-and-wheel assembly in and out to detect any looseness. More horizontal movement is allowed because of the typical ball-joint construction. However, some manufacturers do not accept horizontal movement as indicating ball-joint wear.

_____ 5. If the ball-joint movement exceeds specifications, the ball joint should be replaced. Follow the procedures in the manufacturer's service manual.

INSPECTING WEAR-INDICATING BALL JOINTS

_____ 1. To inspect wear-indicating ball joints, support the vehicle so that the ball joints are loaded, carrying the weight of the vehicle. Wipe the grease fitting to remove all dirt and grease.

_____ 2. Note the position of the grease-fitting nipple. As the ball joint wears, the wear indicator (grease-fitting nipple) moves into the ball-joint socket (Fig. 50-7).

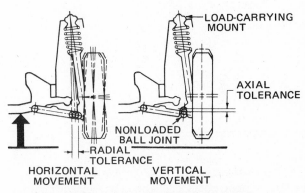

MACPHERSON STRUT—NO UPPER BALL JOINT

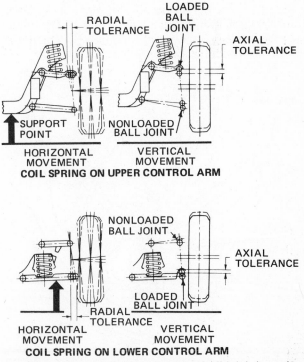

COIL SPRING ON UPPER CONTROL ARM

COIL SPRING ON LOWER CONTROL ARM

Fig. 50-4 Support points for checking ball joints in various front-suspension systems using coil springs. **(Motor Vehicle Manufacturers Association)**

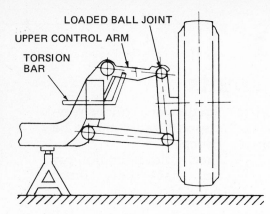

TORSION BAR ON UPPER CONTROL ARM

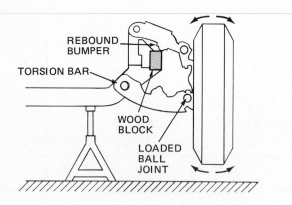

TORSION BAR ON LOWER CONTROL ARM

Fig. 50-5 Support points for checking ball joints in front-suspension systems using torsion bars.

_____ 3. When the ball joint is new, the nipple sticks out of the socket 0.050 inch [1.27 mm]. If the wear is sufficient to move the nipple into the socket 0.050 inch [1.27 mm], the nipple is level with the socket.

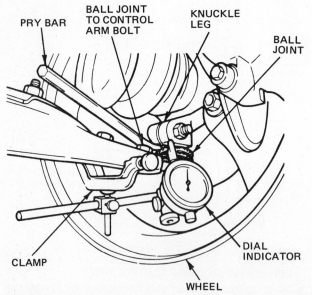

Fig. 50-6 Using a dial indicator to measure ball-joint looseness. (Motor Vehicle Manufacturers Association)

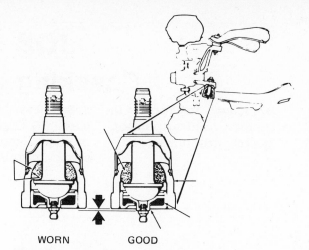

Fig. 50-7 Checking a wear-indicating ball joint. A worn ball joint compared with a good ball joint. (**Chevrolet Motor Division of General Motors Corporation**)

_____ 4. If the ball joint has worn so much that the nipple is level with the socket, the ball joint should be replaced. This much wear can cause failure if the ball joint is not replaced.

_____ 5. Inspect the ball-joint seals. If they are cut, torn, or otherwise damaged, replace the ball joint.

JOB 50-2   MULTIPLE-CHOICE TEST

1. Ball joints without wear indicators are checked
   a. unloaded
   b. with the car weight removed
   c. both a and b
   d. neither a nor b   1. _____

2. Ball joints with wear indicators are checked
   a. with the car weight on the ball joints
   b. with the car weight removed
   c. unloaded
   d. none of the above   2. _____

3. Before checking ball joints,
   a. check tire pressure
   b. perform a chassis lubrication
   c. check the shock absorbers
   d. adjust the front-wheel bearings   3. _____

4. Axial play is
   a. vertical movement
   b. up-and-down movement
   c. both a and b
   d. neither a nor b   4. _____

5. The up-and-down movement in a typical ball joint should not exceed
   a. ¼ inch [6.35 mm]
   b. 1/16 inch [1.6 mm]
   c. 0.050 inch [1.2 mm]
   d. none of the above   5. _____

JOB 50-3

Wheel Alignment

Objective: To learn how to check and adjust wheel alignment.

References: AM ♦50-18, SG Chap. 50, automotive manufacturers' service manuals.
Equipment: Various vehicles.

Tools: Alignment tools, torque wrench, basic hand tools.
Supplies: Alignment shims, as required.

♦ —— ♦

SHOP FACTS

Many conditions besides wheel alignment influence how a vehicle steers. Before caster, camber, toe, turning radius, and steering-axis inclination are checked, other factors should be checked and corrected, if necessary. These include tire pressure and condition, wheel-bearing condition and adjustment, wheel and tire balance and runout, ball-joint and steering-linkage looseness, rear-leaf-spring condition, and front-suspension height. If any of these factors is off, you cannot accurately align the wheels. It is even possible that a "wheel alignment" could make the abnormal conditions worse.

Alignment procedures vary considerably according to the type of equipment being used and the car being checked. When you are assigned a vehicle and specific alignment equipment, study the vehicle manufacturer's service manual and the alignment-equipment instructions before you proceed with the job. Make sure that you understand how to use the alignment equipment. Follow the instructions carefully. If you have any questions, ask your instructor.

SHOP SKILLS

CASTER AND CAMBER ADJUSTMENT

____ 1. A variety of methods have been used to make caster and camber adjustments. In some cars, eccentric pins or bushings are used. They are rotated to move the upper or lower control arms. This changes the caster and camber. Other cars have shim-type adjustments of caster and camber. On such cars, the shims are located between the upper-control-arm shaft and the frame bracket (Fig. 50-8).

____ 2. When shims are added or removed from between the shaft and the frame bracket, the upper arm is moved in or out to vary the position of the upper ball joint. This also changes the caster and camber. Another caster-adjusting method varies the effective length of the strut rod attached to the lower control arm. This moves the outer end of the arm backward or forward. Still other adjustment methods, such as the at-

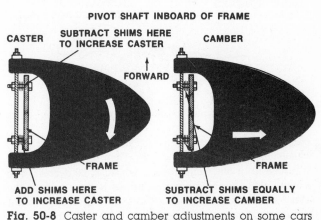

Fig. 50-8 Caster and camber adjustments on some cars using shims. (Chevrolet Motor Division of General Motors Corporation)

tachment-bolt-and-cam assembly, will be found on certain cars. On such cars, the cams are turned to change caster and camber.

TOE

____ 1. After caster and camber have been checked and adjusted, check toe. To adjust toe, change the effective length of the two tie rods by loosening the clamp bolts on the adjustment sleeves and turning the sleeves as required (Fig. 50-9).

____ 2. After the toe-in is correct, lock the adjustment by tightening the clamp bolts to the specified torque. Then check that the clamp bolts are in proper position to prevent interference with other parts of the steering and suspension system.

STEERING-AXIS INCLINATION AND TURNING RADIUS

____ 1. These two factors are not adjustable. However, they should be checked. If they are not within the specifications, a wheel-supporting part or a steering arm is bent. The bent part must be replaced.

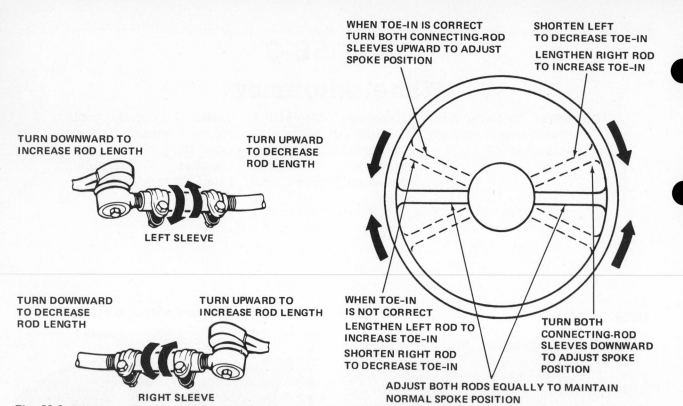

Fig. 50-9 Adjustments for toe-in and steering-wheel alignment. (Ford Motor Company)

____ 2. Toe-out on turns is checked by rolling the front wheels onto turning-radius gauges. Then the steering wheel is turned until one front wheel is angled at 20 degrees. The amount that the other wheel is turned is then read on the other turning-radius gauge. If the turning radius is not within specifications, a steering arm is bent and must be replaced. Front alignment must then be rechecked.

____ 3. Steering-axis inclination is checked with the same equipment used to check caster and camber. It is normally checked at the same time that caster and camber are measured. If the steering-axis inclination is incorrect, even though the caster and camber are within specifications, the spindle probably is bent and must be replaced. Then wheel alignment must be rechecked.

JOB 50-3 MULTIPLE-CHOICE TEST

1. Toe-in
   a. is adjusted by changing the effective length of the tie rods
   b. cannot be adjusted
   c. is adjusted by shims
   d. is adjusted by cams   1. ____

2. One type of device to measure caster and camber is
   a. hung from under the wheel
   b. attached to the lower control arm
   c. placed between the front tires
   d. attached to the front-wheel spindle   2. ____

3. Removal of shims at one of the control-arm attachment bolts and addition of shims at the other results in adjustment of
   a. caster
   b. toe-in
   c. camber
   d. turning radius   3. ____

4. Turning radius
   a. is adjusted by changing the effective length of the tie rods
   b. is adjusted by shims
   c. cannot be adjusted
   d. is adjusted by cams   4. ____

5. Changing the effective length of the strut rod attached to the outer end of the control arm changes the
   a. caster
   b. camber
   c. toe-in
   d. toe-out on turns   5. ____

JOB 51

Automotive Brake Systems

Objective: To learn the construction and operation of automotive brake systems and of power brakes.

References: AM ♦51-1 to 51-35, SG Chap. 51, automotive manufacturers' service manuals.

Equipment: Various vehicles and brake-system components, including assembled, disassembled, and cutaway master cylinders, wheel cylinders, disk-brake calipers; various cars with power brakes; disassembled and cutaway power-brake units.

Tools: Basic hand tools.

SHOP FACTS

Figure 51-1 shows the complete layout on the chassis of the automobile braking system. It is made up of four major parts. First, there must be a source of energy to provide the energy required for braking. On vehicles, brakes may be operated by mechanical, hydraulic, compressed-air, or electrical devices. Second, there must be a control device to apply and release the brake. The foot pedal, operated by the driver, is the control for the service brake. The parking brake has a separate control. It may be either a hand lever or a foot pedal which latches until later released.

The third part that a brake system must have is some means for transmitting the desired force and motion from the control device to the brake mechanism. Figure 51-1 shows the two methods used on cars. The service brake is operated hydraulically by forcing fluid through tubing and hose. This applies force to the friction elements at the brake. The parking brake is mechanically operated. Force and motion are transmitted from the parking-brake control to the brake through rods and cables.

The fourth part of the brake system is the brake mechanism itself. On the car, a brake is located at each wheel. The brake contains the friction elements which are acted on to oppose the motion of the vehicle by retarding the movement of the wheel.

Two completely independent braking systems are used on the car (Fig. 51-1). They are the *service brake* and the *parking brake.*

The service brakes act to slow, stop, or hold the vehicle

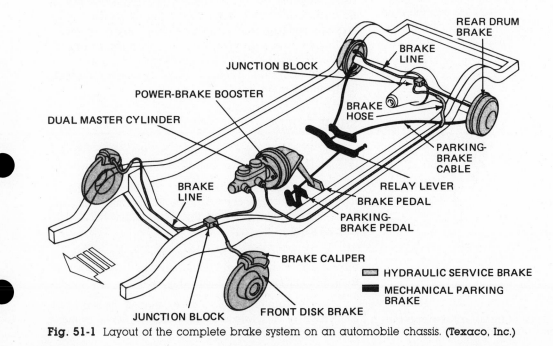

Fig. 51-1 Layout of the complete brake system on an automobile chassis. **(Texaco, Inc.)**

during normal driving as required by the driver. They are foot-operated by the driver depressing and releasing the brake pedal.

The primary purpose of the parking brake is to hold and maintain the vehicle in a stationary position while it is unattended. The parking brake is mechanically operated by the driver when a separate parking-brake foot pedal or hand lever is set.

Basically, all car brakes are friction brakes (Fig. 51-2). When the driver applies the brake, the control device forces brake shoes or pads against the rotating brake drums or disks at the wheels. Friction between the shoes or pads and the drums or disks then slows or stops the wheels so that the car is braked.

In a friction brake, the brake lining wears away during normal operation. This is because parts which do not rotate (shoes and pads shown in Fig. 51-2) are forced against parts which rotate with the wheels (drum and disk shown in Fig. 51-2). Friction between these two parts causes the car to slow down in proportion to the force applied.

Two basic types of friction brakes are used on automobiles. These are the drum brake and the disk brake. Both types are illustrated in Fig. 51-2. Older cars had drum brakes at all four wheels. Later, after disk brakes were introduced, most automotive manufacturers began using the combination drum-and-disk system shown in Fig. 51-1.

In the combination system, disk brakes are used at the front wheels and drum brakes at the rear. By continuing the use of rear drum brakes, the parking brake is easily provided. Now many cars have disk brakes at all four wheels. Various types of parking brakes are used on cars today.

The drum brake has two curved shoes positioned inside a drum (Fig. 51-2). When the brakes are applied, the shoes are forced outward and into frictional contact with the rotating drum. The wheel mounts on the drum so the wheel and drum rotate together. When the brake shoes are forced against the rotating drum, the friction between the two causes the drum and wheel to slow or stop. The same action takes place at all wheels, so the car is braked.

In the disk brake, a disk, or rotor, is attached to the wheel. Brake pads (also called *linings* or *shoes*) are positioned on each side of the disk (Fig. 51-2). When the brakes are applied, the pads press against the disk. This clamps the disk between

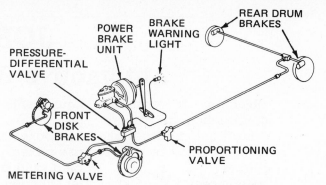

Fig. 51-3 Typical power-brake system using a vacuum booster. **(Bendix Corporation)**

the pads. Friction between the pads and the disk slows or stops the wheel, thereby providing braking action.

In recent years more than 80 percent of all U.S.-built passenger cars have been supplied with power brakes. These are vacuum- or hydraulic-assist systems. Essentially, they all operate in a similar manner. When the brake pedal is moved to apply the service brakes, a valving arrangement is actuated. With the vacuum-assist system, the valves admit atmospheric pressure on one side of a piston or diaphragm and apply vacuum to the other side. The piston or diaphragm then moves toward the vacuum side. This movement transmits most of the hydraulic pressure, through the brake fluid, to the wheel cylinders or calipers.

Vacuum-assisted power brakes can be divided into two general categories: vacuum-suspended and atmospheric-suspended. In the vacuum-suspended type (Fig. 51-3), intake-manifold vacuum is applied to both sides of a piston or diaphragm in the power-brake unit when no braking action is taking place. To produce braking, atmospheric pressure is admitted to one side of the piston or diaphragm. The difference in pressures causes the piston or diaphragm to move, producing the braking action.

The hydraulic-assisted brake booster (Fig. 51-4) uses hydraulic pressure supplied by the power-steering pump to assist in applying the brakes. Figure 51-5 shows the system schematically. Some systems include an oil cooler. Higher pressures and temperatures are developed in the power-steering fluid because of the greater steering and braking demands of vehicle operation. The fluid flows from the pump to the steering gear, hydraulic booster, oil cooler (if used), and then to the pump reservoir.

SHOP SKILLS

____ 1. Examine various cars and locate the master cylinder (Fig. 51-1). Then trace the brake lines running to the wheels.

____ 2. On dual-brake systems, locate the pressure-differential valve that warns if one of the two systems fails. Trace the brake-line routing to and from this valve and also the electric wire attached to the valve.

____ 3. Note the type of brake used at each wheel. The car may have four-wheel drum brakes, four-wheel disk brakes, or front disk and rear drum brakes (Fig. 51-2).

____ 4. On drum brakes, note the location of the brake-line connection to each wheel cylinder and the wheel-cylinder bleeder valve.

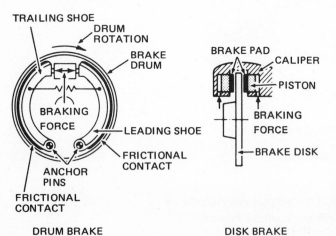

Fig. 51-2 The two basic types of friction brakes used on automobiles. **(Robert Bosch Corporation)**

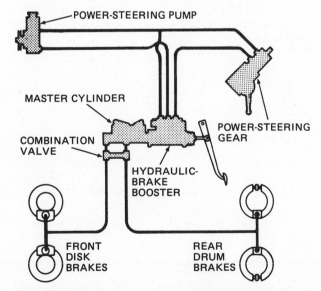

Fig. 51-4 Power-brake system using a hydraulic brake booster. **(Ford Motor Company)**

_____ 5. On disk brakes, determine whether the caliper is of the fixed, floating, or sliding type.

_____ 6. Determine the type of parking brake (Fig. 51-1) used on the car. Then trace the parking-brake cables from the hand lever or foot pedal to the parking brakes on the wheels.

_____ 7. Examine disassembled parts to see how the parts go together to make the completed master cylinder, wheel cylinder, and disk-brake caliper.

_____ 8. Examine various cars with different types of vacuum-assisted power brakes (Fig. 51-3). Note the locations of (1) the power-brake unit and (2) the vacuum line to the intake manifold for the power-brake unit.

_____ 9. Trace all hoses connected to the power-brake unit. Determine whether the system on the car you are inspecting uses a vacuum-reserve tank. Determine how clean fresh air gets into the power brake.

_____ 10. As you inspect power-brake installations, note that power brakes are _add-on_ units. This means that the power-brake unit is connected into the service-brake system on a car between the brake pedal and the master cylinder. If vacuum to the power brake is interrupted because of a leaking hose or diaphragm, the brake system reverts to unassisted hydraulic-brake-system operation.

Fig. 51-5 Hydraulic-brake-booster system, showing the lines between the power-steering pump and the booster.

_____ 11. With the engine off, pump the brake pedal several times. Then, with your foot applying light force to the pedal, start the engine. Note that the pedal lowers as vacuum is applied to the power-brake unit. If the pedal does not move slightly as the engine starts, the vacuum booster is inoperative.

_____ 12. Examine various vehicles with hydraulic brake boosters (Figs. 51-4 and 51-5). Trace the hydraulic lines from the power-steering pump through the circuit back to the power-steering-pump reservoir. This path is shown in Fig. 51-5. Note that the brake-fluid lines from the master cylinder to the wheels are the same regardless of the type of brake booster used.

_____ 13. If a sufficient variety of cars and trucks is available, you will be able to identify the major types of hydraulic- and vacuum-assist power brakes, as described in the references. Make a list of vehicles by make and model year and note the type of power brake used in each.

_____ 14. Examine disassembled or cutaway power-brake units, and identify the different parts. Compare the parts with the various views of power brakes shown in the references. Automotive manufacturers' shop manuals will help you in this identification.

JOB 51 MULTIPLE-CHOICE TEST

1. In the hydraulic brake system, forward movement of the master-cylinder piston forces brake fluid
   a. out of the wheel cylinders
   b. into the power cylinder
   c. into the wheel cylinders or calipers
   d. into the cylinder pistons   1. _____

2. In drum brakes, movement of the wheel-cylinder pistons causes movement of the
   a. brake shoes
   b. brake drum
   c. caliper
   d. brake pedal   2. _____

3. In disk brakes, movement of the caliper pistons forces the brake linings against the
   a. drum
   b. disk
   c. caliper
   d. wheel   3. _____

4. In drum brakes, because the forward momentum of the car throws more weight on the front wheels during braking, the front
   a. wheel-cylinder pistons are larger
   b. drums are larger
   c. shoes are wider
   d. wheels are larger   4. _____

5. Drum brakes and disk brakes are both types of
   a. hydraulic brakes
   b. parking brakes
   c. service brakes
   d. all of the above   5. _____

6. In the vacuum-suspended system, the brakes are applied when
   a. vacuum is applied to both sides of the diaphragm
   b. atmospheric pressure is applied to both sides of the diaphragm
   c. the brake pedal forces the check valve to open
   d. atmospheric pressure is applied to one side of the diaphragm   6. ____

7. In normal operation, the vacuum that operates the vacuum-assist power brake is obtained from the
   a. air compressor
   b. hydraulic accumulator
   c. intake manifold
   d. fuel pump   7. ____

8. The two types of power-brake boosters used on automobiles are
   a. air and vacuum
   b. compressed air and electric
   c. hydraulic and atmospheric
   d. vacuum and hydraulic   8. ____

9. In the hydraulic-assisted brake booster, hydraulic pressure is supplied by the
   a. engine oil pump
   b. windshield-wiper pump
   c. water pump
   d. power-steering pump   9. ____

10. In a system using a hydraulic brake booster, after flowing through the hydraulic booster, the fluid flows to the
   a. pump reservoir
   b. master cylinder
   c. steering gear
   d. none of the above   10. ____

JOB 52-1

Parking-Brake Adjustment

Objective: To learn how to adjust parking brakes.

References: AM ♦52-25 to 52-30, SG Chap. 52, automotive manufacturers' service manuals.

Equipment: Various vehicles with parking brake to be adjusted.

Tools: Basic hand tools.

SHOP FACTS

The parking brake should be adjusted any time the rear brakes have been disconnected and when the parking-brake foot pedal or hand lever travels too far before applying the brakes. The parking brake should be adjusted so that adequate holding action is ensured. On many cars, there should be some pedal or lever reserve. It should not be necessary to move the lever or pedal through its full travel to obtain full braking. However, the adjustment should not be so tight that in the released position the parking brake causes the lining to drag.

Rear-wheel drum brakes use the same shoes for both service brake and parking brake. Any adjustment of the shoe-adjusting wheel will affect both brake systems. For this reason, the parking brake should be checked and adjusted whenever a manual brake adjustment is made on the rear brakes.

Basically all parking brakes are adjusted in some way to ensure that proper tension is restored to the brake cables. This compensates for wear of the brake lining and for stretching of the cables. Typical procedures for adjusting parking brakes are given below. Refer to the manufacturer's service manual for the required specifications.

Rear-wheel disk brakes which have an integral parking brake do not require periodic adjustment. The piston assembly in the caliper contains a self-adjusting mechanism for the parking brake.

SHOP SKILLS

ADJUSTING REAR DRUM PARKING BRAKES

____ **1.** Release or set the parking brake, as required. Then raise the car on a lift.

____ **2.** On most cars with rear-wheel drum brakes, the parking brake pedal or lever is connected to a short front cable (Fig. 52-1). The cable usually has an *equalizer* attached so that an even pull is applied to each of the rear brakes.

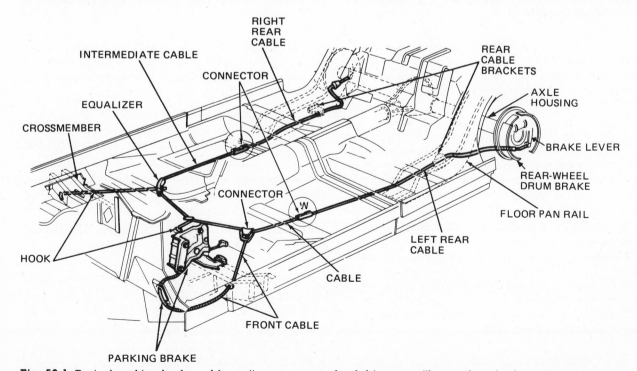

Fig. 52-1 Typical parking-brake cable routing on a rear-wheel-drive car with rear drum brakes. **(Chrysler Corporation)**

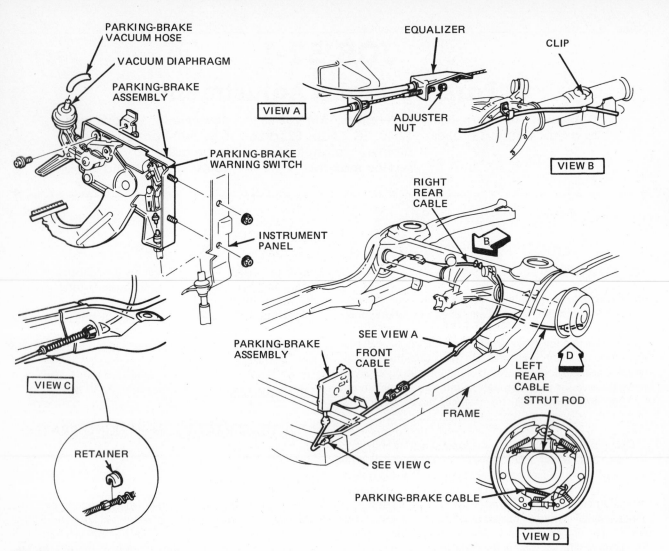

Fig. 52-2 On some cars, the parking-brake cable enters the brake assembly from the rear. (**Cadillac Motor Car Division of General Motors Corporation**)

_____ 3. On some cars, the front cable extends back to where individual cables branch off to the two rear brakes (Fig. 52-1). On other cars, the front cable is routed along the left side of the car through the equalizer, to which the cable is attached (Fig. 52-2).

_____ 4. From the equalizer, the cable continues on as the left rear cable. The cable for the right rear brake is connected to the equalizer and routed around the axle housing to enter the brake assembly from the rear. Note in Fig. 52-2 that the left cable enters the brake assembly from the front.

_____ 5. Adjustment of most parking brakes usually is made by tightening or loosening the equalizer adjuster nut (Fig. 52-2). Another method is by alternately loosening and tightening the check nuts on either side of the equalizer. This moves the equalizer forward or backward to produce the proper tension on the check nuts on either side of the equalizer. This moves the equalizer forward or back to produce the proper tension on the brake cables.

_____ 6. On some brake cables, such as that shown in Fig. 52-1, you must hold the front cable with a wrench to prevent

the cable from turning while moving the adjuster nut. On General Motors cars with the front cable leading to the left rear wheel, adjustment is made by turning the adjuster nut at the equalizer (Fig 52-2).

_____ 7. After making the adjustment, make sure that both check nuts (if two are used) are tight against the equalizer. Apply and release the parking brake several times to check its operation.

_____ 8. Then with the parking brake released, turn each rear wheel by hand to make sure that there is no brake drag.

ADJUSTING DRUM-TYPE PARKING BRAKE IN REAR DISK BRAKES

_____ 1. On rear-wheel disk brakes which include the drum-type parking brake, the parking-brake shoes may require periodic adjustment. Insert the adjusting tool through the backing plate, as shown in Fig. 52-3.

_____ 2. Pivot the adjusting tool on either the splash shield or on the clamp to turn the adjuster star wheel one way or the other, as required.

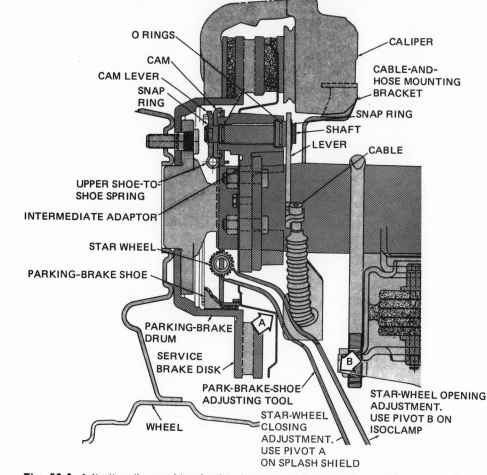

O RINGS
CAM
CAM LEVER
SNAP RING
CALIPER
CABLE-AND-HOSE MOUNTING BRACKET
SNAP RING
SHAFT
LEVER
CABLE
UPPER SHOE-TO-SHOE SPRING
INTERMEDIATE ADAPTOR
STAR WHEEL
PARKING-BRAKE SHOE
PARKING-BRAKE DRUM
SERVICE BRAKE DISK
PARK-BRAKE-SHOE ADJUSTING TOOL
WHEEL
STAR-WHEEL CLOSING ADJUSTMENT. USE PIVOT A ON SPLASH SHIELD
STAR-WHEEL OPENING ADJUSTMENT. USE PIVOT B ON ISOCLAMP

Fig. 52-3 Adjusting the parking-brake shoes on a sliding-caliper disk brake with an independent drum-type parking brake. The two positions of the parking-brake-shoe adjusting tool are shown at A and B. **(Chrysler Corporation)**

JOB 52-1 MULTIPLE-CHOICE TEST

1. The parking brake should be adjusted whenever
   a. the rear brakes have been disconnected
   b. the parking-brake foot pedal travels too far
   c. the parking-brake hand lever travels too far
   d. all of the above   1. ____

2. Whenever rear drum brakes have been adjusted,
   a. no further adjustment of the parking brake is required
   b. the parking brake has been properly adjusted also
   c. the parking brake will require adjustment
   d. none of the above   2. ____

3. Parking brakes are adjusted by
   a. loosening the brake cables
   b. restoring proper tension to the brake cables
   c. refilling the master cylinder
   d. using the brake-shoe adjusting gauge   3. ____

4. The device that provides an even pull to each rear brake is the
   a. equalizer
   b. front cable
   c. left rear cable
   d. right rear cable   4. ____

5. Adjustment of the drum-type parking brake on rear-wheel disk brakes requires a
   a. brake-shoe adjusting gauge
   b. brake adjusting tool
   c. thin-bladed screwdriver
   d. wire hook   5. ____

JOB 52-2

Disk-Brake Service

Objective: To learn how to service disk brakes.
References: AM ♦52-15 to 52-24, SG Chap. 52, automotive manufacturers' service manuals.

Equipment: Various vehicles with disk brakes to be serviced.

Tools: Caliper-piston remover, basic hand tools.
Supplies: New brake pads, as required.

SHOP FACTS

All disk brakes work similarly, although their design and construction varies. There are three general types: fixed-caliper, floating-caliper, and sliding-caliper. The servicing of the floating-caliper disk brake is covered below.

SHOP SKILLS

FLOATING-CALIPER DISK-BRAKE SERVICE

_____ 1. Remove the master-cylinder cover and check the fluid level in the front-wheel reservoir. If the reservoir is more than one-third full, remove fluid until the level drops to one third full. This prevents the reservoir from overflowing when the caliper piston is pushed back into its bore. Never reuse the brake fluid removed from the reservoir.

_____ 2. Raise the car on a lift. Remove the front wheels. Push the piston back into its bore by using a C-clamp (Fig. 52-4).

_____ 3. Remove the two caliper guide pins (also called *mounting bolts*) and positioners that attach the caliper to the steering-knuckle adapter. Take off the caliper. Support the caliper so that the flexible brake hose is not stretched or twisted.

_____ 4. Slide the brake shoes out and remove the shoe support spring. Push the outer bushings from the caliper and discard the bushings. Then slide the inner bushings off the guide pin and discard them.

_____ 5. If the piston seal has leaked, or if the boot is damaged, disconnect the hose from the caliper and take the caliper to the bench. Plug the hose to prevent brake-fluid leakage.

_____ 6. Open the bleeder screw and drain the brake fluid from the caliper.

_____ 7. Clamp the caliper lightly in the soft jaws of a vise. Pad the interior of the caliper with clean cloth and a fiber

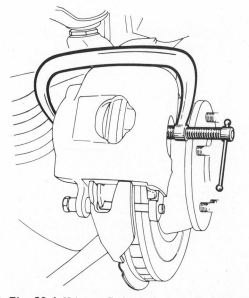

Fig. 52-4 Using a C-clamp to force the piston into the caliper bore. **(Buick Motor Division of General Motors Corporation)**

block. Use compressed air to remove the piston from the cylinder bore by blowing into the caliper inlet hole (Fig. 52-5).

_____ 8. Remove the dust boot. Use a pointed wooden stick to work the seal out of its groove in the piston bore. Then remove the bleeder valve. Never use a metal tool to remove the seal. A screwdriver could scratch the piston bore or burr the edges of the seal groove, ruining the caliper.

_____ 9. Clean the caliper parts with brake fluid. Check the bore for pits and scores. Light scores and stains can be cleaned out with crocus cloth. Deeper scores require replacement of the caliper.

_____ 10. Examine the piston for scoring, nicks, corrosion, and worn or damaged chrome plating. Any surface defects on the piston require replacing it.

_____ 11. To assemble the caliper, lubricate the new piston seal with clean brake fluid. Then install the seal in the groove in the piston bore. Check that the seal is not twisted or rolled.

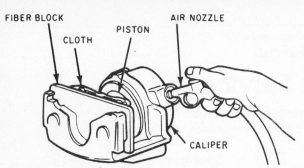

Fig. 52-5 Using compressed air to remove the piston from the caliper. **(Ford Motor Company)**

____ 12. Coat the piston with clean brake fluid. Assemble the new boot into the piston groove so that the fold faces the open end of the piston. Push the piston down until it bottoms in the bore.

____ 13. Position the boot in the caliper counterbore and seat the boot. Install the bleeder valve and torque to specifications.

____ 14. Make sure that the piston is all the way back into its bore. Then install the new bushings. Slide a new inboard shoe into place (Fig. 52-6). Check that the metal part of the shoe is fully in the recess of the caliper and the adapter.

____ 15. Hold the outboard shoe in position and slide the caliper into place. Align guide-pin holes of the adapter and inboard and outboard shoes. On some cars equipped with disk-brake wear indicators, there are left and right inboard shoes. These must be installed properly for the wear indicators to operate.

____ 16. Install the new positioner over the guide pins with the open ends toward the outside and the stamped arrows pointing upward. Install the guide pins, and pressing in on the end of the pins, carefully thread them into the adapter. Avoid cross-threading! Tighten to specifications.

____ 17. Using Channellock pliers, bend both upper ears of the outboard shoe down until no radial clearance exists between the shoe and the caliper housing.

____ 18. Connect the brake hose. Pump the brake pedal several times until a firm pedal is obtained. Bleed the system and refill the master-cylinder reservoir as necessary.

____ 19. Install the front wheels and lower the vehicle.

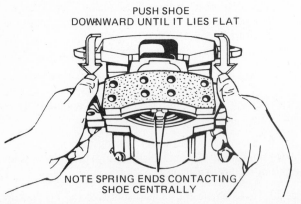

Fig. 52-6 Installing the inboard shoe in the caliper. **(Chevrolet Motor Division of General Motors Corporation)**

CHECKING DISK FOR PARALLELISM AND RUNOUT

____ 1. Before reinstalling the caliper, check the disk for runout and thickness. Use a micrometer and measure thickness at four or more equal points about 1 inch [25 mm] from the edge. Maximum allowable thickness variation usually is about 0.0005 inch [0.013 mm]. If thickness varies excessively, discard the disk and install a new one.

____ 2. Measure runout by first adjusting the wheel bearing to zero end play and then mounting a dial indicator. Rotate the disk, and check runout. Maximum allowable lateral runout usually is about 0.004 to 0.005 inch [0.10 to 0.13 mm]. If it is excessive, discard the disk and install a new one. Light scores and wear of the disk are okay, but if the scores are fairly deep, the disk should be refinished.

____ 3. Readjust wheel bearings.

CAREFUL All vehicles built since 1971 (and some before that) have the specification for the minimum allowable disk thickness cast into the disk. This measurement is the minimum thickness to which the disk can be refinished. If it is necessary to refinish the disk so that its thickness is less than specified, discard it. The disk is too thin to use safely.

JOB 52-2   MULTIPLE-CHOICE TEST

1. Two types of disk brakes are
   a. two-disk and four-piston
   b. fixed-caliper and multiple-disk
   c. sliding-caliper and floating-caliper
   d. all of the above   1. ____

2. Replace the caliper if the piston bore must be honed more than
   a. 0.002 inch [0.05 mm]
   b. 0.001 inch [0.025 mm]
   c. 0.0001 inch [0.0025 mm]
   d. none of the above   2. ____

3. On a floating caliper, shoe replacement can be made
   a. only after caliper is removed
   b. without removing caliper
   c. without removing wheel
   d. after pistons are removed   3. ____

4. The purpose of pumping the brake pedal several times after shoe replacement is to make sure that
   a. a firm pedal is obtained
   b. the pedal works
   c. the reservoir is filled
   d. the disk is properly positioned   4. ____

5. The measurement cast into the disk is
   a. the minimum thickness to which the disk may be worn
   b. the minimum thickness to which the disk can be refinished
   c. the maximum thickness which will fit in the caliper
   d. the maximum thickness which can be used with standard shoes   5. ____

JOB 52-3

Drum-Brake Service

Objective: To learn how to service drum brakes.
References: AM ♦52-1 to 52-14, SG Chap. 52, automotive manufacturers' service manuals.

Equipment: Various vehicles with drum brakes to be serviced.

Tools: Brake tools, basic hand tools.
Supplies: New brake shoes, brake fluid.

SHOP FACTS

Many manufacturers recommend the installation of new shoe-and-lining assemblies, instead of relining the old shoes in the shop. Relining of old shoes, whether bonded or riveted, requires special equipment and training. Some new shoe-and-lining assemblies, such as the Delco cam-ground type, can be used with a drum of any size, from new to discard diameter. Other manufacturers may require that oversize linings be used with brake drums that are 0.060 inch [1.5 mm] or more oversize.

CAREFUL Keep your hands clean while handling shoe-and-lining assemblies, drums, and other brake parts. Never allow oil, grease, or other contaminants to touch the linings.

SHOP SKILLS

REMOVING THE BRAKE SHOES

____ 1. With a car on a lift or on safety stands, remove the wheels and brake drums. Figure 52-8 shows a rear brake with the drum removed and all parts named.

____ 2. If required, install a wheel-cylinder clamp on each wheel cylinder (Fig. 52-9). The clamp prevents fluid leakage and air from getting into the hydraulic system while the shoes are removed. However, not all wheel cylinders require the use of the clamp. Some wheel cylinders have stops which will hold the wheel-cylinder parts in place.

Note Regardless of whether clamps are installed, never press down on the brake pedal after the shoe return springs are removed.

____ 3. Use a brake-spring tool to unhook the brake-shoe return springs from the anchor pin (Fig. 52-10) or from the anchor plate. Then remove the brake-shoe return springs. Be careful not to use the brake-spring tool to remove the adjusting link from the anchor pin or anchor plate.

Note On some cars, the return springs are not directly attached to the anchor pin. One spring may be hooked over the

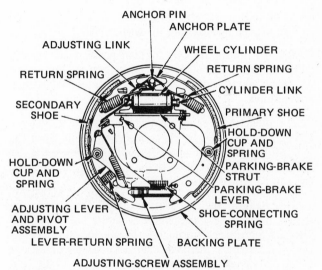

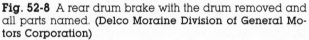

Fig. 52-8 A rear drum brake with the drum removed and all parts named. (**Delco Moraine Division of General Motors Corporation**)

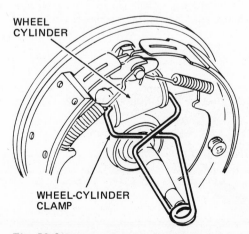

Fig. 52-9 Before removing the brake shoes, place a wheel-cylinder clamp on each wheel cylinder. (**Delco Moraine Division of General Motors Corporation**)

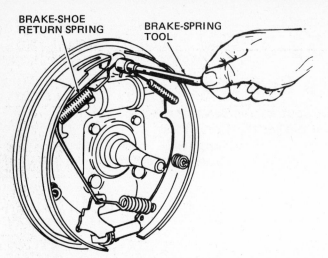

Fig. 52-10 Using a brake-spring tool to unhook the return springs from the anchor pin. (Delco Moraine Division of General Motors Corporation)

adjusting link, as shown in Fig. 52-8. On other cars, both springs may be hooked onto the anchor plate.

CAREFUL Always check the location, position, and color of all springs before removing any spring from the brake. This will enable you to reinstall each spring in its original location and position.

_____ 4. Remove the shoe-retaining cups, or hold-down cups, and springs (Fig. 52-11). Pliers or a special hold-down-cup tool can be used to compress the spring and rotate the cup one-quarter turn in relation to the hold-down pin. Now the cup can be removed from the pin.

_____ 5. Remove the self-adjuster parts. These parts are shown in Fig. 52-8. Take off the actuating link, lever-and-pivot assembly, sleeve (through lever), and the return spring. Do not disassemble the lever-and-pivot assembly unless one of the parts is damaged.

_____ 6. On rear brakes, spread the shoes slightly to free the parking-brake strut (Fig. 52-8). Then remove the strut and its spring.

_____ 7. Next, disconnect the parking-brake lever from the secondary shoe. The lever may be hooked into the shoe, or attached with a retaining clip or bolt. On 1977 and later full-size cars built by General Motors, the parking-brake lever is

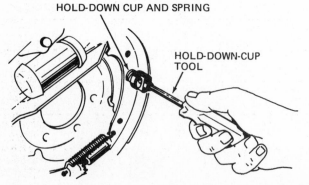

Fig. 52-11 A hold-down-cup tool is used to compress the spring and rotate the cup one-quarter turn so that the cup and spring can be removed from the hold-down pin.

installed on the primary shoe for the right rear brake. This is shown in Fig. 52-8.

_____ 8. If the plate slips off, remove the anchor plate from the anchor pin. If the plate is bolted or riveted on, leave it.

_____ 9. Spread the tops of the shoes apart and disengage them from the wheel-cylinder pins or links (Fig. 52-8), if used. Now remove the shoes (still connected at the bottom by the adjusting screw and spring) as an assembly.

_____ 10. Overlap the tops of the shoes to relieve the spring tension. Then unhook the adjusting-screw spring and remove the adjusting screw.

CLEANING, INSPECTING, AND LUBRICATING

♦ **CAUTION** ♦ Never create dust by cleaning brake parts with a dry brush or compressed air. This could cause asbestos fibers to get into the air. Inhaling dust containing asbestos fibers may cause bodily harm.

_____ 1. Clean, inspect, refinish, or replace the brake drums as necessary.

_____ 2. Using a water-dampened cloth or a water-based solution, clean the backing plates, struts, levers, and other metal parts that will be reused. Wet cleaning prevents asbestos fibers from becoming airborne.

_____ 3. Examine the raised shoe pads on the backing plate. Look for corrosion or any other condition that could prevent the shoes from sliding freely. Remove any surface defects with emery cloth. Then thoroughly clean the backing plate.

_____ 4. On rear-wheel brakes, look for oil or grease leakage past the wheel-bearing seals. This could cause improper brake operation, and indicates that the seal should be replaced or other service work is required.

_____ 5. Check the backing plates. Bent or cracked backing plates must be replaced. Check that the backing-plate bolts and bolted-on anchor pins are torqued to specifications.

_____ 6. Determine the wheel-cylinder condition by inspecting the boots. If they are cut, torn, heat-cracked, or leaking excessively, the wheel cylinders should be repaired or replaced. On cylinders with external boots, pull back the lower edge of the boot. If more than a drop of fluid runs out, the leakage is excessive and the wheel cylinder should be serviced. However, a small amount or trace of fluid behind the boot is normal. This serves to lubricate the pistons. On wheel cylinders with internal boots, remove one of the wheel-cylinder connecting links to check for leakage.

_____ 7. Disassemble the adjusting-screw assembly (Fig. 52-12) and clean the parts. Check that the adjusting screw will thread completely into the pivot nut without sticking or binding. None of the adjusting-screw teeth can be damaged. This would interfere with the operation of the self-adjuster.

_____ 8. Lubricate the adjusting-screw threads with brake lubricant and reassemble the adjusting-screw assembly. Be careful not to get lubricant on the adjusting teeth, or star wheel. Most adjusting-screw assemblies have a thrust washer

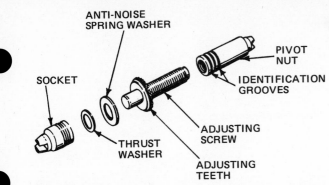

Fig. 52-12 A disassembled adjusting-screw assembly. (Delco Moraine Division of General Motors Corporation)

between the adjusting screw and the socket (Fig. 52-12). Some also have an antinoise spring washer. Thread the adjusting screw into the pivot nut as far as the screw will go.

____ 9. Apply a thin film of brake lubricant to the raised shoe pads on the backing plate. Before installing the brake shoes (as described below), check that there are no burrs on the edges of the shoes where they contact the pads. On rear brakes, lubricate the parking-brake-lever pivot pin.

INSTALLING NEW BRAKE-SHOE-AND-LINING ASSEMBLIES

____ 1. On a clean workbench, place the shoes in the same relative positions as they are to be installed on the backing plates.

____ 2. Hook the adjusting-screw spring between the shoes (Fig. 52-13). Overlap the anchor ends of the shoes, and engage the adjusting-screw assembly between the shoes. Make sure that the adjusting-screw spring is installed with its longer free end over the star wheel of the adjusting-screw assembly. If the spring is not installed in this position, the spring coils will interfere with the operation of the star wheel.

____ 3. Spread the anchor ends of the shoes to retain the adjusting screw in its installed position. Position the shoe assembly on the brake backing plate so that the shoes engage the wheel-cylinder connecting links or pins. If removed, install the anchor plate on the anchor pin over the shoe webs.

____ 4. On rear brakes, spread the shoes slightly and install the parking-brake strut and spring. Connect the parking-

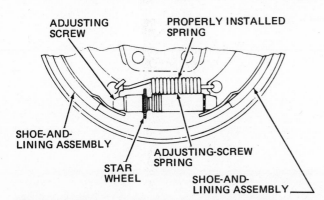

Fig. 52-13 Proper installation of the adjusting-screw spring. (Delco Moraine Division of General Motors Corporation)

brake lever to the secondary shoe. On some 1977 and later General Motors cars, the parking-brake lever for the right rear brake is installed on the primary shoe.

____ 5. Insert the primary-shoe hold-down pin through the holes in the backing plate and shoe, and hold the pin in position. Place the hold-down spring on the pin. Grasp the cup with pliers, and position the cup in front of the pin. Then force the cup into the spring pin, compressing the spring. Twist the pliers one-quarter turn to lock the cup in place. Then release the pliers.

____ 6. Hook one end of the adjusting link over the anchor pin or plate and the other to the lever-and-pivot assembly (Fig. 52-8). Position the lever on the secondary shoe, with the lever return spring in position between the lever and the shoe, and install the sleeve. Install the secondary-shoe hold-down pin, spring, and cup as described in step 4.

____ 7. Hook the shoe return springs into the shoes. Depending on the attachment method, hook the other end of the return spring:
    a. Over the anchor pin, using a brake-spring tool
    b. Onto the bolted-on-type anchor plate
    c. Into the hook on the adjusting link (for some
       secondary-shoe return springs)

CAREFUL Never use a brake-spring tool to remove or install the adjusting link to the anchor pin.

____ 8. Make the preliminary manual adjustment of the self-adjusting brakes. Install the drums and wheels.

____ 9. Make the final adjustments to the service brakes and to the parking brakes (Job 52-1).

JOB 52-3 MULTIPLE-CHOICE TEST

1. Placement of a wheel-cylinder clamp on the wheel cylinder while the brake shoes are removed prevents
    a. brake fluid from leaking out of the hydraulic system
    b. air from getting into the hydraulic system
    c. both a and b
    d. neither a nor b   1. ____

2. You should check the location, position, and color of all brake springs before removing them
    a. to determine whether they have the proper tension
    b. to determine whether they have the proper length
    c. so that you can reinstall each spring in its original location and position
    d. so that you can order a set of replacement springs
              2. ____

3. The parking-brake strut must be removed before removal of the
    a. brake-shoe return springs
    b. brake-shoe hold-down cups
    c. brake-shoe hold-down springs
    d. brake shoes   3. ____

4. On rear-wheel brakes, oil or grease leakage past the wheel-bearing seals indicates that the
    a. wheel bearing should be replaced
    b. seal should be replaced
    c. axle should be replaced
    d. wheel cylinder should be replaced   4. ____

5. When inspecting the condition of a wheel cylinder by pulling back the boots, a few drops of brake fluid run out. Mechanic A says this is the normal amount of fluid that lubricates the pistons. Mechanic B says the leakage is excessive and the wheel cylinder should be rebuilt or replaced. Who is right?
   a. A only
   b. B only
   c. both A and B
   d. neither A nor B   5. _____

JOB 53

Tire Inspection and Service

Objective: To learn to inspect, demount, and mount tires.

References: AM ♦53-1 to 53-33, SG Chap. 53, automotive manufacturers' service manuals.
Equipment: Various vehicles with tire problems.

Tools: Tire changer, tire-mounting band, tire pressure gauge, tread gauge, chalk, basic hand tools.

SHOP FACTS

A tire inspection is basically a visual inspection. A tire pressure gauge and a tread depth gauge are required for some inspection procedures.

When you inspect tires, look for conditions that may cause tires to blow out or fail in use. Tire failure can cause an accident, injure people, and damage property. Here are some factors to keep in mind while performing a tire inspection.

1. A radial tire should never be on the same axle with a bias or belted-bias tire.
2. Tires that are very different in size or type should never be used on the same axle. An example would be one snow tire and one regular tire.
3. Bias-ply or bias-belted tires should not be used on the rear axle when radial-ply tires are used on the front axle. For the best driving conditions, all four tires should be either bias tires or radial tires. Drivers should avoid mixing radial tires and bias tires on the same vehicle.
4. Some state laws require tread inspection and a minimum tread depth.

Wheel inspection also is a visual inspection. To make a complete inspection on an automobile or light truck, remove the hubcaps or wheel covers.

Carefully examine any wheel that is bent from scraping the curb or that has been freshly or heavily painted. A close examination may reveal damage that could cause failure on the road. A wheel may show signs of having been in a collision or having hit a curb with great force. If so, check the wheel for excessive runout. The wheel may be bent.

Some vehicles have offset, or wide-rim, wheels that mount large tires. These large tires may be approved for use on the vehicle. However, certain modified wheels may cause the tire to rub against the wheel well. This can happen during turns and as the wheels move up and down. Contact between the tire and vehicle body may cause tire damage and handling problems.

The recommended wheel and tire inspection procedures are listed below. Take this job sheet, the tire pressure gauge, and the tread depth gauge to the vehicle.

All the steps must be performed on each tire that is touching the ground. Start with the left front tire (LF). Place a check mark to the left of "LF" as you complete each inspection item for the left front tire. Then move to the right front tire (RF). Inspect it by starting over again. Place a check mark to the left of "RF" as you complete each inspection item for the right front tire. Repeat this procedure for each rear tire.

SHOP SKILLS

TIRE INSPECTION

___ 1. ___LF ___RF ___LR ___RR Inspect for tread wear (tire without tread-wear indicators). Check the tread with a tread depth gauge. The tire should be replaced if less than 1/16 inch [1.6 mm] of tread remains in any two adjacent major grooves at three locations spaced about equally around the outside of the tire (Fig. 53-1).

___ 2. ___LF ___RF ___LR ___RR Inspect for tread wear (tire with tread-wear indicators). The tire should be replaced if it is worn so that the tread-wear indicators contact the road at any two adjacent major grooves at three equally spaced locations around the outside of the tire (Fig. 53-2).

LESS THAN 1/16 IN [1.6 MM]

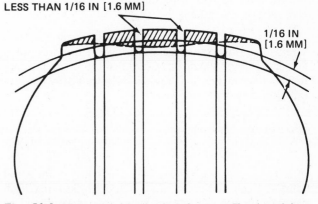

1/16 IN [1.6 MM]

Fig. 53-1 Unacceptable tire-tread wear. The tread has worn down so much that the tread remaining is less than 1/16 inch [1.6 mm].

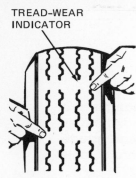

TREAD-WEAR INDICATOR

Fig. 53-2 A tire tread worn down so much that the tread-wear indicators can be seen.

___ 3. ___LF ___RF ___LR ___RR Inspect for cord exposure. The tire should be replaced if it has a worn spot that exposes cord through the tread.

___ 4. ___LF ___RF ___LR ___RR Inspect for tread cuts, snags, and sidewall cracks. The tire should be replaced if it has tread cuts, snags, or sidewall cracks longer than 1 inch [25 mm] in any direction, deep enough to expose the cords.

___ 5. ___1LF ___RF ___LR ___RR Inspect for bumps, bulges, and knots. The tire should be replaced if it has visible bumps, bulges, or knots indicating partial failure or separation of the tire structure.

___ 6. ___LF ___RF ___LR ___RR Inspect for re-grooved or recut tires. The tire should be replaced if it has been regrooved or recut below the original groove depth. An exception would be special tires which have undertread rubber for this purpose and are so marked.

___ 7. ___LF ___RF ___LR ___RR Inspect for mis-matching of tires. The tires on one side of the vehicle should be of the same type or size as the tires on the other side. An example would be radials on one side and bias-ply tires on the other side. An exception would be differences in brand or in tread design; such differences are not causes for rejection.

___ 8. ___LF ___RF ___LR ___RR Inspect for tire size. The tires must not be smaller than the minimum size or larger than the maximum size recommended by the vehicle manufacturer.

___ 9. ___LF ___RF ___LR ___RR Inspect for re-stricted-usage markings on the tires. Tires marked for restricted usage, such as "Farm Implements Only," must not be used on cars and trucks.

___ 10. ___LF ___RF ___LR ___RR Check tire pressure with a tire-pressure gauge. If high or low pressure is found, the driver should be warned that the wrong pressure reduces road traction and drivability. The wrong tire pressure can also cause rapid tire wear.

WHEEL INSPECTION

___ 1. ___LF ___RF ___LR ___RR Inspect for wheel damage. If any part of the wheel is bent, cracked, rewelded, damaged, or has elongated boltholes, the wheel should be replaced. Any of these conditions can lead to wheel failure and an accident.

___ 2. ___LF ___RF ___LR ___RR Inspect for wheel attachment. If any wheel bolts, nuts, studs, or lugs are loose, missing, or damaged, the condition must be corrected.

DEMOUNTING THE TIRE

___ 1. To remove a wheel from a car, first set the parking brake. Block both front and back of the wheel diagonally opposite the wheel to be removed.

___ 2. Loosen the nuts holding the wheel to the hub one-half turn. Raise the car until the tire is about 2 inches [51 mm] off the floor. Place a safety stand under the frame. Then remove the wheel.

___ 3. With chalk, make a mark across the tire and rim so that the tire can be reinstalled on the rim in the same position. This will preserve the balance of the tire and wheel.

___ 4. Place the wheel on a tire changer (Fig. 53-3). Release all air from the tire by holding the tire valve open or by removing the tire-valve core.

___ 5. Push the beads of the tire in toward the center of the rim. Lift the upper bead above the rim. If there is a tube, remove it from inside the tire. Then remove the lower bead from the rim.

Note When a tire goes flat and is driven on at highway speed, remove the tire from the rim. A complete inspection should be made to ensure that no tire damage has occurred.

___ 6. Inspect the inside of the tire for damage such as cracks, separations, plies, stone bruises, and sidewall punctures. Such damage renders the tire unsafe to use. The tire should be discarded.

___ 7. If the tire has a tube, examine the tube for wear and wear spots. Punctures should be repaired or the tube replaced.

___ 8. Check the tire rim for dents, rough spots, or rust. Replace the wheel if the rim is bent or dented. File off any nicks or burrs that could damage the tire bead. Use steel wool to clean off rust spots. Clean the rim flange to remove all dirt and filings.

BEAD BREAKER

HOSE TO SHOP AIR SUPPLY

Rotunda

Fig. 53-3 Using an air-powered tire changer to break the bead so that the tire can be removed from the wheel. **(Ford Motor Company)**

_____ 9. Make sure that the tire valve is in good condition and is tight in the wheel rim.

MOUNTING THE TIRE

_____ 1. To mount a tubeless tire, align the chalk marks on the tire and rim. Coat the beads and rim flanges with a suitable rubber lubricant.

_____ 2. Install the two beads over the rim, using the tire changer. After the tire is on the rim, use a tire-mounting band to spread the beads, if necessary.

_____ 3. Slowly inflate the tire to seat the beads properly.

♦ **CAUTION** ♦ Do not stand over the tire when inflating it! Never exceed an inflation pressure of 40 psi [276 kPa].

_____ 4. When the bead-positioning rings on the tire are evenly visible all around the rim, the beads are seated properly. If they are not evenly visible, deflate and then reinflate the tire. After the beads are properly positioned, inflate the tire to the recommended pressure.

_____ 5. To remount a tire with a tube, first put the tube into the tire. Coat the tire beads and rim flange with a rubber lubricant.

_____ 6. Align the chalk marks and install the tire on the rim, as explained above. Inflate the tube, making sure that it is properly centered in the tire and that the valve stem is centered in the rim hole. Deflate and then reinflate the tube. This ensures good alignment of the tire, tube, and rim.

CAREFUL Never inflate a flat tire on a car. This could cause some part of the tube to stretch and possibly cause a blowout.

JOB 53   MULTIPLE-CHOICE TEST

1. The first step in changing a tire is to
   a. raise the tire off the floor
   b. loosen the wheel nuts
   c. deflate the tire
   d. none of the above   1. _____

2. To remove a tire from the rim, first
   a. deflate the tire
   b. remove the nuts
   c. remove the tube
   d. apply pressure on the tire bead   2. _____

3. When mounting a tubeless tire, the tire-mounting band is used to
   a. align the tube
   b. clean the beads
   c. balance the tire
   d. spread the beads   3. _____

4. When mounting a tire, coat the tire beads and rim flanges with
   a. rubber lubricant
   b. grease or oil
   c. kerosene
   d. water   4. _____

5. When mounting a tubeless tire, first inflate the tire to
   a. recommended pressure
   b. fill out the sidewall
   c. about 40 psi [276 kPa]
   d. about 100 psi [690 kPa]   5. _____

JOB 54

Air-Conditioner Maintenance Checks

Objective: To learn how to make periodic maintenance checks on an automotive air conditioner.

References: AM ♦54-1 to 54-20, SG Chap. 54, automotive manufacturers' service manuals.
Equipment: Automotive air conditioner.

Tools: Belt-tension gauge, antifreeze tester, safety goggles, basic hand tools.

♦ **SAFETY** ♦ *Always wear safety goggles when checking an air conditioner.*

SHOP FACTS

The automotive air conditioner should be operated for a few minutes every week, even in cold weather. This protects the seals from drying out and leaking. It also prevents compressor freeze-up due to loss of lubricating oil from the polished and machined surfaces of the compressor. Below is a general inspection procedure for preventive maintenance or seasonal checks.

SHOP SKILLS

_____ 1. Check the condenser regularly, to make sure that the fins are not plugged with leaves or other trash. Plugged fins reduce the airflow through the condenser. They make the whole system work harder.

_____ 2. Check the evaporator drains regularly for dirt and restrictions.

_____ 3. Check the refrigerant hoses (Fig. 54-1) for brittleness and damage. Check the hose connections for tightness. . Hoses often are burned by rubbing against the hot exhaust manifold. Sometimes they are cut by the fan blades.

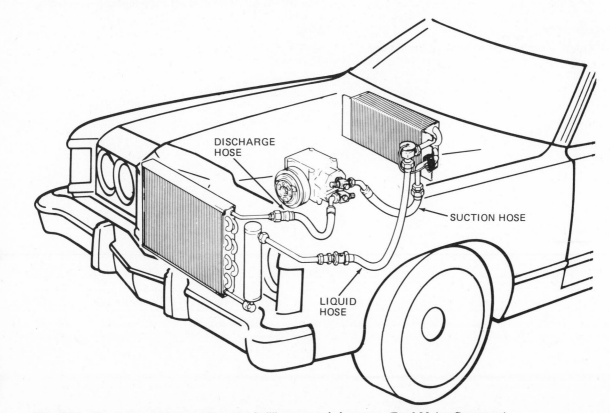

Fig. 54-1 Check the refrigerant hose for brittleness and damage. **(Ford Motor Company)**

____ 4. Periodically check the sight glass with the system in operation. If the sight glass indicates loss of refrigerant, check the system for leaks. Then install the gauge set to measure pressures. Evacuate and recharge the system as necessary.

____ 5. The coolant in the engine cooling system must be protected from freezing down to 15°F [−9.4°C] for summer operation. This will prevent freezing of the coolant in the heater core. However, this does not give enough protection against corrosion. For corrosion protection, add enough antifreeze (Fig. 54-2) to protect to −15°F [−26.1°C].

Chrysler recommends that the engine cooling system be drained and flushed every spring. When draining, flushing, and refilling, set the temperature control for maximum heat. This will allow the heater core to also be drained and flushed. Old antifreeze should not be reused. Instead, use enough new antifreeze to protect the cooling system to at least −15°F [−26.1°C].

____ 6. Check the compressor drive-belt tension and belt condition. Adjust the tension, or replace the belt if necessary.

JOB 54   MULTIPLE-CHOICE TEST

1. To be properly maintained, an air conditioner should be operated briefly about every
   a. day
   b. week
   c. month
   d. year   1. ____

2. If a condenser is plugged with leaves, you must
   a. remove the leaves
   b. replace the condenser
   c. place a screen in front of it
   d. flush the cooling system   2. ____

3. If an air conditioner is equipped with a sight glass, you can check it to determine the
   a. temperature inside the car
   b. temperature under the hood
   c. condition of the engine cooling system
   d. condition of the refrigerant system   3. ____

4. If refrigerant is leaking from a hose, you must
   a. evacuate and recharge the system
   b. check the antifreeze
   c. replace the evaporator
   d. replace the condenser   4. ____

5. When draining, flushing, and refilling a cooling system with antifreeze, you should set the temperature control to
   a. OFF
   b. LOW
   c. MAX
   d. BI-LEVEL   5. ____

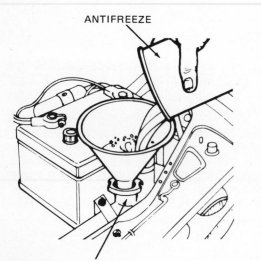

ANTIFREEZE

RADIATOR FILLER NECK

Fig. 54-2 Adding antifreeze to the radiator. **(Chrysler Corporation)**

JOB 55-1

Connecting the Gauge Set and Checking Pressures

Objective: To learn how to connect the gauge set and how to check pressures with it.

References: AM ♦55-1 to 55-9, SG Chap. 55, automotive manufacturers' service manuals, gauge-set and charging-station manufacturers' operating instructions.

Equipment: Automotive air conditioners.

Tools: Gauge set, safety goggles, basic hand tools.

♦ _____ ♦

♦ **SAFETY** ♦ *Always wear safety goggles when connecting and disconnecting a gauge set or a charging station.*

SHOP FACTS

The gauge set (Fig. 55-1) includes a low-pressure gauge for checking the refrigerant pressure on the low-pressure side of the system. It has a high-pressure gauge for checking the refrigerant pressure on the high-pressure side of the system. Gauge sets used to check some air-conditioning systems in Chrysler Corporation cars have a third gauge. This gauge is used to check the pressure at the compressor-inlet service port in the system using the V-type compressor (Fig. 55-2). It is a compound pressure gauge that reads both pressure and vacuum. The third gauge operates independently of the other two gauges and has no connection to the manifold passage.

The high- and low-pressure gauges are connected together by a manifold (metal castings and fittings through which refrigerant can flow), forming a gauge set. The gauge set is sometimes called the *manifold gauge set* or the *gauge-set manifold.* The three-gauge set is sometimes called a *compound manifold gauge set.*

The low-pressure gauge is often called the *suction* gauge. The high-pressure gauge is often called the *discharge* gauge. The purpose of the gauge set is to measure the refrigerant pressures on the high and low sides of the system and thereby determine how the system is operating.

The gauge set is also used when the system is discharged. An important part of discharging, evacuation, and charging is to measure the amount of oil lost during the procedure. This is necessary because the same amount of new, fresh oil must be added along with the new charge of refrigerant.

The refrigerant system has connection points, or *service valves,* at which the hoses from the gauges can be connected.

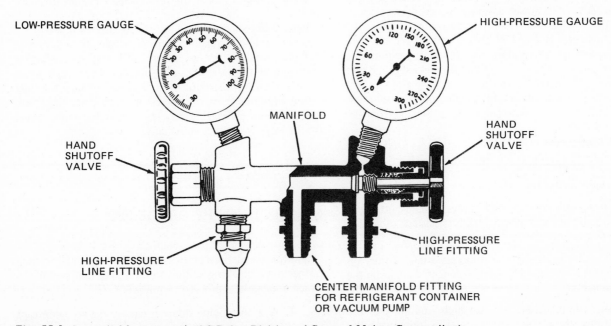

LOW-PRESSURE GAUGE

HIGH-PRESSURE GAUGE

MANIFOLD

HAND SHUTOFF VALVE

HAND SHUTOFF VALVE

HIGH-PRESSURE LINE FITTING

HIGH-PRESSURE LINE FITTING

CENTER MANIFOLD FITTING FOR REFRIGERANT CONTAINER OR VACUUM PUMP

Fig. 55-1 A manifold gauge set. (AC-Delco Division of General Motors Corporation)

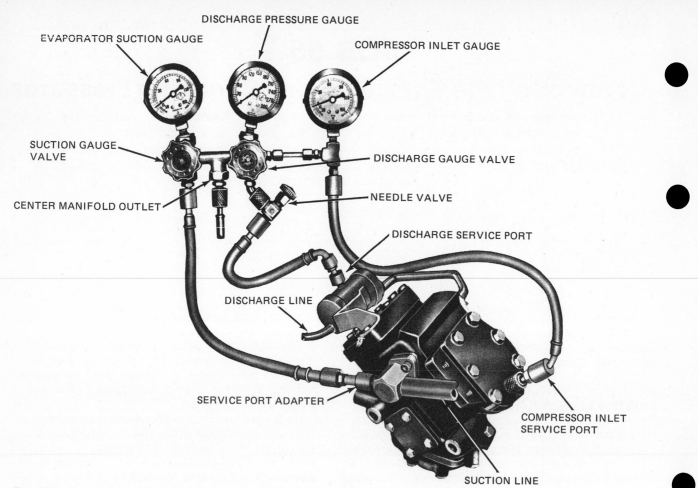

Fig. 55-2 Gauge connections to compressor. **(Chrysler Corporation)**

These service valves are located in various places in the system. One is on the high-pressure side, and the other is on the low-pressure side. There are two types of service valves, the stem type (Fig. 55-3) and the Schrader-valve type (Fig. 55-4).

Each valve has a protective cap which prevents any dirt or moisture from getting into it. The stem-type valve (Fig. 55-3) is used mostly on Tecumseh and York two-cylinder compressors. In the back-seated or normal operating position, the service-gauge port is sealed off. Even if a gauge is connected, it will not register. The midposition is the test position. The valve stem has been turned in so that the service-gauge port is connected to the refrigerant line. The gauge also registers in the front-seated position. This is after the valve stem has been turned in so that the compressor is isolated from the rest of the system.

The Schrader valve is like a tire valve (Fig. 55-4). It is used on General Motors and other late-model systems. Schrader valves are located on both the high-pressure and the low-pressure side, as follows:

High-pressure valve—at the compressor-outlet fitting, or in the liquid line just ahead of the thermostatic expansion valve or the orifice tube

Low-pressure valve—in the compressor-inlet fitting, on the POA valve, on the VIR-inlet connector shell, or on the accumulator

On many late-model systems, the high- and low-pressure valve fittings are of different sizes. This minimizes the chances of making the wrong hose connections. Wrong connections could damage the gauges or the system. Therefore, an adapter is required to attach the gauge-set hose to the high-pressure fitting. In the adapter for 1978- to 1980-model cars, when the adapter and hose are connected to the Schrader valve, a pin in the hose adapter pushes the valve open.

When a hose is connected to or disconnected from the refrigerant system, a small amount of refrigerant and oil may leak out. Usually, the most refrigerant is lost when a hose is disconnected from the high-pressure side. To prevent refrigerant and oil from striking your skin, always turn the hose fitting with a cloth or shop towel in your hand. Make sure that the cloth or towel covers the connection. Also, gloves can be worn to protect your hands.

SHOP SKILLS

CONNECTING THE GAUGE SET

Follow the instructions of the equipment manufacturer when connecting a charging station to the refrigerant system. To attach a gauge set, proceed as follows.

_____ 1. With the engine stopped, remove the protector caps from the system service valves.

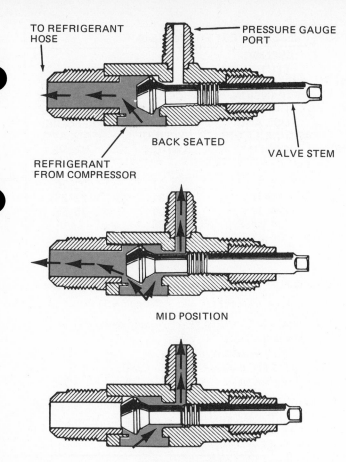

Fig. 55-3 Service-valve positions for a manual, or hand-shutoff, type of valve. **(AC-Delco Division of General Motors Corporation)**

_____ 2. Make sure that all valves on the gauge set are closed (turned in to seat). On most gauge sets, the gauge valve is turned fully clockwise to close off the gauge from the manifold center outlet.

_____ 3. Install the necessary adapters on the gauge-set hoses or on the system service valves.

_____ 4. Leave the center hose on the manifold capped, connected to the storage fitting provided on the manifold, or connected to a refrigerant container through a hose.

_____ 5. Connect the high-pressure gauge hose to the high-side service valve.

_____ 6. Purge the test hoses by opening the high-pressure gauge valve one turn. Open the low-pressure manifold valve slightly, and allow refrigerant vapor to hiss from the low-pressure hose for 3 seconds. Then close both valves.

_____ 7. Connect the low-pressure hose to the low-side service valve. The gauge set is now installed, and the system is ready for pressure checking.

CHECKING PRESSURES WITH THE GAUGE SET

Before you can accurately check the refrigerant-system pressures in an air conditioner, the system must be stabilized.

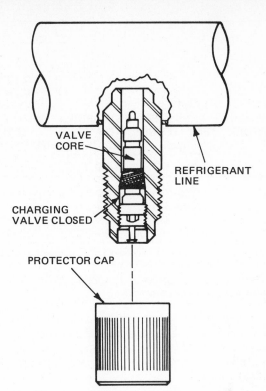

Fig. 55-4 Charging valve with its protector cap removed. **(Ford Motor Company)**

This means that it must be brought to its normal operating condition.

_____ 1. Start the engine, and adjust idle speed to 1500 to 2000 rpm.

_____ 2. Set all air-conditioner controls for maximum cooling. Set the blower control to its high-speed position.

_____ 3. Be sure that the front of the car is at least 5 feet [1.5 m] away from any wall. Then close the car doors and windows.

_____ 4. Operate the air conditioner this way for 5 minutes to stabilize the system.

_____ 5. If it is necessary to test the system on a hot day or when the surrounding air is at a high temperature, place a large fan in front of the car grill. Position the fan to blow air through the condenser and engine radiator.

The pressure readings on the gauges increase as the surrounding air temperature and humidity go up. Higher temperatures and humidities cause the system to work harder. As a result, the pressures in the refrigerant system rise. At idle speed and a surrounding air temperature of 110°F [43.3°C], the high pressure in the system may go as high as 360 psi [2482 kPa].

_____ 6. Read the pressures on the gauges. Compare the pressure readings with the pressures listed in the specifications and in Fig. 55-5. Low pressures in the range of 7 to 15 psi [48 to 103 kPa] may be normal. High pressures in the range of 150 to 250 psi [1034 to 1724 kPa] while the surrounding air temperature is 70°F [21.1°C] are usually considered normal.

AMBIENT (OUTSIDE AIR) TEMPERATURE (°F)	AT HIGH-PRESSURE TEST FITTING* (psi)	AT LOW-PRESSURE TEST FITTING (psi)				
		STV, POA, OR VIR SYSTEMS	CYCLING-CLUTCH SYSTEM WITH TXV AND REC-DEHYD**	CYCLING-CLUTCH SYSTEM WITH EXPANSION (ORIFICE) TUBE AND ACCUMULATOR (CCOT)**	CCOT SYSTEM WITH PRESSURE-CYCLING SWITCH	CHRYSLER CORP. WITH EVAPORATOR-PRESSURE-REGULATOR VALVE
60	120–170	28–31	7–15	—	—	—
70	150–250	28–31	7–15	24–31	24–31	22–30
80	180–275	28–31	7–15	24–31	24–31	22–37
90	200–310	28–31	7–15	24–32	24–31	25–37
100	230–330	28–35	10–30	24–32	24–36	—
110	270–360	28–38	10–35	24–32	—	—

*Pressures may be slightly higher on very humid days or lower on very dry days.
**Pressure just before clutch disengages (cycles off).

Fig. 55-5 Approximate test-pressure ranges for normal operation of various types of air-conditioning systems. (AC-Delco Division of General Motors Corporation)

____ 7. An insufficient refrigerant charge is indicated by the high-side gauge registering lower than normal pressure. The system must be leak-tested and charged. Then accurate tests can be performed to determine whether the system has a leak or is operating properly.

JOB 55-1 MULTIPLE-CHOICE TEST

1. The low-pressure gauge is used to check the system's
   a. charge
   b. high side
   c. low side
   d. temperature   1. ____

2. The discharge gauge checks the
   a. low side
   b. high side
   c. temperature
   d. humidity   2. ____

3. Turning a manifold gauge valve fully clockwise
   a. opens the valve
   b. allows refrigerant to escape
   c. allows air to escape
   d. closes the valve   3. ____

4. Before you can get accurate pressure readings, you must
   a. open the car windows
   b. turn the heater on HIGH
   c. park the car overnight
   d. stabilize the system   4. ____

5. A high-pressure gauge that reads lower than normal indicates that the system is
   a. overheated
   b. overcharged
   c. undercharged
   d. overspeeding   5. ____

JOB 55-2

Charging the System Using a Gauge Set and Small Cans of Refrigerant

Objective: To learn how to charge the air-conditioner refrigerant system using a gauge set and small cans of refrigerant.

References: AM ♦55-1 to 55-13, SG Chap. 55, automotive manufacturers' service manuals.

Equipment: Gauge Set, refrigerant manifold, small cans of refrigerant, safety goggles, basic hand tools.

♦ **SAFETY** ♦ *Always wear safety goggles when charging the refrigerant system or performing any service on or around an air conditioner.*

SHOP FACTS

Many manufacturers make available a refrigerant manifold to which two, three, or four small cans of refrigerant may be attached (Fig. 55-6). The manifold is very convenient, because most air conditioners require from 2 to 4 pounds [0.91 to 1.81 kg] of refrigerant for a complete charge. Also, by using a refrigerant manifold, the technician saves time in not having to change cans so often.

Each can position on the refrigerant manifold has its own shutoff valve. However, the installation of the cans on the refrigerant manifold and the charging procedure are the same as when a single can is used.

The refrigerant-manifold valves should be capped when the manifold is not in use to protect the manifold from moisture and dirt. Keep a supply of can-to-manifold gaskets on hand so that you can use new gaskets when necessary. The seal between the can and the manifold must be tight.

Refrigerant comes in 14-ounce [397-g] and 15-ounce [425-g] cans, often called "pound" cans (Fig. 55-6). It is also available in metal drums and bulk tanks of various sizes. Small cans are very popular because they are so convenient to store and handle. The typical charging procedure outlined below is a vapor-charging procedure. No liquid refrigerant must enter the low side of the compressor, or the compressor will be damaged.

♦ **CAUTION** ♦ Never open the high-pressure gauge valve and attempt to charge the system on the high-pressure side with the procedure listed below. This would admit high pressure to the can, causing it to explode. Anyone nearby could be seriously injured by fragments of the can

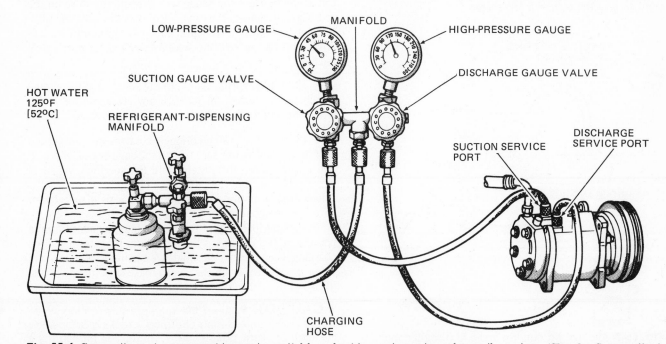

Fig. 55-6 Connections of gauges, refrigerant manifold, and refrigerant cans to recharge the system. **(Chrysler Corporation)**

and by the liquid refrigerant that would fly out. Liquid refrigerant can freeze anything it touches, including your eyes and skin.

SHOP SKILLS

_____ 1. Connect the gauge set to the service valves (Job 55-1). Discharge and evacuate the system. When evacuation is completed, close the vacuum-pump valve.

_____ 2. To use a small can of refrigerant, a special valve and valve retainer must be connected to the can (Fig. 55-7). To install the valve, first lubricate the sealing lip around the top of the can with compressor oil.

_____ 3. Place the valve retainer (or adapter) on the can top, engaging the three tabs of the retainer with the lip on the top of the can. Lock the valve retainer in place by pulling the cam lever on the retainer.

_____ 4. Turn the valve assembly into the threaded hole in the top of the valve retainer until the valve assembly is finger tight. Then screw the valve in to puncture the top of the can (Fig. 55-8). This closes the valve and seals the refrigerant in the can.

_____ 5. Close both gauge-set valves. Connect the center charging hose of the gauge set to the valve on the can or to the fitting on the refrigerant manifold (Fig. 55-6). To purge the air from the charging hose, first loosen it at the gauge set. Then turn the valve in the top of the can (any valve, if you are using a refrigerant manifold) counterclockwise slightly. When refrigerant vapor starts escaping from the loose charging-hose connection, tighten the connection. The charging hose is now purged.

_____ 6. Check the specifications to determine the weight of refrigerant needed to completely charge the system you are servicing. Be sure that you have enough pound cans of refrigerant to give the system a full charge.

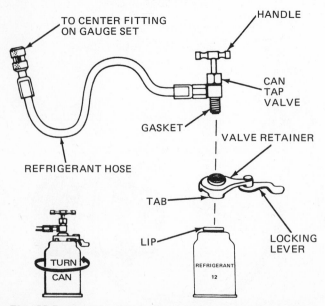

Fig. 55-7 Attaching a can tap valve to a small can of refrigerant. **(ATW)**

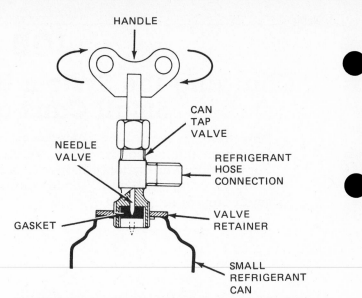

Fig. 55-8 Turning the valve handle down until the needle valve is fully seated will puncture the can. No refrigerant should be lost because the valve is in the closed position. **(Toyota Motor Sales Company, Ltd.)**

_____ 7. Open the low-pressure gauge valve. With the engine off, give the system a partial charge by opening the valve on the can and allowing refrigerant to flow into the system. When the low- and high-pressure gauges both register 60 to 80 psi [413 to 552 kPa] with the ambient (surrounding) temperature about 75°F [24°C], close the valve at the can.

CAREFUL Hold the small can upright during charging. If the can is laid on its side or turned upside down, liquid refrigerant will flow into the system. Liquid refrigerant must never enter the low-pressure side of the compressor. This could overcharge the system and damage the compressor valves.

_____ 8. One small can may not contain enough refrigerant to give the system an adequate partial charge. When the first can is empty, close the gauge-set valve and the valve on the can. Then disconnect the can and connect the valve and valve retainer to another can. Repeat this procedure until enough refrigerant has entered the system to give the proper gauge readings.

_____ 9. With a partial charge in the system and the engine off, check the system for leaks. If any are found, fix them. When the system has no leaks, proceed as follows.

_____ 10. Set the air-conditioner controls for maximum cooling and low blower speed. Start the engine, and let it idle. Add refrigerant to the system until the specified weight of charge has entered. The amount of charge in the system is determined by noting how many pound cans of refrigerant have been emptied.

If ½ pound [0.23 kg] of refrigerant must be added from a pound can, feel the can as the refrigerant flows from it. Stop charging when the extreme cold is felt halfway down the can. Then, if possible, weigh the can to make sure that ½ pound [0.23 kg] of refrigerant was actually added.

♦ CAUTION ♦ Keep the high-pressure gauge valve closed at all times during charging. Cracking or opening the high-pressure gauge valve during this procedure is very dangerous. It allows the high pressure from the air conditioner to pass through the gauge-set manifold into the small can of refrigerant. This high pressure could cause the can to explode violently. Never attempt to charge with a gauge set and small cans on the high-pressure side while the compressor is operating.

_____ 11. If enough refrigerant will not enter the system because the temperature is low, put the refrigerant can in a container of hot water at about 125°F [52°C]. This will increase the pressure in the can and force more refrigerant out.

♦ **CAUTION** ♦ Never heat the refrigerant can with a torch or heat it above 125°F (51.7°C). If overheated, the can will explode violently, possibly injuring or killing anyone nearby.

_____ 12. During charging, the high-pressure side can develop an excessive pressure. This could result from overheating of the engine, an overcharge of refrigerant, a restricted condenser, or high ambient temperatures. Never allow the pressure to go above 240 psi [1655 kPa]. If it does, stop the engine and determine what is wrong.

_____ 13. After the system is fully charged, close off the valve on the refrigerant can. Now check the pressures on the gauges. The low-pressure gauge should read 4 to 25 psi [27 to 172 kPa], and the high-pressure gauge should read 120 to 210 psi [827 to 1448 kPa] with the ambient temperature 70 to 90°F [21 to 32°C].

_____ 14. Check for cold air coming from the outlets in the passenger compartment. If the air conditioner is performing properly, disconnect the gauge hoses from the service valves. Install the protective caps on the system service valves, the gauge hoses, and the refrigerant manifold.

JOB 55-2 MULTIPLE-CHOICE TEST

1. The device to which three small cans of refrigerant may be attached is called a
   a. refrigerant manifold
   b. gauge-set manifold
   c. intake manifold
   d. charging hose   1. ___

2. The charge for most air conditioners weighs from
   a. 1 to 2 pounds [0.45 to 0.91 kg]
   b. 2 to 4 pounds [0.91 to 1.81 kg]
   c. 5 to 10 pounds [2.27 to 4.54 kg]
   d. 10 to 20 pounds [4.54 to 9.07 kg]   2. ___

3. The small cans (called "pound" cans) of refrigerant actually hold
   a. either 14 ounces [397 g] or 15 ounces [425 g]
   b. 1 pound [454 g]
   c. 4 ounces [113 g]
   d. ½ pound [227 g]   3. ___

4. Before you start to charge the system, the charging hose must be purged of
   a. water
   b. refrigerant
   c. compressor oil
   d. air   4. ___

5. If the temperature is too low and refrigerant leaves the small cans slowly, the cans may be placed in a pan of water heated to
   a. 150°F [66°C]
   b. 125°F [52°C]
   c. 70°F [21°C]
   d. 212°F [100°C]   5. ___